TEACHER'S GUIDE

Covering and Surrounding

Two-Dimensional Measurement

Glenda Lappan
James T. Fey
William M. Fitzgerald
Susan N. Friel
Elizabeth Difanis Phillips

Boston, Massachusetts
Upper Saddle River, New Jersey

Connected Mathematics™ was developed at Michigan State University with financial support from the Michigan State University Office of the Provost, Computing and Technology, and the College of Natural Science.

This material is based upon work supported by the National Science Foundation under Grant No. MDR 9150217 and Grant No. ESI 9986372. Opinions expressed are those of the authors and not necessarily those of the Foundation.

The Michigan State University authors and administration have agreed that all MSU royalties arising from this publication will be devoted to purposes supported by the Department of Mathematics and the MSU Mathematics Enrichment Fund.

Acknowledgments appear on page 174, which constitutes an extension of this copyright page.

ISBN 0-13-165663-5
1 2 3 4 5 6 7 8 9 10 09 08 07 06 05

Authors of Connected Mathematics

(from left to right) Glenda Lappan, Betty Phillips, Susan Friel, Bill Fitzgerald, Jim Fey

Glenda Lappan is a University Distinguished Professor in the Department of Mathematics at Michigan State University. Her research and development interests are in the connected areas of students' learning of mathematics and mathematics teachers' professional growth and change related to the development and enactment of K–12 curriculum materials.

James T. Fey is a Professor of Curriculum and Instruction and Mathematics at the University of Maryland. His consistent professional interest has been development and research focused on curriculum materials that engage middle and high school students in problem-based collaborative investigations of mathematical ideas and their applications.

William M. Fitzgerald (*Deceased*) was a Professor in the Department of Mathematics at Michigan State University. His early research was on the use of concrete materials in supporting student learning and led to the development of teaching materials for laboratory environments. Later he helped develop a teaching model to support student experimentation with mathematics.

Susan N. Friel is a Professor of Mathematics Education in the School of Education at the University of North Carolina at Chapel Hill. Her research interests focus on statistics education for middle-grade students and, more broadly, on teachers' professional development and growth in teaching mathematics K–8.

Elizabeth Difanis Phillips is a Senior Academic Specialist in the Mathematics Department of Michigan State University. She is interested in teaching and learning mathematics for both teachers and students. These interests have led to curriculum and professional development projects at the middle school and high school levels, as well as projects related to the teaching and learning of algebra across the grades.

CMP2 Development Staff

Teacher Collaborator in Residence
Yvonne Grant
Michigan State University

Administrative Assistant
Judith Martus Miller
Michigan State University

Production and Field Site Manager
Lisa Keller
Michigan State University

Technical and Editorial Support
Brin Keller, Peter Lappan, Jim Laser, Michael Masterson, Stacey Miceli

Assessment Team
June Bailey and **Debra Sobko** (Apollo Middle School, Rochester, New York), **George Bright** (University of North Carolina, Greensboro), **Gwen Ranzau Campbell** (Sunrise Park Middle School, White Bear Lake, Minnesota), **Holly DeRosia, Kathy Dole,** and **Teri Keusch** (Portland Middle School, Portland, Michigan), **Mary Beth Schmitt** (Traverse City East Junior High School, Traverse City, Michigan), **Genni Steele** (Central Middle School, White Bear Lake, Minnesota), **Jacqueline Stewart** (Okemos, Michigan), **Elizabeth Tye** (Magnolia Junior High School, Magnolia, Arkansas)

Development Assistants
At Lansing Community College *Undergraduate Assistant:* **James Brinegar**

At Michigan State University *Graduate Assistants:* **Dawn Berk, Emily Bouck, Bulent Buyukbozkirli, Kuo-Liang Chang, Christopher Danielson, Srinivasa Dharmavaram, Deb Johanning, Kelly Rivette, Sarah Sword, Tat Ming Sze, Marie Turini, Jeffrey Wanko;** *Undergraduate Assistants:* **Jeffrey Chapin, Jade Corsé, Elisha Hardy, Alisha Harold, Elizabeth Keusch, Julia Letoutchaia, Karen Loeffler, Brian Oliver, Carl Oliver, Evonne Pedawi, Lauren Rebrovich**

At the University of Maryland *Graduate Assistants:* **Kim Harris Bethea, Kara Karch**

At the University of North Carolina (Chapel Hill) *Graduate Assistants:* **Mark Ellis, Trista Stearns;** *Undergraduate Assistant:* **Daniel Smith**

Advisory Board for CMP2

Thomas Banchoff
Professor of Mathematics
Brown University
Providence, Rhode Island

Anne Bartel
Mathematics Coordinator
Minneapolis Public Schools
Minneapolis, Minnesota

Hyman Bass
Professor of Mathematics
University of Michigan
Ann Arbor, Michigan

Joan Ferrini-Mundy
Associate Dean of the College of Natural Science; Professor
Michigan State University
East Lansing, Michigan

James Hiebert
Professor
University of Delaware
Newark, Delaware

Susan Hudson Hull
Charles A. Dana Center
University of Texas
Austin, Texas

Michele Luke
Mathematics Curriculum Coordinator
West Junior High
Minnetonka, Minnesota

Kay McClain
Assistant Professor of Mathematics Education
Vanderbilt University
Nashville, Tennessee

Edward Silver
Professor; Chair of Educational Studies
University of Michigan
Ann Arbor, Michigan

Judith Sowder
Professor Emerita
San Diego State University
San Diego, California

Lisa Usher
Mathematics Resource Teacher
California Academy of Mathematics and Science
San Pedro, California

Field Test Sites for CMP2

During the development of the revised edition of *Connected Mathematics* (CMP2), more than 100 classroom teachers have field-tested materials at 49 school sites in 12 states and the District of Columbia. This classroom testing occurred over three academic years (2001 through 2004), allowing careful study of the effectiveness of each of the 24 units that comprise the program. A special thanks to the students and teachers at these pilot schools.

Arkansas

Magnolia Public Schools
Kittena Bell*, Judith Trowell*; *Central Elementary School:* Maxine Broom, Betty Eddy, Tiffany Fallin, Bonnie Flurry, Carolyn Monk, Elizabeth Tye; *Magnolia Junior High School:* Monique Bryan, Ginger Cook, David Graham, Shelby Lamkin

Colorado

Boulder Public Schools
Nevin Platt Middle School: Judith Koenig

St. Vrain Valley School District, Longmont
Westview Middle School: Colleen Beyer, Kitty Canupp, Ellie Decker*, Peggy McCarthy, Tanya deNobrega, Cindy Payne, Ericka Pilon, Andrew Roberts

District of Columbia

Capitol Hill Day School: Ann Lawrence

Georgia

University of Georgia, Athens
Brad Findell

Madison Public Schools
Morgan County Middle School: Renee Burgdorf, Lynn Harris, Nancy Kurtz, Carolyn Stewart

Maine

Falmouth Public Schools
Falmouth Middle School: Donna Erikson, Joyce Hebert, Paula Hodgkins, Rick Hogan, David Legere, Cynthia Martin, Barbara Stiles, Shawn Towle*

Michigan

Portland Public Schools
Portland Middle School: Mark Braun, Holly DeRosia, Kathy Dole*, Angie Foote, Teri Keusch, Tammi Wardwell

Traverse City Area Public Schools
Bertha Vos Elementary: Kristin Sak; *Central Grade School:* Michelle Clark; Jody Meyers; *Eastern Elementary:* Karrie Tufts; *Interlochen Elementary:* Mary McGee-Cullen; *Long Lake Elementary:* Julie Faulkner*, Charlie Maxbauer, Katherine Sleder; *Norris Elementary:* Hope Slanaker; *Oak Park Elementary:* Jessica Steed; *Traverse Heights Elementary:* Jennifer Wolfert; *Westwoods Elementary:* Nancy Conn; *Old Mission Peninsula School:* Deb Larimer; *Traverse City East Junior High:* Ivanka Berkshire, Ruthanne Kladder, Jan Palkowski, Jane Peterson, Mary Beth Schmitt; *Traverse City West Junior High:* Dan Fouch*, Ray Fouch

Sturgis Public Schools
Sturgis Middle School: Ellen Eisele

Minnesota

Burnsville School District 191
Hidden Valley Elementary: Stephanie Cin, Jane McDevitt

Hopkins School District 270
Alice Smith Elementary: Sandra Cowing, Kathleen Gustafson, Martha Mason, Scott Stillman; *Eisenhower Elementary:* Chad Bellig, Patrick Berger, Nancy Glades, Kye Johnson, Shane Wasserman, Victoria Wilson; *Gatewood Elementary:* Sarah Ham, Julie Kloos, Janine Pung, Larry Wade; *Glen Lake Elementary:* Jacqueline Cramer, Kathy Hering, Cecelia Morris, Robb Trenda; *Katherine Curren Elementary:* Diane Bancroft, Sue DeWit, John Wilson; *L. H. Tanglen Elementary:* Kevin Athmann, Lisa Becker, Mary LaBelle, Kathy Rezac, Roberta Severson; *Meadowbrook Elementary:* Jan Gauger, Hildy Shank, Jessica Zimmerman; *North Junior High:* Laurel Hahn, Kristin Lee, Jodi Markuson, Bruce Mestemacher, Laurel Miller, Bonnie Rinker, Jeannine Salzer, Sarah Shafer, Cam Stottler; *West Junior High:* Alicia Beebe, Kristie Earl, Nobu Fujii, Pam Georgetti, Susan Gilbert, Regina Nelson Johnson, Debra Lindstrom, Michele Luke*, Jon Sorensen

Minneapolis School District 1
Ann Sullivan K–8 School: Bronwyn Collins; Anne Bartel* (Curriculum and Instruction Office)

Wayzata School District 284
Central Middle School: Sarajane Myers, Dan Nielsen, Tanya Ravnholdt

White Bear Lake School District 624
Central Middle School: Amy Jorgenson, Michelle Reich, Brenda Sammon

New York

New York City Public Schools
IS 89: Yelena Aynbinder, Chi-Man Ng, Nina Rapaport, Joel Spengler, Phyllis Tam*, Brent Wyso; *Wagner Middle School:* Jason Appel, Intissar Fernandez, Yee Gee Get, Richard Goldstein, Irving Marcus, Sue Norton, Bernadita Owens, Jennifer Rehn*, Kevin Yuhas

* indicates a Field Test Site Coordinator

Ohio

Talawanda School District, Oxford
Talawanda Middle School: Teresa Abrams, Larry Brock, Heather Brosey, Julie Churchman, Monna Even, Karen Fitch, Bob George, Amanda Klee, Pat Meade, Sandy Montgomery, Barbara Sherman, Lauren Steidl

Miami University
Jeffrey Wanko*

Springfield Public Schools
Rockway School: Jim Mamer

Pennsylvania

Pittsburgh Public Schools
Kenneth Labuskes, Marianne O'Connor, Mary Lynn Raith*; *Arthur J. Rooney Middle School:* David Hairston, Stamatina Mousetis, Alfredo Zangaro; *Frick International Studies Academy:* Suzanne Berry, Janet Falkowski, Constance Finseth, Romika Hodge, Frank Machi; *Reizenstein Middle School:* Jeff Baldwin, James Brautigam, Lorena Burnett, Glen Cobbett, Michael Jordan, Margaret Lazur, Tamar McPherson, Melissa Munnell, Holly Neely, Ingrid Reed, Dennis Reft

Texas

Austin Independent School District
Bedichek Middle School: Lisa Brown, Jennifer Glasscock, Vicki Massey

El Paso Independent School District
Cordova Middle School: Armando Aguirre, Anneliesa Durkes, Sylvia Guzman, Pat Holguin*, William Holguin, Nancy Nava, Laura Orozco, Michelle Peña, Roberta Rosen, Patsy Smith, Jeremy Wolf

Plano Independent School District
Patt Henry, James Wohlgehagen*; *Frankford Middle School:* Mandy Baker, Cheryl Butsch, Amy Dudley, Betsy Eshelman, Janet Greene, Cort Haynes, Kathy Letchworth, Kay Marshall, Kelly McCants, Amy Reck, Judy Scott, Syndy Snyder, Lisa Wang; *Wilson Middle School:* Darcie Bane, Amanda Bedenko, Whitney Evans, Tonelli Hatley, Sarah (Becky) Higgs, Kelly Johnston, Rebecca McElligott, Kay Neuse, Cheri Slocum, Kelli Straight

Washington

Evergreen School District
Shahala Middle School: Nicole Abrahamsen, Terry Coon*, Carey Doyle, Sheryl Drechsler, George Gemma, Gina Helland, Amy Hilario, Darla Lidyard, Sean McCarthy, Tilly Meyer, Willow Nuewelt, Todd Parsons, Brian Pederson, Stan Posey, Shawn Scott, Craig Sjoberg, Lynette Sundstrom, Charles Switzer, Luke Youngblood

Wisconsin

Beaver Dam Unified School District
Beaver Dam Middle School: Jim Braemer, Jeanne Frick, Jessica Greatens, Barbara Link, Dennis McCormick, Karen Michels, Nancy Nichols*, Nancy Palm, Shelly Stelsel, Susan Wiggins

---

* indicates a Field Test Site Coordinator

Reviews of CMP to Guide Development of CMP2

Before writing for CMP2 began or field tests were conducted, the first edition of *Connected Mathematics* was submitted to the mathematics faculties of school districts from many parts of the country and to 80 individual reviewers for extensive comments.

School District Survey Reviews of CMP

Arizona
Madison School District #38 (Phoenix)

Arkansas
Cabot School District, Little Rock School District, Magnolia School District

California
Los Angeles Unified School District

Colorado
St. Vrain Valley School District (Longmont)

Florida
Leon County Schools (Tallahassee)

Illinois
School District #21 (Wheeling)

Indiana
Joseph L. Block Junior High (East Chicago)

Kentucky
Fayette County Public Schools (Lexington)

Maine
Selection of Schools

Massachusetts
Selection of Schools

Michigan
Sparta Area Schools

Minnesota
Hopkins School District

Texas
Austin Independent School District, The El Paso Collaborative for Academic Excellence, Plano Independent School District

Wisconsin
Platteville Middle School

Individual Reviewers of CMP

Arkansas
Deborah Cramer; Robby Frizzell *(Taylor)*; Lowell Lynde *(University of Arkansas, Monticello)*; Leigh Manzer *(Norfork)*; Lynne Roberts *(Emerson High School, Emerson)*; Tony Timms *(Cabot Public Schools)*; Judith Trowell *(Arkansas Department of Higher Education)*

California
José Alcantar *(Gilroy)*; Eugenie Belcher *(Gilroy)*; Marian Pasternack *(Lowman M. S. T. Center, North Hollywood)*; Susana Pezoa *(San Jose)*; Todd Rabusin *(Hollister)*; Margaret Siegfried *(Ocala Middle School, San Jose)*; Polly Underwood *(Ocala Middle School, San Jose)*

Colorado
Janeane Golliher *(St. Vrain Valley School District, Longmont)*; Judith Koenig *(Nevin Platt Middle School, Boulder)*

Florida
Paige Loggins *(Swift Creek Middle School, Tallahassee)*

Illinois
Jan Robinson *(School District #21, Wheeling)*

Indiana
Frances Jackson *(Joseph L. Block Junior High, East Chicago)*

Kentucky
Natalee Feese *(Fayette County Public Schools, Lexington)*

Maine
Betsy Berry *(Maine Math & Science Alliance, Augusta)*

Maryland
Joseph Gagnon *(University of Maryland, College Park)*; Paula Maccini *(University of Maryland, College Park)*

Massachusetts
George Cobb *(Mt. Holyoke College, South Hadley)*; Cliff Kanold *(University of Massachusetts, Amherst)*

Michigan
Mary Bouck *(Farwell Area Schools)*; Carol Dorer *(Slauson Middle School, Ann Arbor)*; Carrie Heaney *(Forsythe Middle School, Ann Arbor)*; Ellen Hopkins *(Clague Middle School, Ann Arbor)*; Teri Keusch *(Portland Middle School, Portland)*; Valerie Mills *(Oakland Schools, Waterford)*; Mary Beth Schmitt *(Traverse City East Junior High, Traverse City)*; Jack Smith *(Michigan State University, East Lansing)*; Rebecca Spencer *(Sparta Middle School, Sparta)*; Ann Marie Nicoll Turner *(Tappan Middle School, Ann Arbor)*; Scott Turner *(Scarlett Middle School, Ann Arbor)*

Minnesota
Margarita Alvarez *(Olson Middle School, Minneapolis)*; Jane Amundson *(Nicollet Junior High, Burnsville)*; Anne Bartel *(Minneapolis Public Schools)*; Gwen Ranzau Campbell *(Sunrise Park Middle School, White Bear Lake)*; Stephanie Cin *(Hidden Valley Elementary, Burnsville)*; Joan Garfield *(University of Minnesota, Minneapolis)*; Gretchen Hall *(Richfield Middle School, Richfield)*; Jennifer Larson *(Olson Middle School, Minneapolis)*; Michele Luke *(West Junior High, Minnetonka)*; Jeni Meyer *(Richfield Junior High, Richfield)*; Judy Pfingsten *(Inver Grove Heights Middle School, Inver Grove Heights)*; Sarah Shafer *(North Junior High, Minnetonka)*; Genni Steele *(Central Middle School, White Bear Lake)*; Victoria Wilson *(Eisenhower Elementary, Hopkins)*; Paul Zorn *(St. Olaf College, Northfield)*

New York
Debra Altenau-Bartolino *(Greenwich Village Middle School, New York)*; Doug Clements *(University of Buffalo)*; Francis Curcio *(New York University, New York)*; Christine Dorosh *(Clinton School for Writers, Brooklyn)*; Jennifer Rehn *(East Side Middle School, New York)*; Phyllis Tam *(IS 89 Lab School, New York)*; Marie Turini *(Louis Armstrong Middle School, New York)*; Lucy West *(Community School District 2, New York)*; Monica Witt *(Simon Baruch Intermediate School 104, New York)*

Pennsylvania
Robert Aglietti *(Pittsburgh)*; Sharon Mihalich *(Freeport)*; Jennifer Plumb *(South Hills Middle School, Pittsburgh)*; Mary Lynn Raith *(Pittsburgh Public Schools)*

Texas
Michelle Bittick *(Austin Independent School District)*; Margaret Cregg *(Plano Independent School District)*; Sheila Cunningham *(Klein Independent School District)*; Judy Hill *(Austin Independent School District)*; Patricia Holguin *(El Paso Independent School District)*; Bonnie McNemar *(Arlington)*; Kay Neuse *(Plano Independent School District)*; Joyce Polanco *(Austin Independent School District)*; Marge Ramirez *(University of Texas at El Paso)*; Pat Rossman *(Baker Campus, Austin)*; Cindy Schimek *(Houston)*; Cynthia Schneider *(Charles A. Dana Center, University of Texas at Austin)*; Uri Treisman *(Charles A. Dana Center, University of Texas at Austin)*; Jacqueline Weilmuenster *(Grapevine-Colleyville Independent School District)*; LuAnn Weynand *(San Antonio)*; Carmen Whitman *(Austin Independent School District)*; James Wohlgehagen *(Plano Independent School District)*

Washington
Ramesh Gangolli *(University of Washington, Seattle)*

Wisconsin
Susan Lamon *(Marquette University, Hales Corner)*; Steve Reinhart *(retired, Chippewa Falls Middle School, Eau Claire)*

Table of Contents

Covering and Surrounding
Two-Dimensional Measurement

Unit Introduction

Covering and Surrounding

Two-Dimensional Measurement

Goals of the Unit

- Use area and relate area to covering a figure
- Use perimeter and relate perimeter to surrounding a figure
- Analyze what it means to measure area and perimeter
- Develop strategies for finding areas and perimeters of rectangular shapes and non-rectangular shapes
- Discover relationships between perimeter and area including that each can vary while the other stays fixed
- Analyze how the area of a triangle and the area of a parallelogram are related to the area of a rectangle
- Develop formulas and procedures, stated in words and/or symbols, for finding areas and perimeters of rectangles, parallelograms, triangles, and circles
- Develop techniques for estimating the area and perimeter of an irregular figure
- Recognize situations in which measuring perimeter or area will help answer practical questions

Developing Students' Mathematical Habits

The overall goal of *Connected Mathematics* is to help students develop sound mathematical habits. Through their work in this and other geometry units, students learn important questions to ask themselves about any situation that is represented and modeled mathematically, such as:

- *How do I know whether area or perimeter of a figure is involved?*
- *What attributes of a shape are important to measure?*
- *What am I finding when I find area and when I find perimeter?*
- *What relationships involving area or perimeter, or both, will help solve the problem?*
- *How can I find the area and perimeter of an irregular shape?*
- *Is an exact answer required?*

Overview

Throughout history we find records of the importance of measurement. In fact, in the early development of mathematics, geometry was synonymous with measurement. Today we are surrounded by increasingly complex measures such as information-access rates, signal strength, and memory capacity.

The overarching goal of this unit is to help students begin to understand what it means to measure. Students study two kinds of measurements: perimeter and area. Since students often have misconceptions about the effects of each of these measures on the other, it is critical to study them together and to probe their relationships. The problems in this unit are structured so that students can build deep understanding of what it means to measure area and what it means to measure perimeter. In the process, they develop strategies for measuring perimeter and area of both rectangular and nonrectangular shapes. As they discuss their strategies, students are supported in formulating rules for finding area and perimeter of rectangles, triangles, parallelograms, and circles.

The name of this unit indicates the theme that binds the investigations together: covering (area) and surrounding (perimeter). A sub-theme running through the unit focuses on questions of what is the greatest and what is the least, since the notions of maximum and minimum are important throughout mathematics. You will recognize connections throughout the *Covering and Surrounding* unit to all the units preceding it in the grade 6 curriculum. The connections to factors and multiples and to fractions are especially strong.

Summary of Investigations

Investigation  1

Designing Bumper Cars

This investigation introduces students to area and perimeter by asking them to create floor plans for bumper-car rides that are made from 1-meter-square floor tiles and 1-meter-long rail sections.

The floor tiles and rail sections allow students to use counting as a way to find the area and perimeter of the plans.

This investigation builds experience with analyzing what it means to measure area and perimeter and develops efficient strategies for finding area and perimeter of rectangles. In addition, students should begin to understand the difference between area and perimeter. They should be aware that shapes with the same area may not have the same perimeter. Similarly, shapes with the same perimeter may not have the same area. By the end of the investigation, students should be able to write rules for finding area and perimeter of a rectangle and be able to explain why these work.

Investigation 2

Changing Area, Changing Perimeter

In this investigation, students explore fixed area and fixed perimeter problems. These problems are sometimes referred to as maximum and minimum problems. Holding one variable constant to study how another variable changes is a powerful mathematical tool used to analyze a wide variety of problems. It also helps strengthen students' understanding of area and perimeter and how they are related.

Investigation 3

Measuring Triangles

In this investigation, students deepen their understanding of area and perimeter by finding the areas and perimeters of triangles. The primary goal is for students to develop, understand, and use the formula for finding the area of a triangle. Students also learn to identify the base and height on a triangle.

Investigation 4

Measuring Parallelograms

In this investigation, students deepen their understanding of area and perimeter by finding the areas and perimeters of parallelograms. The primary goal is for students to develop, understand, and use procedures for finding areas and perimeters of parallelograms.

Investigation 5

Measuring Irregular Shapes and Circles

The first problem in the investigation looks at counting techniques for estimating areas and perimeters of non-regular shapes. These shapes often cannot be covered with whole square units. The counting techniques used to estimate areas and perimeters of non-regular shapes are powerful yet concrete. They let students see the power of formulas to solve some cases and the need to understand the concepts underlying area and perimeter to solve others. Appropriately, this problem pushes students to think about two ideas that are central to this unit: covering and surrounding.

The last three problems in this investigation help students discover how diameter and radius of a circle are related to its circumference and area. These three problems lay the foundation for students to develop an understanding of the number π (pi), which represents the number of diameters needed to surround a circle and the number of radius squares (r^2) needed to cover a circle. Some students will have already seen the expressions $C = \pi d$ (or $C = 2\pi r$) and $A = \pi r^2$ but do not understand what they mean.

Mathematics Background

While this unit does not explicitly focus on the more global aspects of what it means to measure, it does lay the groundwork for teachers to raise issues that help students begin to see relationships and characteristics of all measurements.

The Measurement Process

The measurement process involves several key elements.

- A phenomenon or object is chosen, and an attribute that can be measured is identified. This could involve such disparate properties as height, mass, time, temperature, and capacity.
- An appropriate unit of measurement is selected. The unit depends on the kind of measure to be made and the degree of precision needed for the measure. Units of measurement include centimeters, angstroms, degrees, minutes, volts, and decibels. Instruments for measuring include rulers, calipers, scales, watches, ammeters, springs, and weights.
- The unit is used repeatedly to "match" the attribute of the phenomenon or object in an appropriate way. This matching might be accomplished, for example, by "covering," "reaching the end of," "surrounding," or "filling" the object.
- The number of units is determined. The number of units is the measure of the property of the phenomenon or object.

Measuring Perimeter and Area

Covering and Surrounding highlights two important kinds of measures (perimeter and area) that depend on different units and measurement processes. Counting is a natural and appropriate way for students to find area and perimeter, because measurement is counting. When we measure, we are counting the number of measurement units needed to "match" an attribute of an object.

Measuring perimeter requires linear units. Measuring area requires square units. When finding the perimeter of a figure, students will often say they counted the number of squares along a side to find the length. Students need to be aware that perimeter is a linear measure. To measure the perimeter you count (measure) the number of unit lengths that form the border of the figure.

In the figure at the left below, the 12 square tiles border a 4 by 4 square. This is not the perimeter. Instead, the perimeter comprises 16 unit lengths, shown in the figure below.

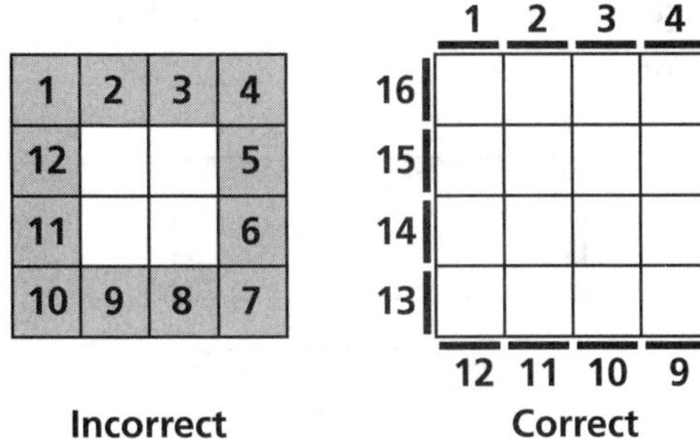

Incorrect   Correct

A strong emphasis on formulas that precedes understanding the methods may contribute to this confusion. While students can become adept at plugging numbers into formulas, they often have a hard time remembering which formula does what. This may be because they have an incomplete fundamental understanding of what the measurement is about and how the formula captures their more informal, intuitive computations.

Many students think that area and perimeter are related in that one determines the other. They may think that all rectangles of a given area have the same perimeter or that all rectangles of a given perimeter have the same area. Alternatively, students may not see any distinction between area and perimeter, giving area answers for perimeter problems or vice versa. The investigations in *Covering and Surrounding* help students realize for themselves the inaccuracy of such notions and help them to analyze the distinctions between the two measures.

In this unit, students work with tiles, transparent grids, grid paper, string, rulers, and other devices of their choice to develop a dynamic sense of *covering* and *surrounding* to find area and perimeter. Once students have an understanding of area and perimeter, they are ready to develop rules or formulas for finding area and perimeter in certain situations. This should be encouraged, but not forced too early. Some students need the help of a more hands-on approach to measuring for quite a while. The payoff for allowing students the time and opportunity to develop levels of abstraction with which they are comfortable is that, through these explorations, they make sense of perimeter and area in a lasting way.

Area and Perimeter of Rectangles

In Investigation 1, students first explore area and perimeter of non-rectangular shapes. After building shapes with square tiles and computing the perimeter and area by counting the units, the students investigate rectangles displayed on a grid. Again they find that they can find the area by counting the number of squares enclosed by the rectangle and the perimeter by counting the number of linear units surrounding the rectangle. Students may have found that, once you have counted the grid squares in one row, you could multiply by the number of rows to find the total number of squares in the rectangle. In other words, you can find the area of a rectangle by multiplying the length by the width.

For example, in this rectangle there are 5 squares in the first row and 7 rows in all. The area of the rectangle is $5 \times 7 = 35$ square units or in general, $\ell \times w$.

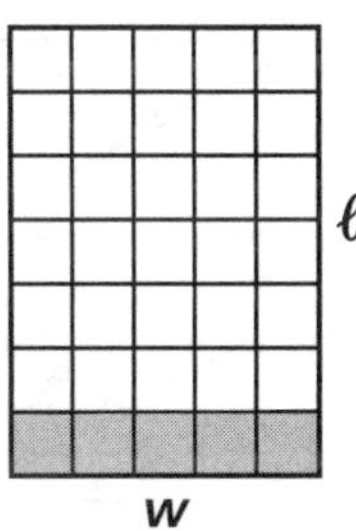

Similarly, the perimeter is $2\ (7 + 5)$ or $2 \times 7 + 2 \times 5$ or in general, $2\ (\ell + w)$ or $2\ell + 2w$.

Parentheses and Order of Operations

The two equivalent forms for the perimeter of a rectangle provide an opportunity to discuss the role of parentheses in expressions and the order of operations. Parentheses indicate that the numbers in them need to be operated on first. In the perimeter formula, *perimeter* = *(length* + *width)* × 2, the parentheses indicate that you need to add the length and width before you multiply by two. Students who are using a scientific calculator, or one that follows order of operations, need to be aware that they must enter the string correctly for it to give the correct answer. For example, for a rectangle with a length of 4 and a width of 3, if you enter the string of numbers and operations as $4 + 3 \times 2$, most calculators will automatically follow the order of operations and multiply 3×2 before adding the 4. If you want to add $4 + 3$ first, either key in $4 + 3$ and press equal to get the sum before keying in to multiply by 2, or use the parentheses keys and key in the following: [( ] 4 [+] 3 [ )] [×] 2 [=] to find the perimeter.

Area of Triangles

In Investigation 3, students use what they have learned from finding the area and perimeter of a rectangle to find the area and perimeter of a triangle. Essentially any triangle can be thought of as half of a rectangle. If we surround a triangle with a rectangle in a particular way, two small triangles are formed, both of which are inside the rectangle and outside the triangle. These are triangles 1 and 4 in the diagram below.

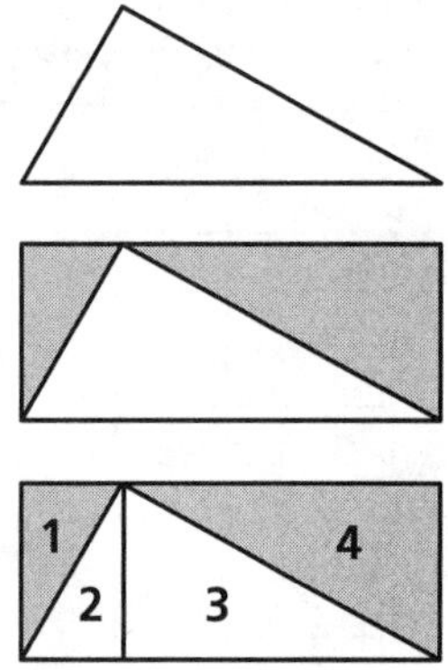

Referencing the grade 6 unit *Shapes and Designs*, students notice that the two triangles created by drawing in the height of the triangle (triangles 2 and 3 in the diagram) are congruent to the other two triangles in the rectangle (that is, triangles 1 and 2 are congruent, as are triangles 3 and 4 in the diagram).

area of triangle 1 +
area of triangle 2 +
area of triangle 3 +
area of triangle 4 = area of rectangle

Since the areas of triangle 1 and triangle 2, as well as triangle 3 and triangle 4, are the same:

2(area of triangle 2) +
2(area of triangle 3) = area of rectangle

Hence the area of the original triangle is $\frac{1}{2} b \times h$ where b is the base of the triangle (or the length of the corresponding rectangle) and h is the height of the triangle (or the width of the rectangle).

Obtuse triangles are reoriented because every obtuse triangle has one orientation where the smallest upright rectangle does not have an area equal to twice the triangle. In the first arrangement below, the rectangle and the obtuse triangle have the same base and height. In the second orientation, the base of the obtuse triangle is shorter than the base of the enclosing rectangle. (In Problem 3.2, students find that the area of a triangle is the same regardless of which side is chosen for the base.)

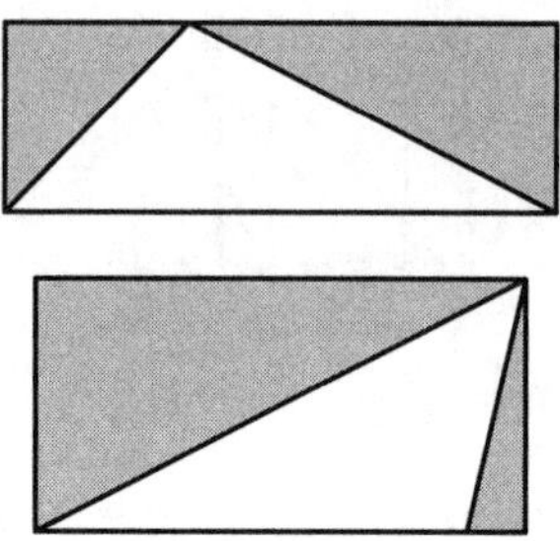

The formula for area of a triangle still holds for obtuse triangles, regardless of orientation. However, the approach modeled in Problem 3.1 does not demonstrate why this is so. Here is a proof of why the formula works for obtuse triangles:

The following obtuse triangle has a base b and a height h. It is embedded in a rectangle. Note that the bottom side of the rectangle is made up of two parts, the base of the obtuse triangle and the base of a right triangle, which is x. From the preceding demonstrations, the area of a right triangle is known. So the length or base of the rectangle is $b + x$ and its height is h.

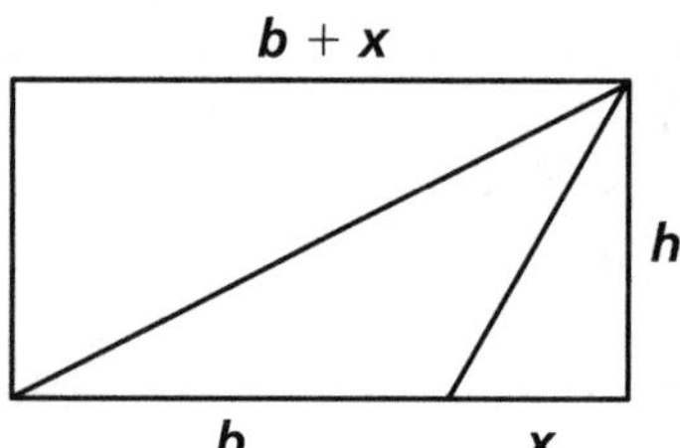

$$\begin{aligned}\text{area of the obtuse triangle} &= \text{area of the rectangle} - \text{area of the two other triangles} \\ &= h(b + x) - \frac{h(b + x)}{2} - \frac{hx}{2} \\ &= \frac{2h(b + x) - h(b + x) - hx}{2} \\ &= \frac{2hb + 2hx - hb - hx - hx}{2} \\ &= \frac{hb + 2hx - 2hx}{2} \\ &= \frac{hb}{2}\end{aligned}$$

Area of Parallelograms

The rule for area of a parallelogram is developed from students' experience finding the area of triangles. This may be a different approach than the one you have used to develop a rule for area of a parallelogram. It is not uncommon to see the rule for area of a parallelogram developed out of the rule for area of a rectangle. When students informally explore ways to find the area of parallelograms, as they will in Problem 4.2, they often offer that they can cut the parallelogram and rearrange it into a rectangle. They can then use their rule for area of a rectangle to find the area of a parallelogram. This approach can be illustrated with this diagram:

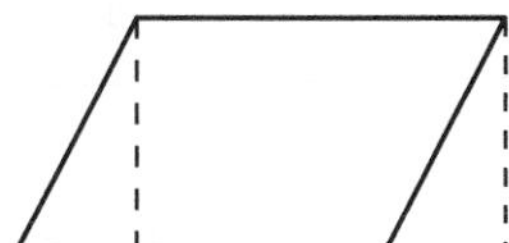

While this method works for most parallelograms, and it should be accepted when students offer it as an informal strategy, it will not work with parallelograms oriented like this one:

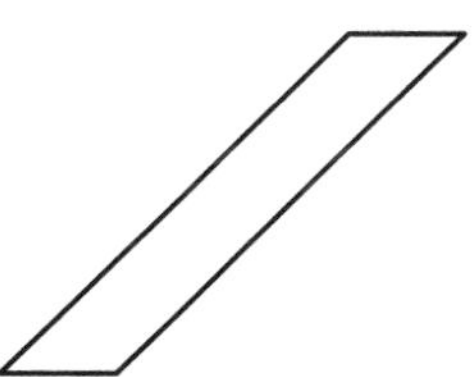

It is not possible to make one vertical cut and rearrange the pieces to form a rectangle. (Of course, one can reorient the parallelogram so that the longer side is the base. Then the rearrangement works.) But, every parallelogram can be divided into two congruent triangles by drawing one diagonal on the parallelogram, as shown:

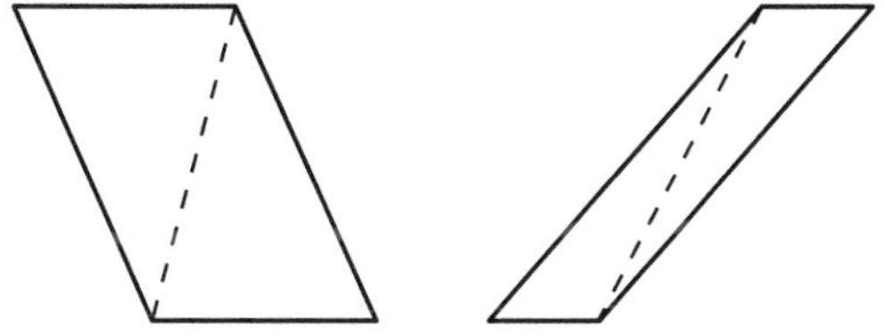

In doing so, the length of the base and height of the parallelogram is the same length as the base and height of the triangle. From this students can see that they find the area of the parallelogram by multiplying the base and height, without dividing by two, as they did when finding the area of a triangle. The area of a parallelogram is $2 \times (\frac{1}{2}b \times h)$, or just $b \times h$.

The height of a parallelogram is the perpendicular distance from the base to the side parallel to the base. As is the case with triangles, the height of a parallelogram depends on the side that is chosen for the base.

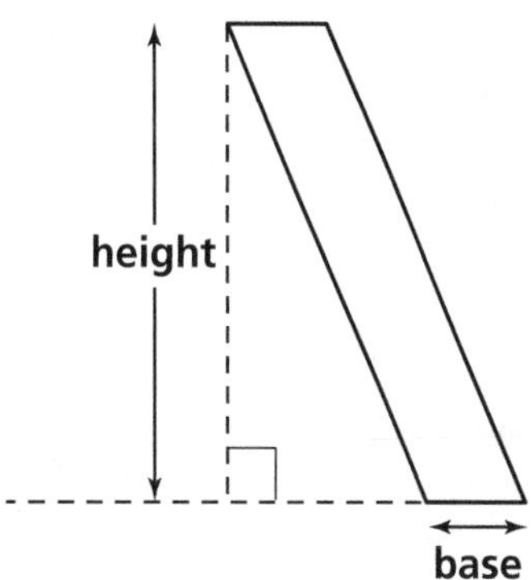

Area and Circumference of Circles

In Investigation 5, the area of a circle is developed by finding the number of squares, whose side lengths equal the radius, that cover the circle. In the diagram, the circle is enclosed in a square. Two perpendicular diameters are drawn which makes four squares whose areas are r^2. The area of the circle is less than $4r^2$. Then by either finding the number of radius squares that cover the circle or by counting the area outside the circle, but inside the larger square, the area of the circle is approximately 3 radius squares $[\pi(r \times r)$ or $\pi r^2]$.

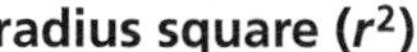

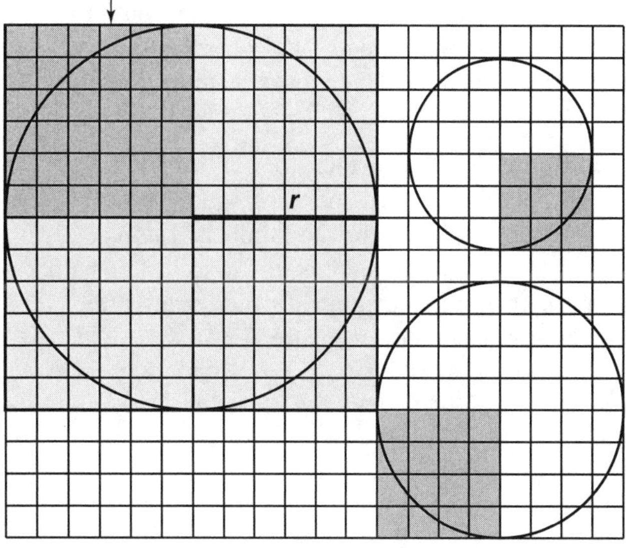

The circumference is found by counting the number of diameter lengths needed to surround the circle. The number is about 3. The circumference of a circle is πd.

Estimating Perimeter and Area of Irregular Figures

Finding an exact measurement for area and perimeter is not always possible or even necessary. However, there are methods that allow for more precise estimates. In the last investigation of the unit before finding the area and circumference of a circle, students will look at irregular shapes, using the context of lakes and shorelines, to explore ways to find reasonable estimates for perimeter and area. When estimating perimeter, students use a string to wrap around the picture of the lake and then measure the length of the string with the appropriate linear measure. A measure of length is always approximate. Once the unit of length has been selected, it can be subdivided to make more accurate measurements because there is less room for error in the approximation.

For example, suppose you approximate the length of the segment measured with two scales below.

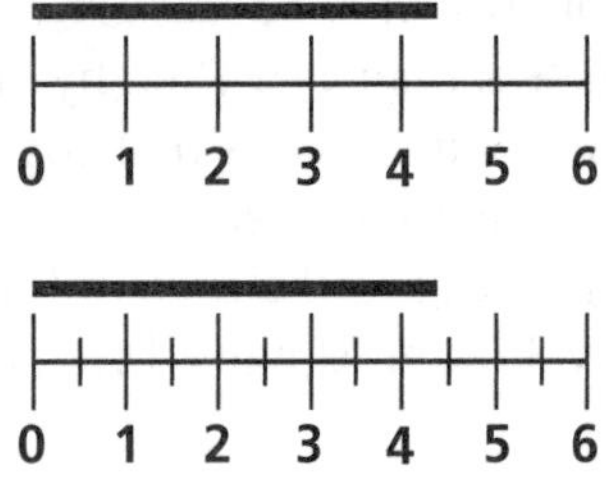

Using the upper measurement scale, you find the length is approximately 4. Using the lower measurement scale, you approximate the length as $4\frac{1}{2}$.

To measure the surface area of the lake, students select a corresponding square unit to cover the surface with. The number of units needed to cover the lake is the area. Just as with length, using smaller units for measuring area gives a more precise measurement.

In the following pictures, the object is measured first with centimeter squares and then with half-centimeter squares.

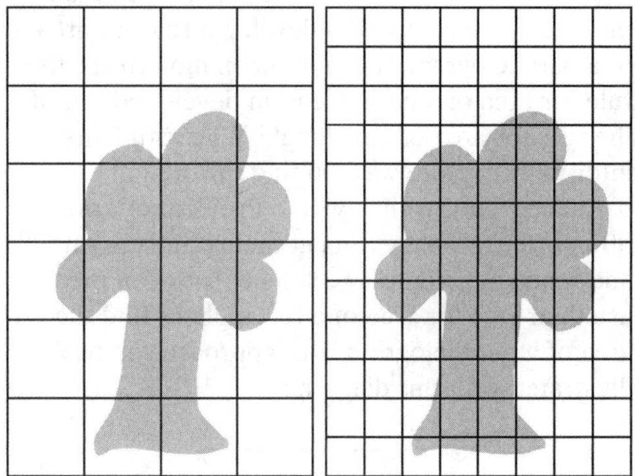

From the pictures you can see more of the tree is covered with whole units of half-centimeter squares, giving a better approximation for the answer.

Accuracy and Error

Measuring objects and comparing data from the whole class is an excellent way to help students begin to see that all measures are approximate. One can fine-tune measurements to get a degree of precision in a particular situation, but no matter how precise the instruments with which a measurement is made, error will always exist.

The investigations in *Covering and Surrounding* primarily involve whole-number situations as students begin to develop methods for finding area and perimeter. But they will also encounter many situations with rational numbers. In addition, students are likely to need fractions or decimals when measuring real objects. Students, especially those uncomfortable with fractions or decimals, may try to round all measurements to whole numbers.

You will need to encourage them to use fractions or decimals so that their measurements are more accurate.

Measurement gives rise to proportional reasoning through measurement conversions, as encountered with the units in the tree example above.

The familiarity of the situation can help students make sense of the relationships. Because they will be working with drawings that represent real objects, students will encounter problems of scale. We have tried to keep these problems manageable by carefully selecting scales that make for easy transitions from the model to the real object. The investigations have a mix of metric and standard measures.

Students will often be asked to estimate or to compare measurements. Comparing and estimating are important skills used in many kinds of quantitative situations, and they will help students develop skills in knowing whether an estimate is reasonable and appropriate, how to make estimates, and how to compare measurements in meaningful ways.

The Relationship Between Shape and Size—Maximum and Minimum

It is important for students to explore how measurements are affected when an attribute such as area or perimeter is held constant. For example, some students hold the misconception that if you know the area of a shape, you can find the perimeter. Yet, for any given area you can make many different shapes with that area, all of which could have varying perimeters. For example, both a 1-by-9 and a 3-by-3 rectangle have an area of 9 square units. The 1-by-9 rectangle is long and thin, and it will have a larger perimeter than the 3-by-3 rectangle that is square in shape. The same is true when perimeter is held constant. For a given perimeter, there are many different areas that can be designed. Of the set of rectangles with a fixed area, the rectangle that is most shaped like a square has the *least* perimeter. With no restrictions specified, there is no rectangle that has a greatest perimeter because we always can divide the width in half and double the length, $2\ell \times \frac{w}{2} = \ell w$, to make the perimeter greater. Where $\ell > w$, $2(2\ell + \frac{w}{2}) > 2\ell + 2w$. Because $4\ell + w > 2\ell + 2w$, the perimeter is greater than the perimeter of the original rectangle with dimensions ℓ and w. If we restrict the dimensions to whole numbers, it would be the rectangle that is the longest.

If the area is 9 square units, then the 1-by-9 rectangle has the greatest perimeter. But if the dimensions are not restricted to whole numbers, then a $\frac{1}{2}$-by-18 rectangle has a greater perimeter and a $\frac{1}{4}$-by-36 rectangle has an even greater perimeter.

Fixed Area

Suppose the area of a rectangle is 24 square units and its dimensions are restricted to whole numbers. The rectangle with the least perimeter is the 4-by-6 rectangle. In the set of real numbers, the rectangle with the least perimeter is the square whose side lengths are $\sqrt{24}$. This will be explored in the *Looking for Pythagoras* unit in eighth grade after they have been introduced to square roots and irrational numbers.

If we allow our shape to be something other than a rectangle (and, in context, if we had flexible walls!), then the best design is a circle with radius of approximately 2.76 meters. The circumference (perimeter) of this circle is approximately 17.37 meters.

When you are working with circles in Investigation 5 you might want to return to this problem and explore what happens to the perimeter when you use a circle with area of 24 square units instead of a rectangle.

Fixed Perimeter

Suppose the perimeter of a rectangle is 24 units and its dimensions are restricted to whole numbers. The rectangle that has the greatest area is the 6-by-6 rectangle. The 1-by-11 rectangle has the least area. If the dimensions are any real numbers, then there is no smallest area. For example, a $\frac{1}{2}$-by-$11\frac{1}{2}$ rectangle has an area of $\frac{1}{2} \times \frac{23}{2} = \frac{23}{4} = 5\frac{3}{4}$ square units, which is smaller than 11 square units. This process could continue infinitely. We could have a perimeter of 24 units with side lengths $\frac{1}{4}$ by $11\frac{1}{4}$. The area would be $\frac{1}{4} \times \frac{45}{4} = \frac{45}{16}$, which is $2\frac{13}{16}$ square units. The relationship between length and area has the shape of a parabola. This relationship will be revisited in the algebra unit, *Frogs, Fleas, and Painted Cubes*.

In Investigation 2, and other places throughout the unit, students will have an opportunity to explore the relationship between shape and size. They will consider situations where area is held constant and perimeter varies as well as situations where perimeter is held constant and area varies. These investigations help develop understanding of area and perimeter. The relationship between size and shape will be revisited when students study volume and surface area in the seventh-grade unit *Filling and Wrapping*. This work also provides a foundation for future studies in calculus.

Content Connections to Other Units

Big Idea	Prior Work	Future Work
Interpreting area as the number of square units needed to cover a two-dimensional shape	Making tessellations *(Shapes and Designs)*	Studying relationships between three-dimensional models and two-dimensional representations of the models *(Ruins of Montarek ©2004);* comparing areas of two-dimensional shapes to test for similarity *(Stretching and Shrinking);* finding surface area and volume of three-dimensional figures *(Filling and Wrapping)*
Interpreting perimeter as the number of (linear) units needed to surround a two-dimensional shape	Side lengths of polygons *(Shapes and Designs)*	Studying two-dimensional (surface area, square units) and three-dimensional (volume, cubic units) measures of figures *(Filling and Wrapping)*
Developing strategies for finding the perimeter and area of irregular two-dimensional shapes	Performing operations with rational numbers; estimating sums of rational numbers *(Prime Time, Bits and Pieces I, Bits and Pieces II)*	Finding the area and side lengths of shapes on a coordinate grid *(Looking for Pythagoras)*
Studying the relationship between perimeter and area in rectangles	Effects of side lengths on shapes of polygons *(Shapes and Designs)*	Studying the relationship between the dimensions and volume of a prism *(Filling and Wrapping)*
Developing strategies and algorithms for finding the perimeter and area of rectangles, triangles, parallelograms, and circles	Performing operations with whole numbers and finding factor pairs of whole numbers *(Prime Time);* subdividing and comparing shapes *(Shapes and Designs);* collecting data and looking for and generalizing patterns *(Prime Time, Shapes and Designs)*	Developing and applying algorithms for performing decimal calculations *(Bits and Pieces III);* developing strategies and algorithms for finding the surface area and volume of prisms, cones, and spheres *(Filling and Wrapping);* developing the Pythagorean Theorem and other equations to model algebraic and geometric patterns *(Thinking With Mathematical Models; Looking for Pythagoras; Growing, Growing, Growing; Frogs, Fleas, and Painted Cubes; Say It With Symbols; The Shapes of Algebra)*

Planning for the Unit

Pacing Suggestions and Materials

Investigations and Assessments	Pacing 45–50 min. classes	Materials for Students	Materials for Teachers
1 Designing Bumper Cars	4 days	Labsheets 1.2, 1.3; square tiles; cm grid paper; string (optional)	Transparencies 1.1, 1.2, 1.3A–C; square tiles; string (at least 18 cm long)
Mathematical Reflections	$\frac{1}{2}$ day		
2 Changing Area, Changing Perimeter	5 days	Labsheets 2.1, 2.3, 2ACE 3–5, 2ACE 10–12, 2ACE 23; square tiles; string; scissors; inch grid paper; several 24-cm loops of string (optional)	Transparencies 2.1A, 2.1B, 2.2, 2.3A, 2.3B; 4-by-6 rectangle cut from inch (or two-inch) grid paper or transparency
Mathematical Reflections	$\frac{1}{2}$ day		
Assessment: Check Up	$\frac{1}{2}$ day		
3 Measuring Triangles	5 days	Labsheets 3.1, 3.2A, 3.2B, 3ACE 1–6, 3ACE 26–31; scissors; cut-outs from a transparency copy of Labsheet 3.2 (optional); cm grid paper	Transparencies 3.1A–D, 3.2A, 3.2B, 3.3; transparent cm ruler (optional); shape T from Shapes Set (optional)
Mathematical Reflections	$\frac{1}{2}$ day		
Assessment: Partner Quiz	1 day		
4 Measuring Parallelograms	5 days	Labsheets 4.1, 4.2A, 4.2B, 4ACE 1–7, 4ACE 14–19, 4ACE 39; cut-outs from a transparency copy of Labsheet 4.2 (optional); scissors	Transparencies 4.1A, 4.1B, 4.2, 4.4A, 4.4B
Mathematical Reflections	$\frac{1}{2}$ day		
5 Measuring Irregular Shapes and Circles	5 days	Labsheets 5.1, 5.3A, 5.3B, 5.4, 5ACE 1 and 2, 5ACE 3 and 4; string; rulers; tape measures; several circular objects of different sizes; scissors; glue; construction paper (optional); cm grid paper; transparency of cm grid	Transparencies 5.1, 5.2A, 5.2B, 5.3, 5.4A, 5.4B
Mathematical Reflections	$\frac{1}{2}$ day		
Looking Back and Looking Ahead	$\frac{1}{2}$ day		
Assessment: Unit Project	Optional		
Assessment: Self Assessment	Take Home		
Assessment: Unit Test	1 day		

Total Time **$29\frac{1}{2}$ days**

For detailed pacing for Problems within each Investigation, see the Suggested Pacing at the beginning of each Investigation.

For pacing with block scheduling, see next page.

Materials for Use in All Investigations	
Calculators, blank transparencies and transparency markers (optional), student notebooks	Blank transparencies and transparency markers (optional)

Pacing for Block Scheduling (90-minute class periods)

Investigation	Suggested Pacing	Investigation	Suggested Pacing	Investigation	Suggested Pacing
Investigation 1	**$2\frac{1}{2}$ days**	**Investigation 3**	**3 days**	**Investigation 5**	**3 days**
Problem 1.1	$\frac{1}{2}$ day	Problem 3.1	1 day	Problem 5.1	$\frac{1}{2}$ day
Problem 1.2	$\frac{1}{2}$ day	Problem 3.2	$\frac{1}{2}$ day	Problem 5.2	$\frac{1}{2}$ day
Problem 1.3	1 day	Problem 3.3	$\frac{1}{2}$ day	Problem 5.3	$\frac{1}{2}$ day
Math Reflections	$\frac{1}{2}$ day	Problem 3.4	$\frac{1}{2}$ day	Problem 5.4	1 day
Investigation 2	**3 days**	Math Reflections	$\frac{1}{2}$ day	Math Reflections	$\frac{1}{2}$ day
Problem 2.1	1 day	**Investigation 4**	**3 days**		
Problem 2.2	$\frac{1}{2}$ day	Problem 4.1	$\frac{1}{2}$ day		
Problem 2.3	$\frac{1}{2}$ day	Problem 4.2	1 day		
Problem 2.4	$\frac{1}{2}$ day	Problem 4.3	$\frac{1}{2}$ day		
Math Reflections	$\frac{1}{2}$ day	Problem 4.4	$\frac{1}{2}$ day		
		Math Reflections	$\frac{1}{2}$ day		

Vocabulary

Essential Terms Developed in This Unit	Useful Terms Referenced in This Unit	Terms Developed in Previous Units
area	center	diagonal
base	concentric circles	isosceles
circumference	congruent	parallelogram
diameter	dimension	perpendicular
height	fixed (in the sense of unchanging)	rectangle
length	irrational number	right angle
perimeter	maximum area/perimeter	right triangle
pi (π)	minimum area/perimeter	scalene
radius	pentomino	trapezoid
width	size	triangle

Program Resources

Go Online
PHSchool.com
For: Teacher Resources
Web Code: amk-5500

Components

Use the chart below to quickly see which components are available for each Investigation.

Investigation	Labsheets	Additional Practice	Transparencies		Formal Assessment		Assessment Options	
			Problem	Summary	Check Up	Partner Quiz	Multiple-Choice	Question Bank
1	1.2, 1.3	✔	1.1, 1.2, 1.3A, 1.3B, 1.3C				✔	✔
2	2.1, 2.3, 2ACE 3–5, 2ACE 10–12, 2ACE 23	✔	2.1A, 2.1B, 2.2, 2.3A, 2.3B		✔			✔
3	3.1, 3.2A, 3.2B, 3ACE 1–6, 3ACE 26–31	✔	3.1A, 3.1B, 3.1C, 3.2, 3.3				✔	✔
4	4.1, 4.2A, 4.2B, 4ACE 1–7, 4ACE 39	✔	4.1A, 4.1B, 4.2, 4.4A, 4.4B			✔		
5	5.1, 5.3A, 5.3B, 5.4, 5ACE 1–2, 5ACE 3–4	✔	5.1, 5.2A, 5.2B, 5.3, 5.4A, 5.4B				✔	✔
Unit Project							✔	✔
For the Unit	Grid paper (half-cm, cm, quarter-in., half-in., in.)	*ExamView* CD-ROM, Web site			Unit Test, Unit Project, Notebook Check, Self Assessment		Multiple-Choice, Question Bank, *ExamView* CD-ROM	

Also Available for Use With This Unit

- Parent Guide: take-home brochure for the unit
- Implementing CMP
- Spanish Assessment Resources
- Additional online and technology resources

Technology

The Use of Calculators

Connected Mathematics was developed with the belief that calculators should be available and that students should learn when their use is appropriate. For this reason, we do not designate specific problems as "calculator problems."

Student Interactivity CD-ROM

Includes the interactive activities Areas and Perimeters of Shapes and Images and GeoExplore Tool.

Also available online at PHSchool.com, Web Code amk-5500.

PHSchool.com

For Students Multiple-choice practice with instant feedback, updated data sources, data sets for Tinkerplots data software.

For Teachers Professional development, curriculum support, downloadable forms, and more.

See also www.math.msu.edu/cmp for more resources for both teachers and students.

ExamView® CD-ROM

Create multiple versions of practice sheets and tests for course objectives and standardized tests. Includes dynamic questions, online testing, student reports, and all test items and practice items in Spanish. Also includes all items in the *Assessment Resources* and *Additional Practice*.

Teacher Express™ CD-ROM

Includes a lesson planning tool, the Teacher's Guide pages, and all the teaching resources.

LessonLab Online Courses

LessonLab offers comprehensive, facilitated professional development designed to help teachers implement CMP2 and improve student achievement. To learn more, please visit PHSchool.com/cmp2.

Assessment Summary

Ongoing Informal Assessment

Embedded in the Student Unit

Problems Use students' work from the Problems to informally check student understanding.

ACE exercises Use ACE exercises for homework assignments to assess student understanding.

Mathematical Reflections Have students summarize their learning at the end of each Investigation.

Looking Back and Looking Ahead At the end of the unit, use the first two sections to allow students to show what they know about the unit.

Additional Resources

Teacher's Guide Use the Check for Understanding feature of some Summaries and the probing questions that appear in the *Launch, Explore,* or *Summarize* sections of all Investigations to check student understanding.

Self Assessment

Notebook Check Students use this tool to organize and check their notebooks before giving them to their teacher. Located in *Assessment Resources*.

Self Assessment At the end of the unit, students reflect on and provide examples of what they learned. Located in *Assessment Resources*.

Formal Assessment

Connected Mathematics provides many options for assessment so that you can choose the instructional materials that are appropriate for your students.

Assessment	For Use After	Focus	Student Work
Check Up	Invest. 2	Skills, rich problems	Individual
Partner Quiz	Invest. 4	Rich problems	Pair
Unit Project	The Unit	Rich problems	Individual, pair
Unit Test	The Unit	Skills, rich problems	Individual

Additional Resources

Multiple-Choice Items Use these items for homework, review, a quiz, or add them to the Unit Test.

Question Bank Choose from these questions for homework, review, or replacements for Quiz, Check Up, or Unit Test questions.

Additional Practice Choose practice exercises for each Investigation for homework, review, or formal assessments.

***ExamView* Test Generator** Create practice sheets, quizzes, and tests with this dynamic software. Give online tests and receive student progress reports. *(All test items are also available in Spanish.)*

Spanish Assessment Resources

Includes Partner Quizzes, Check Up, Unit Test, Multiple-Choice Items, Question Bank, Notebook Check, and Self Assessment. Plus, the *ExamView* Test Generator has all test items in Spanish.

Correlation to Standardized Tests

Investigation	NAEP	Terra Nova CAT6	Terra Nova CTBS	ITBS	SAT10	Local Test
1 Designing Bumper Cars	M1h, M2b, M2f	✔	✔	✔	✔	
2 Changing Area, Changing Perimeter	G1d, G2d, M2f	✔	✔	✔	✔	
3 Measuring Triangles	G5a, M2a, M1h	✔	✔		✔	
4 Measuring Parallelograms	M2a, M2d, G3f	✔	✔		✔	
5 Measuring Irregular Shapes and Circles	M1b, M1C M1g					

NAEP National Assessment of Educational Progress
CAT6/Terra Nova California Achievement Test, 6th Ed.
CTBS/Terra Nova Comprehensive Test of Basic Skills
ITBS Iowa Test of Basic Skills, Form M
SAT10 Stanford Achievement Test, 10th Ed.

Launching the Unit

Introducing Your Students to *Covering and Surrounding*

One way to introduce your students to this unit is to ask them to think about measurement. What aspects of a classroom could we measure? Examples might include the temperature, the number of students that can fit inside, the height of the ceiling, etc. When students mention *size*, press them to be specific about how to measure size. What do they mean when they say one classroom is larger than another? Tell students that in this unit, we will focus on two measures: area and perimeter. Listen to know what students already know about these measurements. Ask the class what other types of things are measured (time, temperature, rates, etc. . . .).

Using the Unit Opener

Briefly discuss the questions posed on the opening page of the Student Edition, which are designed to start students thinking about the kinds of questions and mathematics in the unit. Don't look for "correct" answers at this time. Do, however, present an opportunity for the class to discuss the questions and to start to think about what is needed to answer them. You may want to revisit these questions as students learn the mathematical ideas and techniques necessary to find the answers.

Mathematical Highlights

The Mathematical Highlights page in the Student Edition provides information to students, parents, and other family members. It gives students a preview of the mathematics and some of the overarching questions that they should ask themselves while studying *Covering and Surrounding.*

As they work through the unit, students can refer back to the Mathematical Highlights page to review what they have learned and to preview what is still to come. This page also tells students' families what mathematical ideas and activities will be covered as the class works through *Covering and Surrounding*.

Using the Unit Project

Plan a Park is the final assessment for *Covering and Surrounding*. The project gives students an opportunity to think about the amount of area things occupy. They will need to use measurement skills, concepts of area and perimeter, and reasoning about size and space to create their design. This project could be assigned as an individual, partner, or small-group project.

Assign the project near the end of the unit (during or after Investigation 5). Although this project will take several hours to complete, most of the work can be done outside of class. You may want to take 15 to 20 minutes to launch the project in class and then have students finish the project as homework. Read through the description of the unit project, in the Student Edition, with the class. Make sure everyone understands the project, including the idea that students are asked that the park be divided into two parts, but that half the total area be reserved for what the city council has specified. The elements the city council requires (the playground area, the picnic area, and the trees) can be located anywhere in the park.

See the Guide to the Unit Project on page 134 for detailed information about assigning and assessing the project, a scoring rubric, and sample projects.

Designing Bumper Cars

Mathematical and Problem-Solving Goals

- Learn that the area of a figure is the number of square units needed to cover it
- Learn that the perimeter of an object is the number of units of length needed to surround it
- Understand that two figures with the same area may have different perimeters
- Use the relationship between length and width to develop formulas for the area and perimeter of a rectangle

In the context of bumper-car rides, students study perimeter, area, and relationships between them. This investigation involves simple shapes constructed from square tiles and leads to formulas for area and perimeter of rectangles. Rectangles are presented in a variety of ways: on grids, off grids, and described by dimensions alone.

Mathematics Background

For background on the measuring process, see page 4.

Summary of Problems

Problem 1.1 Designing Bumper-Car Rides

Problem 1.1 is an introduction to area, perimeter, and the study of relationships between them through a motivating discussion of bumper-car designs.

Problem 1.2 Pricing Bumper-Car Rides

Students compare costs of bumper-car rides, demonstrating that shapes with the same area need not have the same perimeter.

Problem 1.3 Decoding Designs

Students develop formulas for area and perimeter of rectangles.

	Suggested Pacing	Materials for Students	Materials for Teachers	ACE Assignments
ll	4 days	Calculators, student notebooks, centimeter grid paper	Blank transparencies and transparency markers (optional)	
.1	1 day	Square tiles (24 per student or pair)	Transparency 1.1, square tiles	1–6
.2	1 day	Square tiles (24 per student or pair), Labsheet 1.2	Transparency 1.2, square tiles	7–15, 28–30, 34, 35, 39, 40
.3	$1\frac{1}{2}$ days	Labsheet 1.3, string (one piece at least 18 cm long per student, optional)	Transparencies 1.3A, 1.3B, 1.3C; string (one piece at least 18 cm long)	16–27, 31–33, 36–38, 41, 42
IR	$\frac{1}{2}$ day			

1.1 Designing Bumper-Car Rides

Goals

- Learn that the area of a figure is the number of square units needed to cover it
- Learn that the perimeter of an object is the number of units of length needed to surround it

In this problem, students are asked to design two bumper-car floor plans: one with an area of 36 m^2 and a perimeter of 26 m and a second with an area of 36 m^2 and "many" rail sections. The last question introduces the terms *area* (for covering) and *perimeter* (for surrounding).

Launch 1.1

Launch the problem by telling students about the fictitious Midway Amusement Rides company. You might help your students with the context by adding to the story.

- *These tiles are similar to what the designers use to make their models of bumper-car floor plans. (Hold up a tile.) Each tile represents 1 m^2.*
- *Let's think of this tile as the world's simplest bumper-car floor plan. A design that consists of only one tile represents a 1 m^2 design that would require 4 m of bumper rail to surround it. Of course, this would only hold a very small car!*

Begin a table on the board for recording data.

- *Now make a bumper-car floor plan from two tiles.*

Make sure the class understands that the tiles of bumper-car floor plans must fit together edge to edge.

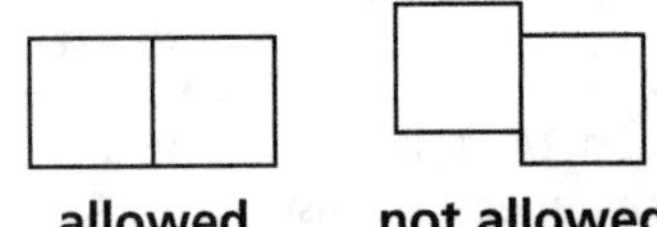

Suggested Questions

- *How many meters of railing would this floor need?* (6)
- *I notice that some of you have your tiles arranged this way. (Hold up, or display on the overhead projector, the following arrangements.)*

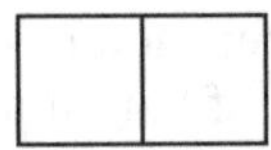

- *And some of you have your tiles arranged this way.*

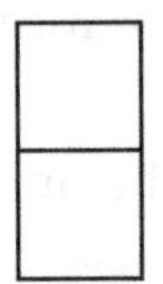

- *Did you get the same number of rails for each of these arrangements?* (yes)
- *Since the different orientations use the same number of tiles and the same number of rails, we can list the information once.* (Add 2 to the "Number of Tiles" column and 6 to the "Number of Rails" column.)

Number of Tiles	Number of Rails
1	4
2	6

- *Show me a design made of 3 m^2. How many meters of railing does it need?*
- *Some of you have arranged your tiles this way.* (Show the following arrangement.)

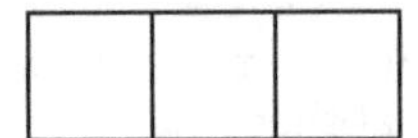

- *And some of you have arranged your tiles this way.*

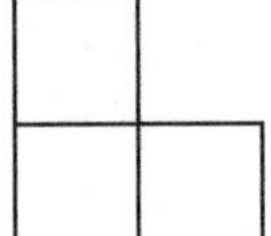

- *Do these two arrangements require the same number of rail sections?* (Yes; add the information about three tiles to the chart.)

Number of Tiles	Number of Rails
1	4
2	6
3	8

- *Show me a design with 4 m² of flooring. How many meters of railing does it need?*
- *Some possible designs are shown.*

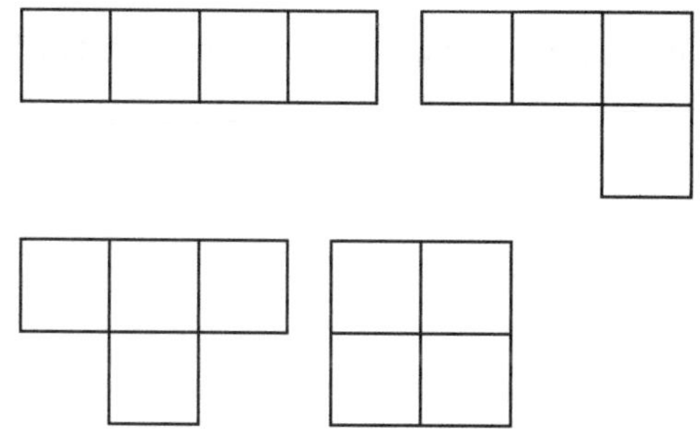

The first three designs require 10 m of railing. The 2-by-2 design requires only 8 m of railing. Record both possibilities on the chart.

Number of Tiles	Number of Rails
1	4
2	6
3	8
4	10
4	8

Ask students whether there are other numbers of tiles that can be arranged in more than one way so that different numbers of rail sections are required. Do not try to find a definite answer at this time. Leave the question for students to think about.

Students should now be ready to tackle Problem 1.1. Have students make sketches of their designs on grid paper so that they can reuse their tiles for the next part of the problem.

Have students work in pairs.

Explore 1.1

Students will need time to talk about and experiment with the tiles. As you visit with them, be sure their sketches for Questions A and B are complete and clearly show 36 tiles have been used in each design. If students are still struggling with constructing designs for a given number of tiles or figuring out how many rails are needed to surround a design, you may want to continue the exploration by asking students to design bumper-car floors with 12 tiles.

Here are a few possible arrangements.

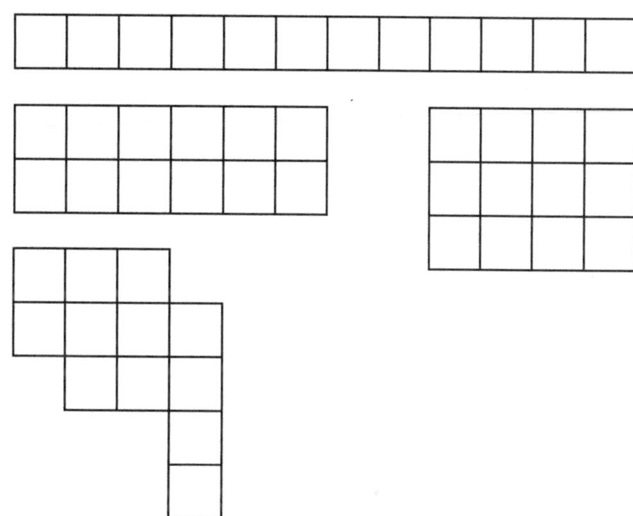

You would need 26 rail sections for the 1-by-12 rectangle, 16 for the 2-by-6 rectangle, 14 for the 3-by-4 rectangle, and 18 for the given nonrectangular shape.

Students could put their designs on poster paper to use in the summary.

Summarize 1.1

Have pairs share their results for Questions A and B. Ask students to explain why their designs meet the requirements. Keep students focused on the mathematics and what is happening to the perimeter (the number of rails needed) as they look at the variety of designs with the same area.

Suggested Questions Discuss the ideas and questions presented in Question C. Talk about the labels for area and perimeter measure by relating each to what is being counted.

- *What are you actually counting when you measure area?* (The number of square tiles covering the figure.)
- *What are you actually counting when you measure perimeter?* (The number of units of length surrounding the figure.)
- *How are these measurements different from each other?* (The kinds of units being counted are different; squares in one case, lengths in the other.)

Push students to talk about how area is labeled in square units because it is a measurement of how many squares of a certain size are needed to cover a shape. Perimeter is labeled in units of length such as a foot or a centimeter (linear units), because it is a measurement of how many segments of a specific length are needed to surround a shape. Talk with students about the importance of labeling measures. The label tells what units are being used.

You can also begin a conversation about fixed area.

- *Look at the floor plans that have an area of 36 m^2. Which one has the least perimeter? The greatest perimeter?*

This summary can help launch Problem 1.2.

1.1 Designing Bumper-Car Rides

At a Glance

PACING 1 day

Mathematical Goals

- Learn that the area of a figure is the number of square units needed to cover it
- Learn that the perimeter of an object is the number of units of length needed to surround it

Launch

Tell students about the bumper-car rides.

- *Let's think of this tile as the world's simplest bumper-car floor plan. A design that consists of only one tile represents a 1-m^2 design that would require 4 m of bumper rail to surround it.*

Begin a table on the board for recording data. Have students find the possible ways to arrange 2 tiles. Make sure the class understands that the tiles of bumper-car floor plans must fit together edge to edge. Discuss and record on the table. Repeat with 3 tiles.

- *Show me a design with 4 m^2 of flooring. How many meters of railing does it need?*

Ask students whether there are other numbers of tiles that can be arranged in more than one way so that different numbers of rail sections are required. Do not try to find a definite answer at this time. Leave the question for students to think about.

Have students make sketches of their designs on grid paper in pairs.

Materials

- Square tiles (24 per student or pair)
- Centimeter grid paper

Explore

Students will need time to talk about and experiment with the tiles. As you visit with them, be sure their sketches for Questions A and B are complete and clearly show 36 tiles have been used in each design.

If students are still struggling with constructing designs for a given number of tiles or figuring out how many rails are needed, continue by asking students to design bumper-car floors with 12 tiles.

Summarize

Have pairs share their results for Questions A and B. Ask students to explain why their designs meet the requirements. Keep students focused on the mathematics and what is happening to the perimeter (the number of rails needed) as they look at the variety of designs with the same area.

Talk about the labels for area and perimeter measure by relating each to what is being counted.

- *What are you actually counting when you measure area?*

Materials

- Transparency 1.1
- Student notebooks

Vocabulary

- area
- perimeter

continued on next page

Summarize
continued

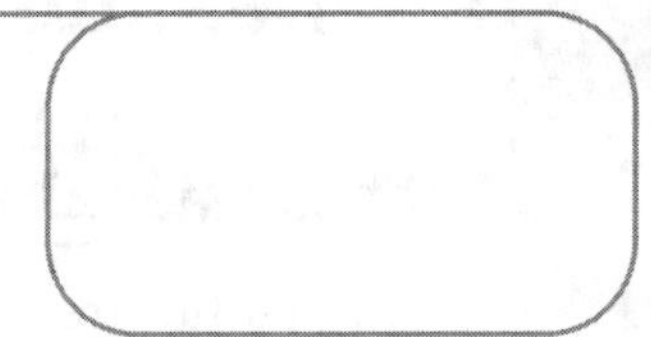

- *What are you actually counting when you measure perimeter?*
- *How are these measurements different from each other?*

Talk with students about the importance of labeling measures.

ACE Assignment Guide for Problem 1.1

Core 1–5

Other *Applications* 6

Adapted For suggestions about adapting Exercise 6 and other ACE exercises, see the CMP *Special Needs Handbook.*

Answers to Problem 1.1

A. Possible answers: The floor plan could be a 9-by-4 rectangle, or a 5-by-7 rectangle with an additional square somewhere.

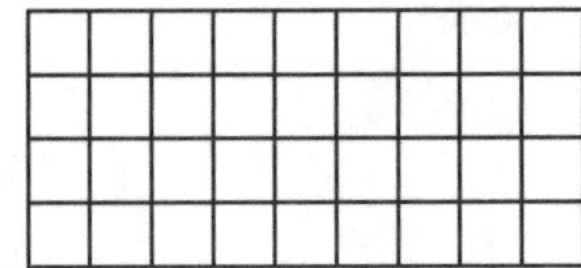

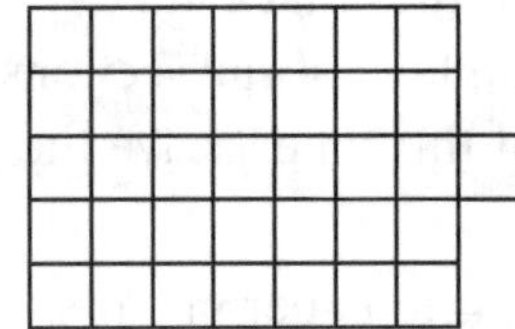

B. Possible answer:

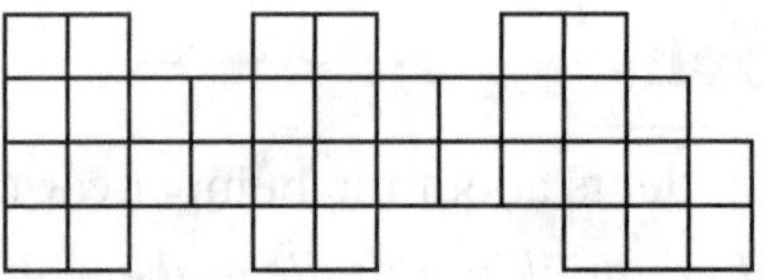

The area is 36 m^2. The perimeter is 40 m.

The largest perimeter possible for 36 squares and whole-number dimensions is a 1-by-36 rectangle with a perimeter of 74 m, but it wouldn't make a very interesting bumper-car design. NOTE: There are other, nonrectangular arrangements with this same perimeter.

C. **1.** area: 45 m^2; perimeter: 32 m

2. Possible answer: Area is probably a better measure, because it indicates the amount of space available for the bumper cars to move around on.

1.2 Pricing Bumper-Car Rides

Goals

- Learn that the area of a figure is the number of square units needed to cover it
- Learn that the perimeter of an object is the number of units of length needed to surround it
- Understand that two figures with the same area may have different perimeters

In this problem, students examine several different floor plans. They continue to find perimeters and areas. They will also consider how perimeter and area affects the cost of building different designs. For example, how is cost affected when plans have the same area but different perimeters or the same perimeter but different areas?

Launch 1.2

Provide students with a copy of Labsheet 1.2. Discuss the challenge of the problem with your class. See the summary of Problem 1.1 as a possible launch to this problem.

As you talk about the chart students are to make in Question A, revisit the definitions of area and perimeter. Talk with students about what area and perimeter mean as well as what each one is measuring. Depending on your students, you might find it helpful to work as a class to fill in the table for Design A.

Allow students to continue working on the problem, individually or in pairs.

Explore 1.2

As you observe students working, help those who are still confused about perimeter. Some may be counting the squares that line the edge of the figure instead of counting the side lengths around the outside of the figure (see pages 4 and 5). Have some tiles ready for students who want to make the shapes themselves.

Look to see if students understand what Question B is asking. Figures with the same area may have different perimeters.

Question D asks students to design bumper-car floor plans. As students work, look for interesting floor plans. Ask these students to make an overhead transparency of their floor plan to share in the summary.

Also be on the lookout for students who are struggling with the cost computations. You may want to have such students break down the cost calculations systematically by adding columns for rail cost, floor cost and total cost to their tables.

Going Further

You might ask some students to design two floor plans with the same cost, but different areas.

Summarize 1.2

Have students share the information in their charts and push them to talk about what they were actually measuring or counting when they arrived at their solutions. As you move the discussion from Question A to Question B, encourage students to look for relationships between area and perimeter.

Suggested Questions For Question A, ask:

- *What is the area of Design A?* (16 square units)
- *How did you find it?* (counting; multiplying length by width)
- *What were you counting?* (squares inside the shape)
- *What is the perimeter of Design A?* (16 units)
- *How did you find it?* (counting; adding two sides, then doubling the result)
- *What were you counting?* (the exposed sides of the square tiles that form the boundary)

Question B, part (1), does not explicitly indicate whether it is asking for area or perimeter. Students have to realize that floor tiles measure area.

- *Which part of the table, area or perimeter, did you use to answer Question B, part (1)? Why?*

You could discuss Question B by grouping the designs by area. Discussion should emphasize that although many floor plans have the same area, the perimeter and cost vary. Use questions like these:

- *Do any other designs have an area of 16 m^2?* (Yes; Design B does also.)
- *Do all designs with 16 m^2 of floor space cost the same?* (no)

Be sure to ask students to explain what causes designs with the same area and different perimeters to have different costs.

- *What is causing the difference in cost? Why?* (They have the same area, but the perimeters are different.)

Question C does not involve cost, but continues to explore perimeter and area relationships. Be sure to ask students to explain their reasoning.

- *Can you find two designs, each with a perimeter of 18 m?* (yes; B, D, and F)
- *Do all of these designs have the same area?* (no)

For Question D, part (1), ask students to share their floor plans and talk about how they found the area, perimeter and cost. There is no single correct answer for part (2), but students should be able to argue their choice in some way.

Throughout the summary have students talk about how they found area and perimeter. Verify that students can at least find each measurement by counting. By this point in the unit, all students should be able to count squares to find area and count exposed edges to find perimeter. If some are still struggling, find a way for them to get additional help and practice with these concepts.

1.2 Pricing Bumper-Car Rides

At a Glance

PACING 1 day

Mathematical Goals

- Learn that the area of a figure is the number of square units needed to cover it
- Learn that the perimeter of an object is the number of units of length needed to surround it
- Understand that two figures with the same area may have different perimeters

Launch

Provide students with a copy of Labsheet 1.2. Read through the problem with your class. Revisit the definitions of area and perimeter. You might find it helpful to work as a class to fill in the table for Design A. Allow students to continue working on the problem, individually or in pairs.

Materials

- Square tiles (24 per student or pair)
- Labsheet 1.2

Explore

Help those students who are still confused about perimeter. Have some tiles ready for students who want to make the shapes themselves.

Look to see if students understand what Question B is asking. For part (2), see if students chose designs with a common area.

Question D asks students to design bumper-car floor plans. As students work, look for interesting floor plans. Ask these students to make an overhead transparency of their floor plan to share in the summary.

As an extra challenge, you might ask some students to design two floor plans with the same cost, but different areas.

Materials

- Transparency 1.2

Summarize

Ask students to share the information in their charts. Encourage students to look for relationships between area and perimeter.

- *What is the area of Design A? How did you find it? What were you counting?*
- *What is the perimeter of Design A? How did you find it? What were you counting?*

Check that students have found area for Question B, part (1).

- *Which part of the table, area or perimeter, did you use to answer Question B, part (1)? Why?*

Discussion should emphasize that although many floor plans have the same area, the perimeter and cost vary.

- *Do any other designs have an area of 16 m^2? Do all designs with 16 m^2 of floor space cost the same?*

Ask students to explain what causes designs with the same area and different perimeters to have different costs.

Be sure to ask students to explain their reasoning in Question C.

Materials

- Student notebooks

continued on next page

Summarize

continued

- *Can you find two designs, each with a perimeter of 18 m? Do all of these designs have the same area?*

Throughout the summary have students talk about how they found area and perimeter. Verify that students can at least find each measurement by counting.

ACE Assignment Guide for Problem 1.2

Core 7, 9–15, 28

Other *Applications* 8; *Connections* 29, 30, 34, 35; *Extensions* 39, 40; unassigned choices from previous problems

Adapted For suggestions about adapting ACE exercises, see the CMP *Special Needs Handbook*.

Connecting to Prior Units 34: *Prime Time, Bits and Pieces I*

Answers to Problem 1.2

A.

Design	Area (m^2)	Perimeter (m)
A	16	16
B	16	18
C	12	26
D	18	18
E	12	26
F	12	18
G	15	20
H	18	38

B. 1. Designs A and B each have an area of 16 m^2; Designs C, E, and F each have an area of 12 m^2; Designs D and H each have an area of 18 m^2.

2. Design A has a perimeter of 16 m and Design B has a perimeter of 18 m. Design C has a perimeter of 26 m, Design E has a perimeter of 26 m, and Design F has a perimeter of 18 m. Design D has a perimeter of 18 m and Design H has a perimeter of 38 m.

3. In any set, the design with the largest perimeter (B, C/E, H) will cost the most and the design with the smallest perimeter (A, F, D) will cost the least. The area is the same in each design making the cost of the flooring the same for each. Therefore, the perimeter determines the cost. The design with the largest perimeter requires the most rail sections and, as a result, costs more to build. Likewise, the design with the smallest perimeter requires the fewest rail sections and costs less to build.

C. 1. 18 tiles can be arranged to make each of these rectangles and perimeters:

Rectangle	Perimeter
18 m by 1 m	38 m
9 m by 2 m	22 m
6 m by 3 m	18 m

No; the perimeters are different because longer, thinner rectangles have more tiles with exposed edges. The rectangles that are wider have fewer tiles with exposed edges and more tiles in the middle.

2. No; the designs may have the same perimeter but they do not have the same area. Design B is arranged using 16 tiles. Design D uses 18 tiles.

D. 1. Designs will vary and costs are dependent on the number of tiles and rail sections used. Two possible answers:

7 m by 5 m: area = 35 m^2, perimeter = 24 m, cost = \$1,650.00

6 m by 6 m: area = 36 m^2, perimeter = 24 m, cost = \$1,680.00

2. Answers will vary. For the designs offered in part (1), a possible explanation might be to get the 6-by-6 floor plan, which has more area for the same perimeter. Another possible answer is that the 7-by-5 floor plan is almost the same area and the same perimeter for \$30 less.

1.3 Decoding Designs

Goal

- Use the relationship between length and width to develop formulas for the area and perimeter of a rectangle

This problem is laid out so that students shift from finding the area of rectangles drawn on grid paper to rectangles whose dimensions (length and width) are described in words. In Question A, students work with the two types of rectangles on grid paper shown in the figure below.

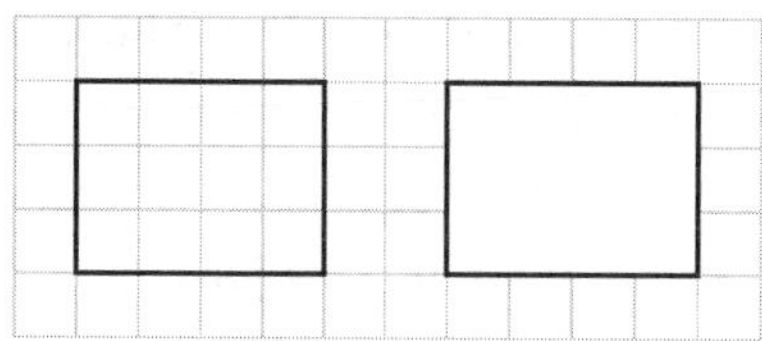

In Question B, the grids are removed and students work with diagrams of rectangles with labeled dimensions. In Question C, a rectangle's dimensions are described in words. A picture is not provided. Across Questions A–C you will want to focus on the strategies that students use to find the area of rectangles. Continue to monitor how students are making sense of area and perimeter, and what each is measuring.

In Question D students are introduced to the term *dimension*. They will be asked to write rules for finding the area and the perimeter of any rectangle. Students will use these rules in Investigation 2. Any rectangle can be described by two dimensions. It is standard to call these dimensions *length* and *width*. It is not generally agreed which dimension is which, however. In both the Student Edition and Teacher's Guide of this unit, length will sometimes be used to describe the horizontal side of a rectangle, and sometimes the vertical side. You may wish in certain problems to agree as a class on which dimension to call length and which width in order to make conversation easier.

Bear in mind though, that this decision is arbitrary and not standard in the world of mathematics.

You will want to consider your students when deciding how to structure work on Problem 1.3. Working with a partner will be helpful. You may choose to have students work on Questions A–C, then stop and discuss these parts before moving on to Question D. Alternatively, you may choose for your students to work through all the problems before summarizing.

Launch 1.3

Suggested Questions Give students some time to think about the questions in the Getting Ready on their own. Then discuss the Getting Ready with the class.

- *What do you think the student did next?* (The next thing that she did was she stretched out the string and measured it. She was finding the perimeter of the figure. She got the same answer that she got by counting, 18 cm.)

Help them to see that the student would get the same measurement for the perimeter if she counted the exposed side lengths of each centimeter square, or if she used a centimeter ruler to measure the string. This transition from counting to measuring is an important one for student learning of measurement concepts, and can be difficult for many students. Students may notice that the string measurement may not be as accurate as counting since the string does not fit as nicely on the perimeter. Later in this unit, students will need to measure the perimeters of figures for which they cannot count whole units. It is important to help students now to understand that both techniques give the same result so that they are ready to use strings when counting no longer works.

- *How could this student find the area?* (Count all the squares.)

Give each student a copy of Labsheet 1.3. Briefly explain the problem to the students. Be sure they understand that Questions A, B, and C ask them to consider bumper-car floor plans that come with different types of diagrams and descriptions: gridded, diagrams with dimensions labeled, and written descriptions.

Question D introduces the term *dimension*, although you may wish to do this in the launch.

Suggested Question Ask students to think about Problem 1.2, Question C, where they were asked to make rectangular bumper-car floor plans using 18 floor tiles.

- *What are the dimensions, or the length and width, of a rectangle you can make with 18 floor tiles?* (3 by 6; 9 by 2; 1 by 18)

Students can work on this problem in groups of 2 or 3.

Explore 1.3

As students are working, look at the different explanations students write for Questions A, parts (1) and (2).

Listening to Students

Consider the following questions as you watch students work on this problem:

- *What strategies are students using to find area and perimeter?*
- *What are students counting when they find area?*
- *What are students counting when they find the perimeter?*
- *Do students have other strategies besides counting for finding area and perimeter?*
- *Do they use the terms* length *and* width *in conversation?*

Have students share their strategies in the summary. Ask the class to discuss each strategy.

If students have trouble with Question C, you might suggest that they draw a diagram of the bumper-car floor plan that is described and label the length and width.

Summarize 1.3

The goal of the summary is to develop rules for finding the area and perimeter of rectangles. As students share their solutions also have them share their strategies for finding area and perimeter. Having overhead transparencies of the bumper-car floor plans in Question A will be helpful when trying to share strategies. Compared to area, describing a rule for perimeter may be more difficult and several patterns may emerge in the discussion. Help students to make sense of these patterns.

Begin by asking students to describe their strategies for finding area and perimeter using words. Wait until Question D to focus on symbolizing the patterns students describe. You may want to discuss area first, then perimeter, rather than proceeding through the parts of the problem in order.

Students may say they found area by multiplying the length and width. Write their ideas on the board using the number they multiplied (e.g., 6 × 3) or words (length × width), according to what students say. Here are some examples of strategies that students may offer. Share them with the class:

Mari *There are 6 squares in a row and 6 rows, so I multiplied 6 × 6 to get 36.*

Notice that Mari does not use the words *length* or *width*. She talks about rows as well as numbers. Her reasoning is sensible and she is talking about counting squares, the unit of measure for area. Mari does not mention a label for area and you might want to ask her to do so. On the board you might write:

number of squares in a row	×	number of rows	=	area
6 squares	×	6	=	36 squares

Erik *I just multiplied the length and the width.*

Erik has noticed that you can multiply the length and the width together to get the area. This is helpful when you do not have a picture with squares or rows to count. You might ask how Erik's idea of length × width is similar to Mari's idea.

Suggested Questions

- *Will Erik's idea work on the design Mari was using?* (Yes)
- *What is the length of the rectangle in Design I?* (6 units) *The width?* (6 units)
- *Could we label Mari's equation 6 × 6 = 36 so it is labeled with length and width?* (Yes. We could write length for the first 6 and width for the second 6.)

Ask other students if they agree with an idea when it is offered. If they have not already done so, ask them to explain why a rule or strategy works. You might ask them to try their rule on other rectangles.

In Question D of the problem you can ask students how they would write a rule to find area using ℓ for length and w for width. This should lead to the introduction of the area formula $A = \ell \times w$. Relate this formula back to Questions A–C or with some problems you offer.

Suggested Questions You can use the rectangle below to check students' understanding.

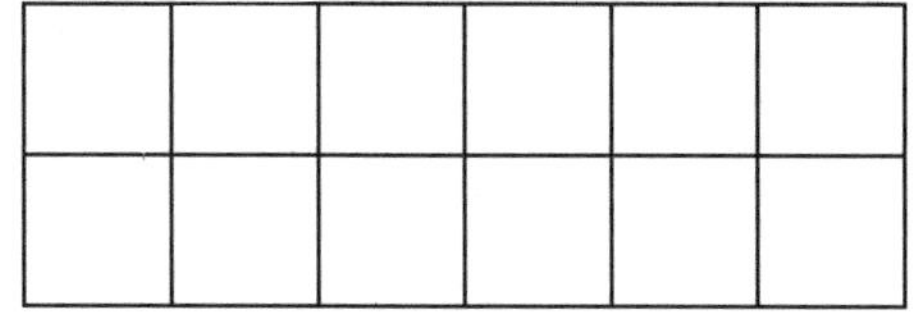

- *What is the length and the width of this rectangle?* (6 cm and 2 cm)
- *What are the dimensions of this rectangle?* (6 cm by 2 cm)
- *What does the 6 tell us about this rectangle?* (There are 6 cm^2 in a row.)
- *What does the 2 tell us about this rectangle?* (There are two rows with 6 cm^2 in each.)
- *How would you use the rule $length \times width = area$ to find the area of this rectangle?* (by multiplying 6 by 2)
- *Would this give you the same result as counting the squares individually?* (Yes)

As you move the discussion to perimeter, let students offer solutions, explain why they make sense, and perhaps try these solutions on other rectangles. There are several strategies that may emerge as you work across Questions A, B, and C. Have students relate their strategies and operations to a diagram that everyone can see.

Some students may describe the perimeter as the sum of the four sides of the rectangle:

$$perimeter = length + width + length + width$$

Some may say that they found the sum of the length and width and then doubled to get the answer. They may offer this in words and you can notate it in the following way:

$$perimeter = (length + width) \times 2$$

Other students may double the length and the width and then add them:

$$perimeter = 2 \times length + 2 \times width$$

Be sure students understand what is happening here. Doubling the length (or width) is equivalent to adding the two lengths (or widths) together. It is very similar to the following adding strategy:

$$\begin{aligned} perimeter &= (length + length) + (width + width) \\ &= (2 \times length) + (2 \times width) \end{aligned}$$

NOTE: Talk with students about why you are using parentheses in certain formulas.

Once strategies have been offered, it might help to apply them using the same rectangle so students can see how the same numbers play out with different approaches to perimeter.

Students will get a chance to deepen their understanding of area and perimeter of rectangles in the next investigation and throughout the unit. You can use Question 2 of the Mathematical Reflections as a launch into Investigation 2.

Mathematics Background

For background on parentheses and order of operations, see page 5.

1.3 Decoding Designs

At a Glance

PACING $1\frac{1}{2}$ days

Mathematical Goal

- Use the relationship between length and width to develop formulas for the area and perimeter of a rectangle

Launch

Discuss the Getting Ready with students.

Give each student a copy of Labsheet 1.3. Read through the problem with the students. Be sure they understand that Questions A, B, and C ask them to consider bumper-car floor plans that come with different types of diagrams and descriptions: gridded diagrams with dimensions labeled, and written descriptions.

Introduce the term *dimension*.

Ask students to think about Problem 1.2, Question C, where they were asked to make rectangular bumper-car floor plans using 18 floor tiles.

- *Tell me the dimensions or the length and width of a rectangle you can make with 18 floor tiles.*

Have students work in groups of 2 or 3.

Materials

- Transparency 1.3A
- Labsheet 1.3
- String: one piece at least 18 cm long per student (optional)

Explore

As students work, look at the different explanations students write for Question A, parts (1) and (2).

- What strategies are students using to find area and perimeter?
- What are students counting when they find area?
- What are students counting when they find the perimeter?
- Do students have other strategies besides counting for finding area and perimeter?
- Do they use the terms *length* and *width* in conversation?

If students have trouble with Question C, suggest they draw a diagram of the bumper-car floor plan and label the length and width.

Materials

- Transparency 1.3B

Summarize

Ask students to describe their strategies for finding area and perimeter in words. Discuss area first, then perimeter rather than proceeding through the parts of the problem in order.

Write students' ideas on the board according to what students say. For example:

Mari: There are 6 squares in a row and 6 rows, so I multiplied 6×6 to get 36.

Materials

- Transparency 1.3C
- Student notebooks

Vocabulary

- dimension

continued on next page

Summarize

continued

On the board, you might write:

number of squares in a row × number of rows = area
6 squares × 6 = 36 squares

Erik: I just multiplied the length and the width.

You might ask how Erik's idea of *length* × *width* is similar to Mari's idea.

Question D leads to the introduction of the area formula $A = \ell \times w$. Relate this formula back to Questions A–C or with some problems you offer.

Repeat this sequence with perimeter: have students share their strategies while you record and push towards a formula.

ACE Assignment Guide for Problem 1.3

Core 16–21, 31

Other *Applications* 22–27; *Connections* 32, 33, 36–38; *Extensions* 41, 42; unassigned choices from previous problems

Adapted For suggestions about adapting ACE exercises, see the CMP *Special Needs Handbook.*

Connecting to Prior Units 31: *Prime Time*

Answers to Problem 1.3

A. 1. Design I: 36 m^2

Design II: 40 m^2

Design III: 55 m^2

Design IV: 54 m^2

Design V: 77 m^2

Strategies for finding area may vary. Any reasonable strategy, including counting the number of squares, is acceptable.

2. Design I: 24 m

Design II: 26 m

Design III: 32 m

Design IV: 30 m

Design V: 36 m

Strategies for finding perimeter may vary. Any reasonable strategy is acceptable.

B. area: 48 m^2; perimeter: 32 m

C. 1. area: 510 m^2

2. perimeter: 94 m

D. 1. Possible answers include:
$P = \ell + w + \ell + w$, or
$P = (\ell + w) \times 2$, or
$P = 2 \times \ell + 2 \times w$

2. Area $= \ell \times w$ or $A = \ell \times w$

Investigation 1

ACE Assignment Choices

Problem 1.1

Core 1–5
Other *Application* 6

Problem 1.2

Core 7, 9–15, 28
Other *Applications* 8; *Connections* 29, 30, 34, 35; *Extensions* 39, 40; unassigned choices from previous problems

Problem 1.3

Core 16–21, 31
Other *Applications* 22–27; *Connections* 32, 33, 36–38; *Extensions* 41, 42; unassigned choices from previous problems

Adapted For suggestions about adapting Exercise 6 and other ACE exercises, see the CMP *Special Needs Handbook.*
Connecting to Prior Units 31, 34: *Prime Time*; 34: *Bits and Pieces I*

Applications

1. **a.** Possible answers:

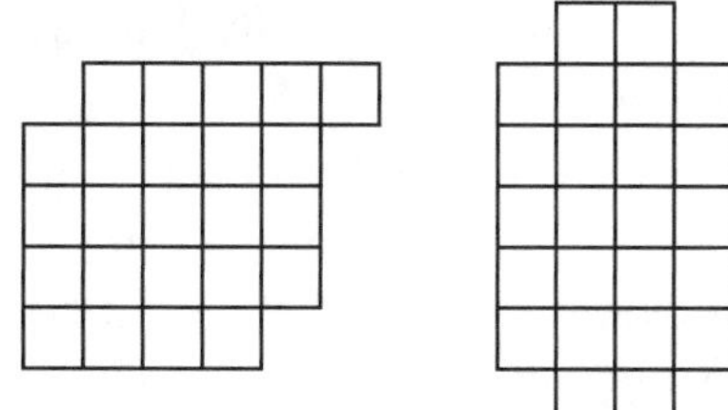

b. The bumper-car ride has an area of 24 m^2, which is the total number of square meters used to cover the floor plan of the bumper-car ride. The perimeter of 22 m is the total number of rail sections that are needed to surround the bumper-car ride.

2. Answers will vary. Maximum perimeter for whole-number dimensions is 34 units, minimum is 16 units. Possible answers:

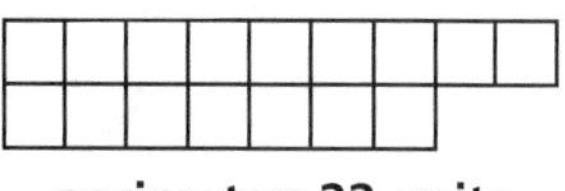

perimeter: 22 units

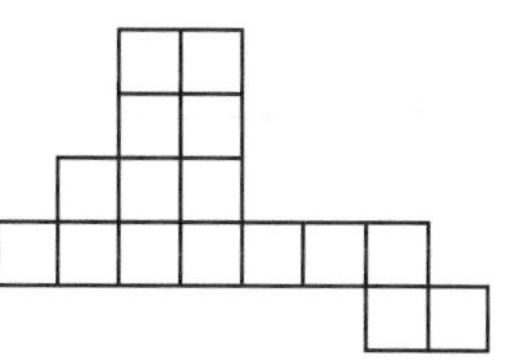

perimeter: 26 units

3. Answers will vary. Maximum area for whole-number dimensions is 16 square units, minimum is 7 square units. Possible answers:

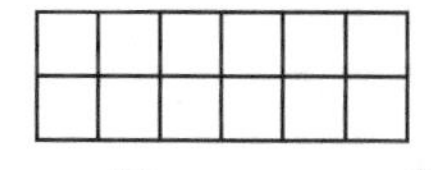

area: 12 square units

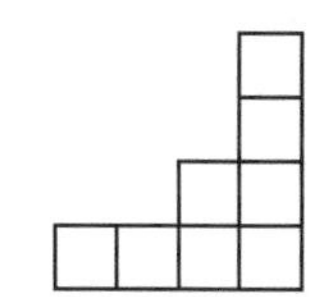

area: 8 square units

4. Answers will vary. Possible answers:

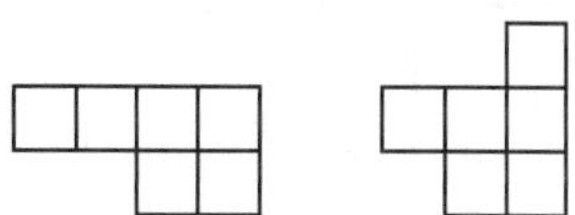

5. Answers will vary. Possible answers:

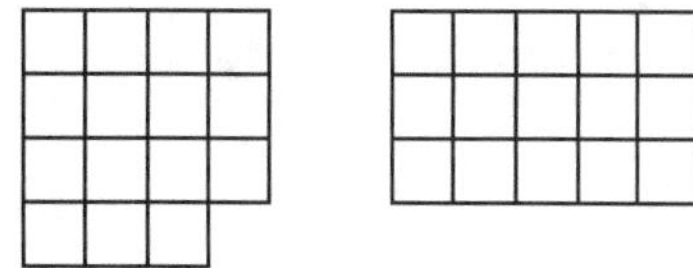

6. a. This is possible. (Note that the area of the original rectangle is 18 square units.) Examples will vary. Possible answer:

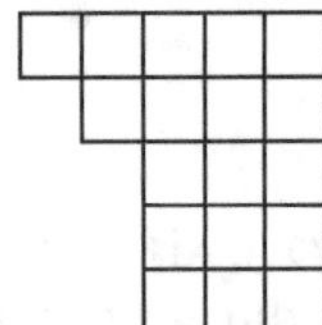

b. This is possible. Examples will vary. Possible answer:

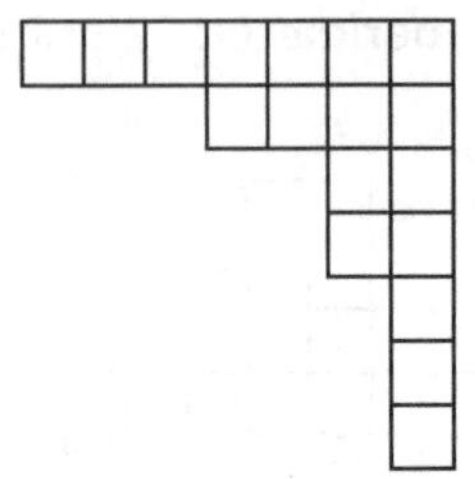

7. Possible answers: No, because I counted the number of units around the edge of each figure and found that their perimeters were different. Or, Design J has the maximum perimeter for designs with this area, while Design K has some interior tiles and so must have less than the maximum perimeter.

8. 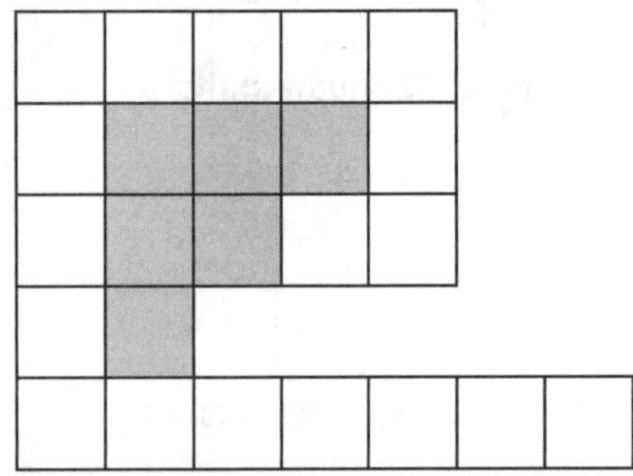

Adding these six tiles reduced the perimeter of the figure. Only two of the new tiles have exposed edges, while together they cover ten previously exposed edges in the original figure.

9. $P = 4 \times 12$ ft $= 48$ ft, $A = 12$ ft $\times 12$ ft $= 144$ ft^2

10. $P = 22 \times 12$ ft $= 264$ ft,
$A = 144$ ft$^2 \times 21 = 3{,}024$ ft^2

11. $P = 30 \times 12$ ft $= 360$ ft,
$A = 144$ ft$^2 \times 26 = 3{,}744$ ft^2

12. $P = 26 \times 12$ ft $= 312$ ft,
$A = 144$ ft$^2 \times 20 = 2{,}880$ ft^2

13. $P = 16$ units, $A = 7$ units^2

14. $P = 16$ units, $A = 16$ units^2

15. $P = 16$ units, $A = 12$ units^2

16. A $1\frac{1}{4}$ unit-by-$4\frac{1}{4}$ unit rectangle has $P = 11$ units, $A = 5\frac{5}{16}$ units^2.

17. $A = 28$ cm^2, $P = 32$ cm

18. $A = 100$ in.^{2}, $P = 40$ in.

19. $A = 75$ m^2, $P = 40$ m

20. $A = \ell w$, $P = \ell + \ell + w + w$ or $P = 2\ell + 2w$ or $P = 2(\ell + w)$

21. (Figure 2) Check students' sketches.

22. $A = 65$ cm^2, $P = 38$ cm

23. $A = 36$ cm^2, $P = 36$ cm

24. a. Possible answer: You could draw two imaginary horizontal lines across the room, dividing the floor into three rectangles: one by the door, one by the nook by the window, and a large one taking up the majority of the floor's surface. You would then measure the length and width of each rectangle (in yards) and multiply the two measurements to find the areas (in square yards) of each rectangle. Add the areas together, and multiply the sum by the cost per square yard.

Alternatively, you could get a square that is 1 yd by 1 yd and lay it over the room and to find about how many it would take to cover it. You could take that number and multiply it by the cost for each square yard.

Figure 2

Rectangle	Length (in.)	Width (in.)	Area (square in.)	Perimeter (in.)
A	5	6	30	22
B	4	13	52	34
C	$6\frac{1}{2}$	8	52	29

b. Possible answer: You could lay a ruler all around the base edges of the walls of the room, counting as you go. You would multiply the total by the cost per foot.

Alternatively, you could measure the length of each wall and add the results.

25. **a.** $6 \text{ ft} \times 8\frac{1}{2} \text{ ft} = 51 \text{ ft}^2$

b. 29 ft of molding

c. Two walls have an area of $6 \text{ ft} \times 6 \text{ ft} = 36 \text{ ft}^2$, and two walls have an area of $6 \text{ ft} \times 8\frac{1}{2} \text{ ft} = 51 \text{ ft}^2$. The total surface area would be $36 + 36 + 51 + 51 = 174 \text{ ft}^2$. You would need 4 pints of paint because $174 \text{ ft}^2 \div 50 \text{ ft}^2 = 3.48$, and you round up to 4 so that you will have enough paint.

d. Answers will vary.

26. **a.** $40 \times 120 = 4{,}800$. $4{,}800 \times \$95 = \$456{,}000$

b. $4{,}800 \div 100 = 48$ cars

27. Yes, both rules are correct. The only difference is that Chuck multiplied the lengths and widths by 2 and then added them, and Ruth added the length and width first and then multiplied their sum by 2.

Connections

28. C

29. Possible answers: A tile on the classroom floor is about 1 ft^2. A coffee table is about 1 yd^2.

30. **a.** 1 yd^2 is larger. It is 9 ft^2.

b. They are the same length. 5×12 in. $= 60$ in.

c. 12 m is larger because 120 cm is 1.2 m.

d. 120 ft is larger because 12 yd is 36 ft.

e. They are the same length. 50 cm = 500 mm.

f. One square meter is larger because a meter is longer than a yard.

31. **a.**

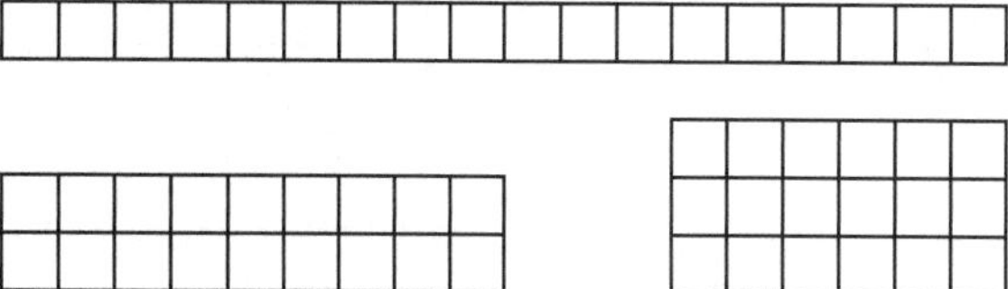

b. (Figure 3) **c.** (Figure 4)

d. The factors of a number and the dimensions of the rectangles that can be made from that number of tiles are the same. For example, the factors of 25 are 1, 5, and 25, so each number can be at least one dimension of a rectangle with 25 square units of area.

32. **a.** $31\frac{45}{100}$ or $31\frac{9}{20}$ **b.** 50

c. $23\frac{29}{32}$ **d.** $1\frac{11}{24}$

33. **a.** 8 **b.** 16 **c.** 6

34. **a.** Possible answer:

Each brownie is 2 in. by 2 in.

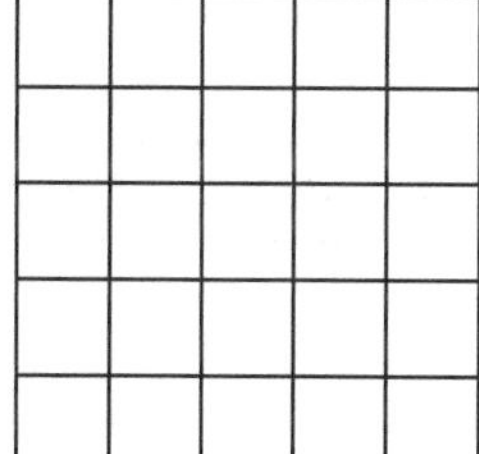

b. Possible answer:

Each brownie is $2\frac{1}{2}$ in. by 2 in.

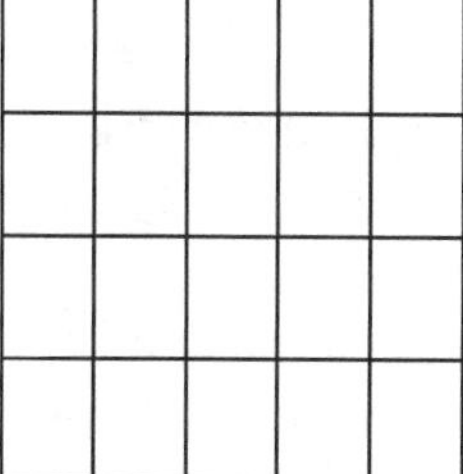

Figure 3

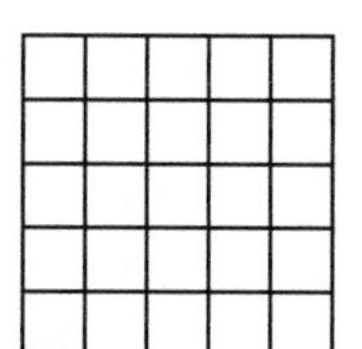

Figure 4

c. Possible answer:

Each brownie is 2 in. by $1\frac{2}{3}$ in.

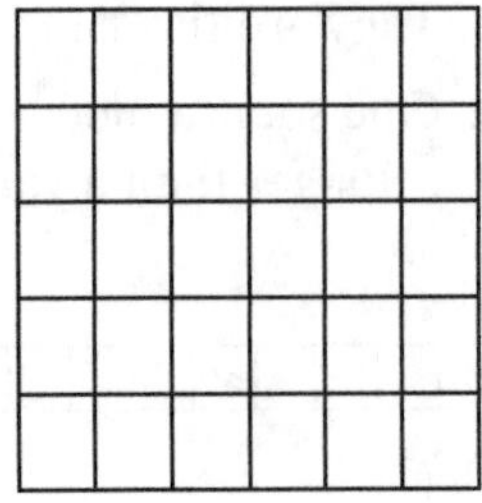

35. a. If they make 20 brownies, then each could be 2 in. by $2\frac{1}{2}$ in. The area of the bottom of the brownie is 5 in.^{2}.

b. If they make 30 brownies then each could be 2 in. by $1\frac{2}{3}$ in. The area of the bottom of the brownie is $3\frac{1}{3}$ in.^{2}.

36. a. $A = 5{,}000$ yd^2, $P = 300$ yd

b. $A = 45{,}000$ ft^2, $P = 900$ ft

c. $20 \times 25 = 500$ ft^2,
$45{,}000 \div 500 =$ about 90 classrooms

37. a. $A = 86{,}250$ ft^2, $P = 1{,}210$ ft

b. $A = 86{,}250 \div 9 = 9{,}583\frac{1}{3}$ yd^2, $P = 403\frac{1}{3}$ yd

c. 15 ft $\times$ 25 ft $= 375$ ft^2,
$86{,}250 \div 375 =$ about 230 classrooms

38.

Length (ft)	Width (ft)
1.25	16
0.625	32

Extensions

39. This is always true, because $E + E + E + E = E, O + O + O + O = E$, and $E + E + O + O = E$, where E stands for an even number, O for an odd number. Alternatively, the formula $2(\ell + w)$ shows that 2 is a factor of any perimeter with whole-number length and width.

40. 3 cm-by-6 cm rectangle

41. No; there are many different combinations of lengths and widths that could add up to a certain perimeter. A square, on the other hand, has four equal sides, so you can find the length of one of the sides by dividing the perimeter by 4.

42. You would need 28 tiles to cover this floor. One possible explanation: I used copies of the given tile to cover the floor plan. Alternate explanation: I found the area of the figure and knew it would take half this many tiles to cover the floor since each tile has an area of 2.

Possible Answers to Mathematical Reflections

1. Area is the number of unit squares needed to cover a shape. The perimeter is the distance around a shape.

2. Yes, it is possible to have the same area and different perimeters. In the figure below, both floor plans have an area of 12 cm^2. The first picture has a perimeter of 14 cm and the second picture has a perimeter of 16 cm.

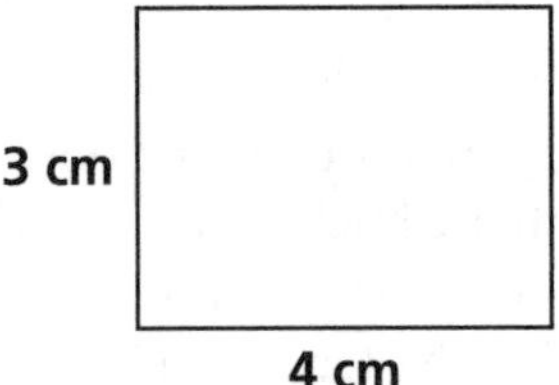

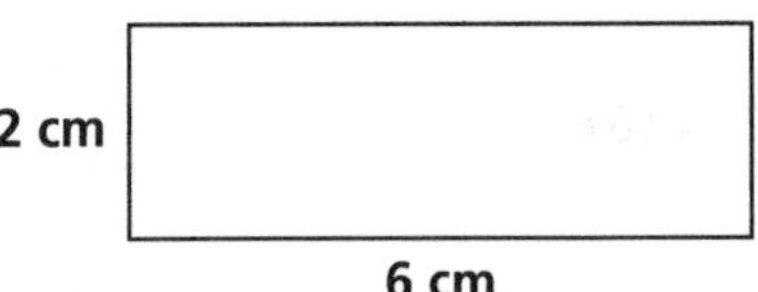

3. You can multiply a rectangle's length and width to get the area. This works because the length tells you how many rows of squares you have and the width tells you how many squares are in each row.

4. You can add the length and width of a rectangle and double this sum to get the perimeter. This works because the perimeter is the distance around the rectangle, so by adding the length and the width you will be halfway around the outside distance. If you double this, you will get the total distance around a rectangle. (There are several approaches students might offer. See the Investigation 1.3 summary for other approaches and explanations.)

Investigation 2 Changing Area, Changing Perimeter

Mathematical and Problem-Solving Goals

- Explore questions of maximum and minimum in the context of finding the largest and smallest perimeter for rectangles of fixed area
- Understand that the perimeters of rectangles with a fixed area can vary considerably
- Continue to develop facility using formulas for finding perimeter and area of rectangles
- Continue to develop a conceptual understanding of area and perimeter
- Find the minimum and maximum area of a rectangle with a fixed perimeter
- Distinguish the case of fixed area from fixed perimeter
- Construct diagrams, tables, and graphs to organize and represent data
- Apply understanding of the relationship between area and perimeter to nonrectangular figures

In this investigation, students explore fixed area and perimeter problems. Some of these problems are maximum and minimum problems. Holding one variable constant to study how another variable changes is a powerful mathematical tool used to analyze a wide variety of problems.

In the first two problems, area is held constant while students explore how perimeter varies. In the last two problems, students will have a fixed perimeter and explore how area varies. These two kinds of problems will provide opportunities for students to reason about and use the formulas for area and perimeter of rectangles that they developed in Investigation 1. This investigation will also set the stage for finding areas of triangles in Investigation 3 and parallelograms in Investigation 4.

Summary of Problems

Problem 2.1 Building Storm Shelters

Students investigate how the perimeters of rectangles vary when they have the same area.

Problem 2.2 Stretching the Perimeter

Students continue to investigate perimeters for a constant area but they are no longer restricted to rectangular arrangements.

Problem 2.3 Fencing in Spaces

Students find the maximum and minimum possible areas for a rectangle with a perimeter of 24 m.

Problem 2.4 Adding Tiles to Pentominos

Students add tiles to a given figure to form shapes with a common perimeter. They find all the ways the perimeter can change by adding or subtracting a single tile.

	Suggested Pacing	Materials for Students	Materials for Teacher	ACE Assignments
All	5 days	Calculators, student notebooks, centimeter grid paper	Blank transparencies and transparency markers (optional)	
2.1	$1\frac{1}{2}$ days	Square tiles (24 per student or pair; Labsheets 2.1, 2ACE Exercises 3–5	Transparencies 2.1A, 2.1B	1–6, 16, 17, 20, 21
2.2	1 day	String, scissors, inch grid paper	Transparency 2.2, 4-by-6 rectangle cut from inch (or two-inch) grid paper or transparency	7, 18, 19
2.3	1 day	Square tiles (at least 36 per student or pair); several 24-cm loops of string (optional); Labsheets 2.3, 2ACE 10–12, 2ACE 23	Transparencies 2.3A, 2.3B (optional)	8–14, 22–25, 27, 29
2.4	1 day	Square tiles (about 25 per student)		15, 26, 28
MR	$\frac{1}{2}$ day			

2.1 Building Storm Shelters

Goals

- Explore questions of maximum and minimum in the context of finding the largest and smallest perimeter for rectangles of fixed area
- Understand that the perimeters of rectangles with a fixed area can vary considerably
- Continue to develop facility using formulas for finding perimeter and area of rectangles
- Continue to develop a conceptual understanding of area and perimeter

In this problem, students begin by finding all the possible rectangles with whole-number side lengths in order to determine the least expensive way to build a storm shelter with a floor that is 24 m^2. In one part students will explore a situation with fractional lengths. The goal is to explore a collection of rectangles all having the same area in order to determine which rectangles will have the largest and the smallest perimeters, and why. As students work they will have many opportunities to find the area and perimeter of rectangular shapes using the rules they developed in Investigation 1.

Launch 2.1

Before they start working on the problem, help students understand the mathematical context. Question 3 of the Mathematical Reflections for the last investigation can be used as part of the launch.

Suggested Questions

- *We have been finding areas and perimeters of several shapes. In this problem we will look at a specific shape, a rectangle. We want to find all the rectangles that can be made with a given area.*

Ask students to use 12 of their tiles to build a rectangle.

- *We call the length and width of a rectangle its dimensions. Tell me what rectangle you built by giving me its dimensions.* (Example: 3 units and 4 units)
- *Also, give the perimeter and area of your rectangle.* (For the above example, the perimeter is 14 units and the area is 12 square units.)

Record the length, width, perimeter, and area of each rectangle on the board. As students offer examples, it will be helpful if you sketch the rectangles they are describing. Encourage students to talk about how they found the area and the perimeter of each rectangle. Look for opportunities to relate their work on this problem to the rules they developed for finding area and perimeter of rectangles in Investigation 1. Collect students' ideas until all possible rectangles have been found.

If you include reversals—such as 1 unit by 12 units and 12 units by 1 unit—there are six possibilities. Many students do consider a 1 unit-by-12 unit rectangle and a 12 unit-by-1 unit rectangle to be different. Students will make a table and a graph of the lengths and perimeters of the rectangles in this problem. In order for useful patterns to be displayed in the table and graph, students will need to record both rectangles.

Length (units)	Width (units)	Area (square units)	Perimeter (units)
1	12	12	26
2	6	12	16
3	4	12	14
4	3	12	14
6	2	12	16
12	1	12	26

Suggested Question

- *How do you know we have found all the rectangles that can be made using 12 tiles?* (All the possible factor pairs have been given as lengths and widths.)

Read about building storm shelters with your class. Make sure students understand the problem.

- *As you work on this problem, record your findings in a table similar to the one we used to find the rectangle with an area of 12 square units.*

Question C asks students to graph the relationship between the length and perimeter. Your class may need help with making coordinate graphs. Summarize Questions A and B and then use the data from the rectangles with a fixed area of 12 square units to demonstrate or review how to make a coordinate graph. Once the graph is sketched, discuss the relevance of the shape of the graph. Students might say: "As the length increases the perimeter decreases to a certain point and then it begins to increase." Now let the class do Questions C and D.

Students worked on a similar problem in Problem 2.1 of *Prime Time*.

Let the class work in pairs.

Explore 2.1

Observe students while they work. Make sure students are making sketches as well as completing the chart. Some students may choose not to use tiles because they can see patterns without them. This is fine. Using tiles to make models of the shelters should not be a mandate; tiles are simply tools to help make sense of the problem.

Question C may be challenging for students. Be prepared to help students plot points on their graphs. Some students will want to plot a vertical line or a bar from the x-axis. Help such students to understand how plotting a single point gives two pieces of information—the length and the perimeter of a rectangle.

Summarize 2.1

Suggested Questions You might begin the summary by collecting the data students recorded for Question A.

- *Did anyone find a shelter design with an edge length of 1 m? What is the width of that shelter?* (24 m)
- *What is the perimeter?* (50 m)
- *How did you find the perimeter?* (Possible answer: I added the length and width to get 25 m, then I doubled that to get 50 m.)
- *Did anyone find a shelter design with an edge length of 2 m? What is the width of that shelter?* (12 m)
- *What is the perimeter?* (28 m)
- *How did you find it?*

Continue with this line of questioning for edge lengths of 3, 4, 5, 6, 7, 8, 12, and 24. Asking for edge lengths of 5 and 7 should give rise to a short discussion about factors. If students state that they don't need to list 6, 8, 12, and 24 because they are reversals, then stop listing, but be sure to ask them how they know they have found all possible rectangles.

Suggested Questions As students discuss their solutions for Question B, help them use the information in the table to visualize what the shelters with the largest and smallest perimeters look like.

- *Which of the shelters with an area of 24 m^2 has the smallest perimeter?* (4 m by 6 m)
- *What does it look like?* (It's more square-like.)
- *What is the perimeter of this design?* (20 m)
- *Which of the shelters with an area of 24 m^2 has the largest perimeter?* (1 m by 24 m)
- *What does this shelter look like?* (It is long and skinny.)
- *Why do some floor plans use more wall panels than others?* (larger perimeter)
- *Which floor plan would make a good shelter? Explain your reasoning.* (Possible answer: The 4 m-by-6 m shelter will give a lot of open space so people won't bump into each other as much.)

Display Transparency 2.1B.

- *We said that the design with the smallest perimeter is 4 m by 6 m. How should we display this on the graph?* [This design shows up as two points, one at (4, 20), the other at (6, 20).]
- *How can we tell from the graph that this is the design with the smallest perimeter?* (These two points will be lower on the graph than any other points.)
- *How will we display the design with the largest perimeter?* [Again, with two points: one at (1, 50), the other at (24, 50).]
- *Why does one rectangle show up with two points?* (We are recording it with two orientations: lying down and standing up. Or, we are using 1 as the length and 24 as the width, then reversing them.)

Finish by discussing Question D.

- *If you were going to build a rectangular shelter with an area of 36 m^2, which design would cost the most to build? Why?*

Help students to see that a 1 m-by-36 m shelter would cost the most. This shelter has the largest perimeter of any other arrangement of 36 m^2, so it would require the most wall sections and have the highest cost.

- *If you were going to build a rectangular shelter with an area of 36 m^2, which design would cost the least to build? Why?* [The 6-by-6 shelter would be the least expensive, because it is the most compact and therefore has the smallest perimeter (24 m). In the tile models, this arrangement of tiles has the fewest exposed edges to contribute to the perimeter.]

Suggested Questions Put up the graph and repeat some of the questions.

- *Where on the graph is the rectangle with the smallest perimeter?* [(4, 20) or (6, 20)]
- *What are its dimensions?* (4 m by 6 m)
- *What is the perimeter of a rectangle whose length is 8 m?* (22 m) *What is the width of the rectangle?* (3 m)
- *What is the length of a rectangle whose perimeter is 28 m?* (12 m or 2 m) *What is the width?* (2 m or 12 m)

To review fractions, choose some points that are not necessarily whole numbers.

- *What is the perimeter of the rectangle if the length is 18 m?* ($1\frac{1}{3}$ m)
- *What is the length of the rectangle if the perimeter is 32?*

Have students state a general rule about maximizing and minimizing perimeters for rectangles with fixed area and whole-number dimensions.

- *In general, if I have a bunch of rectangles with a fixed area, how will I know which one has the smallest perimeter? How will I know which has the largest?* (The one with the smallest perimeter is the one that is most "square-like." The one with the largest perimeter has dimensions 1 unit by whatever the fixed area is.

2.1 Building Storm Shelters

At a Glance

PACING $1\frac{1}{2}$ days

Mathematical Goals

- Explore questions of maximum and minimum in the context of finding the largest and smallest perimeter for rectangles of fixed area
- Understand that the perimeters of rectangles with a fixed area can vary considerably
- Continue to develop facility-using formulas for finding perimeter and area of rectangles
- Continue to develop a conceptual understanding of area and perimeter

Launch

Help students understand the mathematical context.

Ask students to use 12 of their tiles to build a rectangle.

- *We call the length and width of a rectangle its dimensions. Tell me what rectangle you built by giving me its dimensions.*

Record the length, width, perimeter, and area of each rectangle on the board. Sketch the rectangles students describe. Relate their work on this problem to the rules for area and perimeter of rectangles. Collect students' ideas until all possible rectangles have been found.

- *How do you know we have found all the rectangles that can be made using 12 tiles?*

Read about building storm shelters with your class.

- *As you work on this problem, record your findings in a table similar to the one we used to find the rectangle with an area of 12 square units.*

Have students work in pairs.

Materials

- Square tiles (24 per student or pair)
- Labsheet 2.1
- Transparencies 2.1A, 2.1B

Explore

Make sure students make sketches and complete the chart. Help students plot points on their graphs when necessary. Help students understand that each point gives two pieces of information.

Summarize

Collect the data students recorded for Question A.

- *Did anyone find a shelter design with an edge length of 1 m? What is the width of that shelter? The perimeter? How did you find the perimeter?*

Continue with this line of questioning for edge lengths of 3, 4, 5, 6, 7, 8, 12, and 24.

- *Which of the shelters with an area of 24 m^2 has the smallest perimeter? What does it look like? What is the perimeter of this design?*
- *Which of the shelters with an area of 24 m^2 has the largest perimeter? What does this shelter look like?*
- *Why do some floor plans use more wall panels than others?*

Materials

- Student notebooks

Vocabulary

- fixed area
- maximum area
- minimum area

continued on next page

Summarize

continued

Go over the graph and its meaning with students.

- *We said that the design with the smallest perimeter is 4 m by 6 m. How should we display this on the graph?*

Have students state a general rule about maximizing and minimizing perimeters for rectangles with fixed area.

ACE Assignment Guide for Problem 2.1

Core 1, 2

Other *Applications* 3–6; *Connections* 16, 17, 20, 21 Labsheet 2ACE Exercises 3–5 is provided if Exercises 3–5 are assigned.

Adapted For suggestions about adapting Exercise 3 and other ACE exercises, see the CMP *Special Needs Handbook.*

Connecting to Prior Units 17, 20, 21: *Bits and Pieces II*

Answers to Problem 2.1

A.

Length (m)	Width (m)	Perimeter (m)	Area (m^2)
1	24	50	24
2	12	28	24
3	8	22	24
4	6	20	24
6	4	20	24
8	3	22	24
12	2	28	24
24	1	50	24

B. 1. Perimeter; possible explanation: Perimeter is the distance or length around the outside of a shape. The walls fit around the outside so the number of panels depends on how long the distance around the outside is.

2. The 1 m-by-24 m (or 24 m-by-1 m) shelter is the most expensive to build. The floor plan is long and skinny, with the least open space and the most wall sections.

3. The 4 m-by-6 m (or 6 m-by-4 m) shelter is the least expensive to build. The floor plan is the most square-like of the possibilities. The floor plan would have the most open space and the fewest panels.

C. 1.

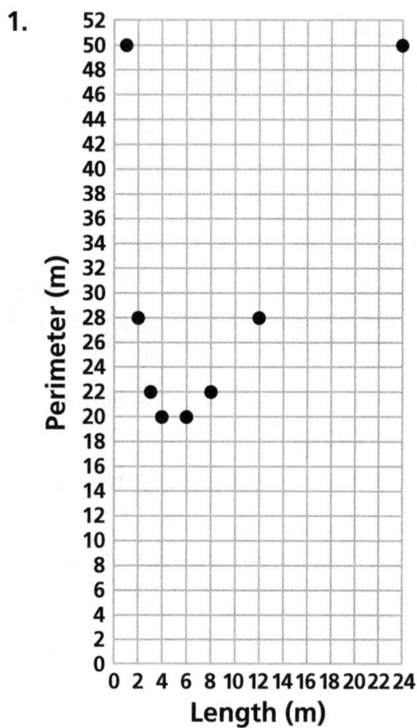

2. The graph is curved. As we move from left to right, the points are lower and lower, then begin to rise. This is because if one side of the storm shelter is very short, the other is very long and the perimeter will be large. As the two dimensions become close to each other, the perimeter becomes smaller. Past a certain point, the perimeter becomes large again.

D. 1. The 6 m-by-6 m floor plan would have the least perimeter and the 36 m-by-1 m floor plan would have the greatest perimeter.

2. A long, skinny rectangle has the largest perimeter for a fixed area, while the rectangle that is most square-like has the smallest perimeter for a fixed area.

2.2 Stretching the Perimeter

Goals

- Understand that the perimeters of rectangles with a fixed area can vary considerably
- Explore questions of maximum and minimum in the context of finding the largest and smallest perimeter for rectangles of fixed area
- Continue to develop facility using formulas for finding perimeter and area of rectangles
- Continue to develop a conceptual understanding of area and perimeter

In this section, students continue to investigate perimeters for a constant area of 24 m^2. However, they are no longer restricted to rectangular shapes. The question in this problem is: Can you make a shape with a larger perimeter than a rectangle with the same area?

Launch 2.2

This problem can serve as a summary to the ideas that were explored in the last problem. Use the Getting Ready to model the procedure with a 4 in.-by-6 in. rectangle, cutting it as described in the Student Edition. Slide your piece and tape it to the opposite edge.

Suggested Questions

- *What is the area of this new shape? How do you know?* (The area is still 24 square units; the area of the original rectangle.)
- *How can we find the perimeter of this shape?* (The lengths of the straight edges are 6 units each. You can use string to find the lengths of the other edges.)
- *What are the areas and perimeters of the next two figures?* (The first example has a perimeter of 32 units. The second example has a perimeter of just over 30 units. Each of these is larger than the original perimeter of 20 units. When we perform this procedure, the distance that the scissors cut replaces the 4-unit edge on each side of the rectangle. The scissor cut must be longer than the original 4 units, so we are increasing the perimeter, while leaving the area alone.)
- *Theoretically, there is no limit to the potential length of the perimeter that can be created by this technique.*
- *How do the area and perimeter of this new shape compare with the area and perimeter of the 4-by 6-rectangle?* (The area stays the same, but the perimeter changes.)

Once students understand the problem, let them work individually using inch grid paper.

Explore 2.2

Students should make their own shapes and answer the questions individually, then meet with their groups to share and compare answers. As students work, make sure they are taking time to measure accurately enough to see the differences in perimeters. Suggest that students who finish early try to make another figure with an even greater perimeter than the one they just made. Ask what strategy they are using to accomplish this task.

You could have students cut string the length of the perimeter of their figures, which makes it easier to compare perimeters. Later, you could display the shapes and their perimeters (the lengths of string) to help students better visualize the relationship between constant area and changing perimeter.

Summarize 2.2

Have groups share their findings for each question. Focus on the fact that each figure has an area of 24 square units, yet the perimeters vary.

Suggested Questions Ask students to display their figures. Use the ideas brought out in Questions A, B, and C to discuss what is the same and what is different.

- *Look at the areas and perimeters of the shapes that we made. How are they the same and how are they different?* (The areas are always the same and the perimeters are different.)
- *Why are the areas always the same?* (The areas are the same because we are rearranging the original 24 square units. No square units are being removed or added.)

- *Let's look at perimeter. Let's arrange these three figures from the shortest perimeter to the longest. Why is the perimeter of this figure longer than the perimeter of this one?*

Use the conversation on the changing perimeter to lead into Question E.

- *Does someone have a figure with a longer perimeter than these?* (Place the new figure by the others.)
- *Why does this figure have a longer perimeter?*

Ask the student with the longest perimeter to display his or her figure.

- *Can you make a figure with 24 square units that has a longer perimeter than the one here? How?*

Turn the conversation toward discussing the smallest perimeter. The goal is for students to see that shorter cuts will increase the perimeter, but less than longer cuts will.

- *Who has the shortest perimeter? Why?*
- *Was anyone able to make a perimeter that was shorter than the original rectangle's perimeter of 20 units?*
- *Is this possible?* (No, it is not. For this rectangle, once you cut a curve in it the curve is longer than the original side length of 4 units. When you reattach the cutout to the other end of the shape, the perimeter will be longer.)

Have the class present their reactions to Talecia's statement in Question D. You might ask them to use the figures that the class made as a way to show whether Talecia's idea makes sense or not. Focus on the idea that for one area, there are many possible perimeters.

Depending upon your students, you might want to push them to think about what they did with rectangles and area in Problem 2.1. This question pushes students to think about how in this problem, the 4 unit-by-6 unit rectangle has the smallest perimeter (when compared to the nonrectangular shapes). Yet, there are other shapes with an area of 24 square units that have a smaller perimeter than the 4 unit-by-6 unit rectangle.

- *In this problem, you cut a 4 unit-by-6 unit rectangle to make a nonrectangular shape. We said that the smallest perimeter you could make by cutting and sliding would be very close in length to the perimeter of the rectangle itself.*
- *Are there other rectangular shapes with an area of 24 square units that would have a perimeter less than 20 units? What about rectangular shapes with fractional side lengths?* (In Exercise 17, the storm shelter with dimensions 5 meters and $4\frac{4}{5}$ meters had a smaller perimeter of $19\frac{4}{5}$ m. Also, a square with an area of 24 will have side lengths of approximately $4\frac{9}{10}$ units, making the perimeter about $19\frac{3}{5}$ units.)

2.2 Stretching the Perimeter

At a Glance

PACING 1 day

Mathematical Goals

- Understand that the perimeters of rectangles with a fixed area can vary considerably
- Explore questions of maximum and minimum in the context of finding the largest and smallest perimeter for rectangles of fixed area
- Continue to develop facility using formulas for finding perimeter and area of rectangles
- Continue to develop a conceptual understanding of area and perimeter

Launch

Use the Getting Ready to model the procedure with a 4 in.-by-6 in. rectangle, cutting it as described in the Student Edition.

- *What is the area of this new shape? How do you know?*
- *How can we find the perimeter of this shape?*
- *How do the area and perimeter of this new shape compare with the area and perimeter of the 4 in.-by-6 in. rectangle?*

Once students understand the problem, let them work individually using inch grid paper.

Materials

- Transparency 2.2
- String, scissors, inch grid paper
- 4-by-6 rectangle cut from inch (or 2-inch) grid paper or transparency

Explore

As students work, make sure they take time to measure accurately enough to see the differences in perimeters. Suggest that students who finish early try to make another figure with an even greater perimeter than the one they just made.

Have students cut string the length of the perimeter of their figures, which makes it easier to compare perimeters.

Summarize

Have groups share their findings for each question. Focus on the fact that every new figure has an area of 24 square units, yet the perimeters vary.

- *Look at the areas and perimeters of the shapes we made. How are they the same and how are they different?*
- *Why are the areas always the same? Why is the perimeter of this figure longer than the perimeter of this one?*

Use the conversation on the changing perimeter to lead into Question E.

Turn the conversation toward discussing the smallest perimeter. The goal is for students to see how shorter cuts will reduce the perimeter and longer cuts increase the perimeter.

Materials

- Student notebooks

continued on next page

Summarize
continued

Have the class present their reactions to Talecia's statement in Question D. If necessary, refer the class to the figures they have just made. Wrap up by referring back to Problem 2.1.

- *Are there other rectangular shapes with an area of 24 square units that would have a perimeter less than 20 units?*

ACE Assignment Guide for Problem 2.2

Core 7

Other *Connections* 18, 19; unassigned choices from previous problems

Adapted For suggestions about adapting ACE exercises, see the CMP *Special Needs Handbook*.

Answers to Problem 2.2

A. Areas will all be 24 square units; perimeters will vary but will be greater than 20 units.

B. The perimeters of the new figures will all be greater than 20 units. When you cut the new piece, the edge is longer than the original 4-unit side of the rectangle.

C. The area of the new figure will always be 24 square units. When you cut and rearrange the rectangle, you still have 24 square units. They have been moved to a new place, but the number you have does not change.

D. There are many possible perimeters for a given area. For example, an area of 12 square units can be made with a 1 unit-by-12 unit rectangle or a 3 unit-by-4 unit rectangle. Both of these rectangles have the same area, but they each have a different perimeter.

E. Possible answer: Yes, by cutting and sliding a piece from the rectangle that has a longer cut edge than any of the previously made figures.

2.3 Fencing in Spaces

Goals

- Find the minimum and maximum area of a rectangle with a fixed perimeter
- Understand that the areas of rectangles with a fixed perimeter can vary considerably
- Construct diagrams, tables, and graphs to organize and represent data
- Continue to develop facility using formulas for finding perimeter and area of rectangles

In this problem, students are asked to find all the rectangles with whole-number dimensions that have a fixed perimeter of 24 units. Many students will find this problem to be more difficult than Problem 2.1, in which area was fixed. When students complete this problem, they should be able to describe the largest or smallest possible area for a rectangle with whole-number dimensions that has a fixed perimeter.

Launch 2.3

Tell the class about the context of the problem. Before students start designing dog pens, make sure they understand the mathematical context.

- *Before Problem 2.1, we found all the rectangles that could be made with an area of 12 square units and whole-number side lengths. Now I want you to think about all the rectangles that can be made with a perimeter of 12 units. This time, we are holding the perimeter fixed.*
- *Once you think you have an example, use your tiles and build your rectangle. Share your results with someone near you. Convince that person that you have built a rectangle with a perimeter of 12 units.*
- *Tell me what you built by giving me the dimensions (the lengths of the sides), the perimeter, and area for your rectangle.*

On the board, record the length, width, perimeter, and area of each rectangle students suggest. (You may want to use a table formatted like the one started in the Student Edition.) Continue collecting examples until all possibilities have been found. If you include reversals, there are five possibilities.

Use some of this time to revisit strategies for finding area and perimeter. Ask students to talk about how they found the area and the perimeter. As students describe strategies in words, link them to the formulas that were developed in Investigation 1.

Suggested Question

- *How do we know we have found all the rectangles we can make with whole-number dimensions and a perimeter of 12 units?*

Your students may not be able to answer this question now. If they are struggling, ask them to continue to think about this question and return to it in the summary.

Question B asks the students to graph the relationship between the length and area. If the class still needs help with graphs, this is a good time to review how to make a graph using the data for length and area for rectangles with a perimeter of 12 units.

Because working with constant perimeter is more difficult than working with constant area, you may want to have students work with a partner to find all possible rectangles with whole-number dimensions. Each student should keep a record of the pair's findings.

Explore 2.3

As you circulate, you may notice that some students are frustrated with trying to find examples. Encourage them to try adding on or taking off more tiles so as to maintain a rectangle, or to try changing only one dimension at a time. You could also have some 24-centimeter loops of string made in advance and give one to any student who is struggling to visualize the perimeter. Have these students look for rectangles the string would enclose perfectly on centimeter grid paper.

When students are trying to answer Question C, part (2), it might help them to sketch out the rectangles in Questions A and C, part (1), to see that they are becoming more and more like a square.

Summarize 2.3

Suggested Questions You might begin the summary by collecting the data students recorded for Question A.

- *Did anyone find a rectangular dog pen with a perimeter of 24 m and an edge length of 1 m? What is the width of that dog pen? What is the area? What does this dog pen look like?*
- *Did anyone find a rectangular dog pen with perimeter of 24 m and an edge length of 2 m? What is the width of that dog pen? What is the area? What does this dog pen look like?*

Continue with this line of questioning until all possible rectangles with whole-number dimensions have been given.

For some students, a diagram of each rectangle in the table can be helpful when trying to understand and talk about the relationship between fixed perimeter and area. One way to display some of the rectangles is to make the rectangles on grid paper or dot paper and line them up along the chalkboard. They can also be sketched out directly on the chalkboard.

For Questions B and C, ask students to talk about why certain rectangles have the most or least area. Encourage them to look across the data in the table to consider how the shapes of the rectangles are changing.

Suggested Questions

- *Why does the 1 m-by-11 m rectangle have a smaller area than the 6 m-by-6 m rectangle?* (because 1 times 11 is less than 6 times 6)
- *If you compare the pictures of these two rectangles, can you show why the 1 m-by-11 m rectangle has the smallest area and the 6 m-by-6 m has the largest?* (Yes; there are more squares in the 6 m-by-6 m rectangle than in any other, and fewer in the 1 m-by-11 m.)
- *What is happening to the shape of the rectangles as the length increases from 1 m to 6 m?* (They are becoming more compact.)
- *From 6 m to 11 m?* (They are becoming longer and skinnier.)

Some students may talk in terms of numbers or dimensions and others will describe the shape. Encourage both.

Some students may notice that in all the problems the length and width total 12 m. This is related to a formula for perimeter: $P = (\ell + w) \times 2$. Help students to see differences from working with fixed area. With fixed area students used factors of the area to generate side lengths.

Some students will talk about how the 1-by-11 rectangle is long and skinny with every square creating part of the perimeter. With the 6-by-6 rectangle, some of the squares are on the inside of the rectangle and do not make up any of the perimeter. This is what Question D is about. The more square-like a shape is, the more of the square units there are on the inside of the shape and less that touch the edge. When fewer edge units touch the edge, the perimeter is smaller.

Prompt students to use the data in the table and the diagrams of the rectangles to support their reasoning when answering Question C. If students struggled in the launch to explain how they know when they have found all the rectangles, revisit this now.

Suggested Question

- *How do you know you have found all the rectangles?*

2.3 Fencing in Spaces

At a Glance

PACING 1 day

Mathematical Goals

- Find the minimum and maximum area of a rectangle with a fixed perimeter
- Understand that the areas of rectangles with a fixed perimeter can vary considerably
- Construct diagrams, tables, and graphs to organize and represent data
- Continue to develop facility using formulas for finding perimeter and area of rectangles

Launch

Read the introduction to the problem with the class. Before students start designing dog pens, make sure they understand the mathematical context.

- *Before Problem 2.1, we found all the rectangles that could be made with an area of 12 square units and whole-number side lengths. Now I want you to think about all the rectangles that can be made with a perimeter of 12 units and whole-number dimensions. This time, we are holding the perimeter fixed.*
- *Tell me what you built by giving me the dimensions (the lengths of the sides), the perimeter, and area for your rectangle.*

Record the length, width, and area of each rectangle students suggest. Use some of this time to revisit strategies for finding area and perimeter. Ask students to talk about how they found the area and the perimeter.

- *How do we know we have found all the rectangles we can make with a perimeter of 12 units and whole-number dimensions?*

Return to this question in the summary.

Read the context of the dog-pen problem with your class. Make sure students understand the problem.

Materials

- Transparencies 2.3A, 2.3B
- Square tiles (at least 36 per student or pair)
- Several 24-centimeter loops of string (optional)
- Labsheet 2.3

Explore

Encourage students to try adding on or taking off more tiles so as to maintain a rectangle, or to try changing only one dimension at a time. You could also have some 24-centimeter loops of string made in advance and give one to any student who is struggling to visualize the perimeter. When students are trying to answer Question D, it might help them to sketch out the rectangles in Questions A and C.

Summarize

Begin by collecting the data students recorded for Question A. Display the rectangles in some way to facilitate conversation.

For Questions B and C, have students discuss why certain rectangles have the largest or smallest area. Some students may talk in terms of numbers or dimensions and others will describe the shape. Encourage both.

Materials

- Student notebooks

continued on next page

Summarize *continued*

If students struggled in the launch to explain how they know when they have found all the rectangles with whole-number dimensions, revisit this now.

ACE Assignment Guide for Problem 2.3

Differentiated Instruction
Solutions for All Learners

Core 8, 13, 14
Other *Applications* 9–12; *Connections* 22–25; *Extensions* 27, 29; unassigned choices from previous problems
Labsheets 2ACE Exercises 10–12 and 2ACE Exercise 23 are provided if Exercises 10–12 and 23 are assigned.

Adapted For suggestions about adapting ACE exercises, see the CMP *Special Needs Handbook.*
Connecting to Prior Units 22: *Bits and Pieces II,* 25: *Prime Time*

Answers to Problem 2.3

A. 1.

Length (m)	Width (m)	Perimeter (m)	Area (m^2)
1	11	24	11
2	10	24	20
3	9	24	27
4	8	24	32
5	7	24	35
6	6	24	36
7	5	24	35
8	4	24	32
9	3	24	27
10	2	24	20
11	1	24	11

2. For rectangles with whole-number dimensions and a perimeter of 24 m, a 1 m-by-11 m (or 11 m-by-1 m) rectangle will have the smallest area and a 6 m-by-6 m rectangle (a square) will have the largest area.

B. 1.

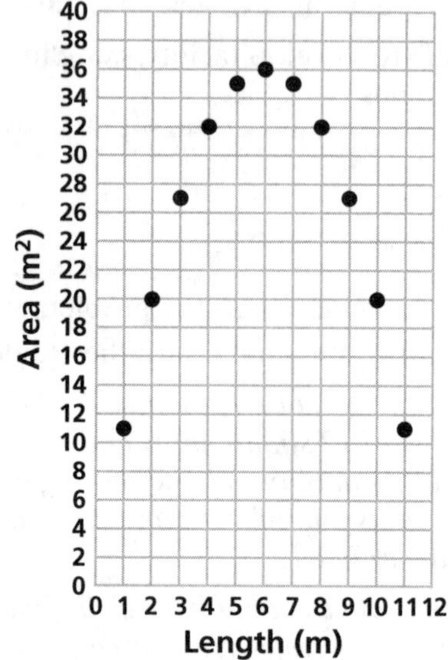

2. The graph is curved. As you read it from left to right, the points rise to a certain place, then go down. As the length decreases in the table, the width increases, and so does the area. Once we have a square, the area is maximized and so increasing the length further begins to decrease the area.

3. This graph is curved like the other one was, but the curve is different. The other graph was decreasing to a minimum, then increasing. This curve increases to a maximum, then decreases. This graph is symmetrical, the other was not. The two graphs show different relationships: the possible areas for a fixed perimeter and the possible perimeters for a fixed area.

C. With 36 m of fencing, the rectangle with whole-number side lengths that has the smallest area will be 17 m by 1 m (or 1 m by 17 m). The largest area is formed with a 9 m-by-9 m rectangle (square).

D. The longest and thinnest shape has the least area for a fixed perimeter. A square shape has the most area for a fixed perimeter.

2.4 Adding Tiles to Pentominos

Goals

- Distinguish the case of fixed area from fixed perimeter
- Apply understanding of the relationship between area and perimeter to nonrectangular figures
- Continue to develop a conceptual understanding of area and perimeter

In this problem, students continue to investigate fixed perimeter and changing area; however, they are no longer restricted to rectangular arrangements. They now consider how adding tiles to a pentomino changes the perimeter of the figure. They explore the patterns of change that occur as tiles are added that touch existing tiles on one, two, or three sides. As students try to find as many different figures with a perimeter of 18 as they can, they will also explore how perimeter changes when a tile is removed from along an edge or a corner of a shape.

There are three ideas about adding tiles that should emerge from this problem:

Case 1: You can add a tile so that it touches one edge of the figure. This adds three exposed edges and eliminates one, increasing the perimeter by 2 units.

Case 2: You can add a tile in a corner so that it touches two tiles. This adds two exposed edges and eliminates two, leaving the perimeter unchanged.

Case 3: You can slip a tile into a space surrounded by three tiles. This adds one exposed edge and eliminates three, decreasing the perimeter by 2 units.

For a diagram of each case, see the answers to Problem 2.4.

As students begin to articulate the various ways in which adding (or subtracting) tiles in different places on a figure affects the perimeter, they become able to purposefully manipulate tiles to create figures that meet the problem constraints. This realization will occur in the explore phase of the lesson for some students, but do not feel this is an expectation for all students when they are exploring. For some, these ideas may not emerge until the summary.

Launch 2.4

Draw the following pentomino on the board and have students construct the pentomino with their tiles.

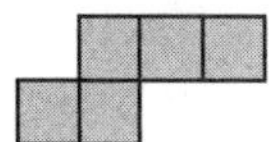

Suggested Questions

- *What is the area of this figure?* (5 square units)
- *What is the perimeter?* (12 units)

Tell students they must keep these five tiles in this arrangement as part of any figure they construct. Discuss with students how to add tiles to the pentomino. Give students examples of ways they are *not* permitted to add tiles. For example, the white tiles in the figure below are not "legal" additions.

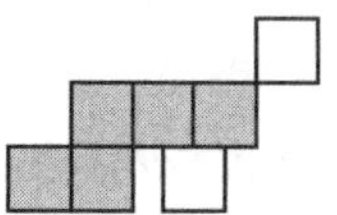

Students must add tiles to the pentomino so that edges match up exactly. If the tiles students are using come in more than one color, you might suggest that they use one color for the pentomino and another color for the tiles they add. Each figure they create will have a perimeter of 18 units but the areas will vary. It will be helpful to have students record the area of each figure beside the figure they sketch on their labsheet.

Before starting, it is important they understand the questions being asked. Make students aware of what Questions B and C are asking so that they can think about these ideas as they work on Question A. This is a nice problem for students to do with a partner, but have each student keep a record of findings on their own grid paper or notebook paper.

Explore 2.4

If students struggle with Questions B and C, ask them to experiment with how the perimeter of the figure changes when they add or subtract a tile in different places such as a corner or an edge. As students identify ways that adding or subtracting tiles affects perimeter, ask them to talk with their partner and try to figure out why this is happening.

Students who finish early can work on ACE Exercise 28, which is also about pentominos.

Summarize 2.4

As students talk about how adding and subtracting tiles in various locations affects perimeter, help others understand what is happening by demonstrating with diagrams or tiles.

Suggested Questions Ask students to reflect on the relationship between area and perimeter using the following questions:

- *When you add a tile, it increases the area by one square unit. Will the perimeter increase too?* (Not necessarily.)
- *If you remove a tile and decrease the area, will the perimeter decrease too?* (Maybe, but not necessarily.)
- *Why or why not?* (Depending on where the tile is added or removed, the perimeter could increase, decrease or stay the same. What matters is how many edges are being covered up and exposed.)

Move to discussing Questions B and C.

- *What is the fewest number of tiles you can add to the pentomino to get a perimeter of 18 units?* (3) *Show us your arrangement on the board.*

Have two or three students show different arrangements. There are several possibilities. Here is one possibility:

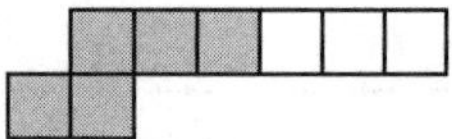

- *Where should you add the three tiles to get the perimeter to increase as quickly as possible?* (On an edge, so that only one side of each new tile touches any other tile.)
- *What is the greatest number of tiles you can add to get a perimeter of 18 units?* (15)
- *What does the figure you got with the maximum area and a perimeter of 18 units look like?* (It is a 4 unit-by-5 unit rectangle.)

Compare this shape to the others and talk about why the 4-by-5 rectangle has such a large number of tiles or area for the fixed perimeter of 18 units. It might help to provide a specific figure with a smaller area and perimeter of 18 units to use as a comparison. Display both and ask:

- *Both of these figures have a perimeter of 18 units. Why is the area of the 4-by-5 rectangle so much larger than the area of this figure?* (The first figure is long and thin with lots of tiles making up the edge of the figure or the perimeter. The rectangle is compact or has a lot of tiles in the middle of the figure that are not part of the edge so they don't increase the perimeter, but they do increase the area.)

Check for Understanding

- *If the perimeter of a rectangle with whole-number dimensions is 36 units, what is the smallest/largest area?* [If dimensions are whole numbers, the smallest/minimum area is 17 square units (1 by 17). The largest/maximum area is 81 square units (9 by 9).]
- *If the area of a rectangle with whole-number dimensions is 36 square units, what is the smallest/largest perimeter?* [The minimum perimeter is 24 units (6 by 6). The maximum perimeter is 74 units (1 by 36).]

2.4 Adding Tiles to Pentominos

At a Glance

PACING 1 day

Mathematical Goals

- Distinguish the case of fixed area from fixed perimeter
- Apply understanding of the relationship between area and perimeter to nonrectangular figures
- Continue to develop a conceptual understanding of area and perimeter

Launch

Draw the pentomino on the board and have students construct it with their tiles.

- *What is the area of this figure? What is the perimeter?*

Tell students they must keep these five tiles in this arrangement. Have students record the area of each figure beside the figure they sketch on their labsheet.

Read through the problem with the students. Make students aware of what Questions B and C are asking so that they can think about these ideas as they work on Question A.

Have students work in pairs, but record their work individually.

Materials

- Square tiles (about 25 per student)

Explore

If students struggle with Questions B and C, ask them to experiment with how the perimeter of the figure changes when they add or subtract a tile in different places such as a corner or an edge.

Summarize

Help students to understand by demonstrating with diagrams or tiles.

- *When you add a tile it increases the area by one square unit. Will the perimeter increase, too?*
- *If you remove a tile and decrease the area, will the perimeter decrease, too? Why or why not?*

Discuss Questions B and C.

- *What is the fewest number of tiles you can add to the pentomino to get a perimeter of 18 units?*

Have two or three students show different arrangements. There are several possibilities.

- *Where should you add the three tiles to get the perimeter to increase as quickly as possible?*
- *What is the greatest number of tiles you can add to get a perimeter of 18 units?*
- *What does the figure you got with the maximum area and a perimeter of 18 units look like?*

Materials

- Student notebooks

ACE Assignment Guide for Problem 2.4

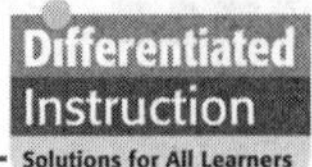

Core 15, 26

Other *Extensions* 28; unassigned choices from previous problems

Adapted For suggestions about adapting ACE exercises, see the CMP *Special Needs Handbook*

Answers to Problem 2.4

A. Answers will vary. Possible answers:

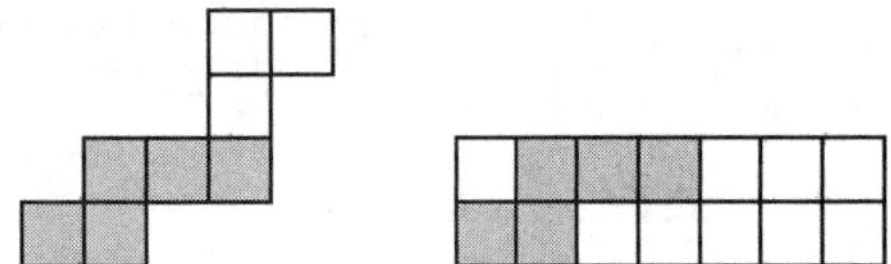

B. 3; possible answers (each of the three tiles must touch only one edge as they are added):

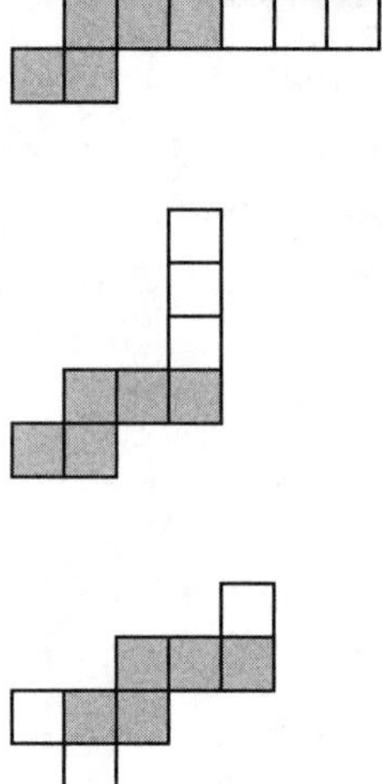

C. 15; possible answers (each figure must enclose the pentomino in a 4-by-5 rectangle)

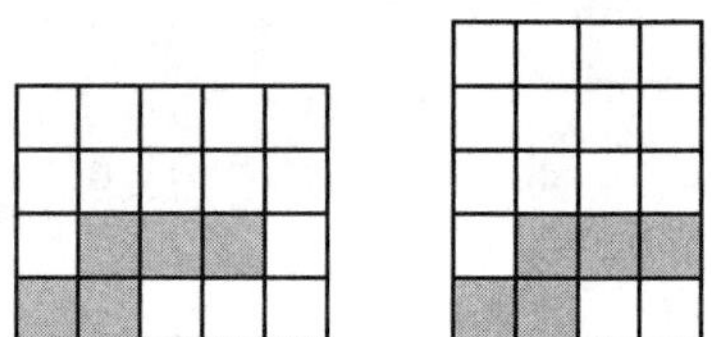

Investigation 2

ACE Assignment Choices

Differentiated Instruction
Solutions for All Learners

Problem 2.1

Core 1, 2
Other *Applications* 3–6; *Connections* 16, 17, 20, 21

Problem 2.2

Core 7
Other *Connections* 18, 19; unassigned choices from previous problems

Problem 2.3

Core 8, 13, 14
Other *Applications* 9–12; *Connections* 22–25; *Extensions* 27, 29; unassigned choices from previous problems

Problem 2.4

Core 15, 26
Other *Extensions* 28; unassigned choices from previous problems

Adapted For suggestions about adapting Exercise 3 and other ACE exercises, see the CMP *Special Needs Handbook.*
Connecting to Prior Units 17, 20–22: *Bits and Pieces II*; 25: *Prime Time*

Applications

1. A 4 ft-by-4 ft square requires the least amount of material for the sides—16 ft of board.

2. a.

Length (ft)	Width (ft)
1	240
2	120
3	80
4	60
5	48
6	40
8	30
10	24
12	20
15	16

b. Possible answer: A car needs at least 8 ft for the length, so the 8 ft-by-30 ft design would probably be too snug. The 10 ft-by-24 ft, 12 ft-by-20 ft, and 15 ft-by-16 ft designs would all be appropriate as garages.

3. a.

Length (m)	Width (m)	Area (m^2)	Perimeter (m)
1	30	30	62
2	15	30	34
3	10	30	26
5	6	30	22
6	5	30	22
10	3	30	26
15	2	30	34
30	1	30	62

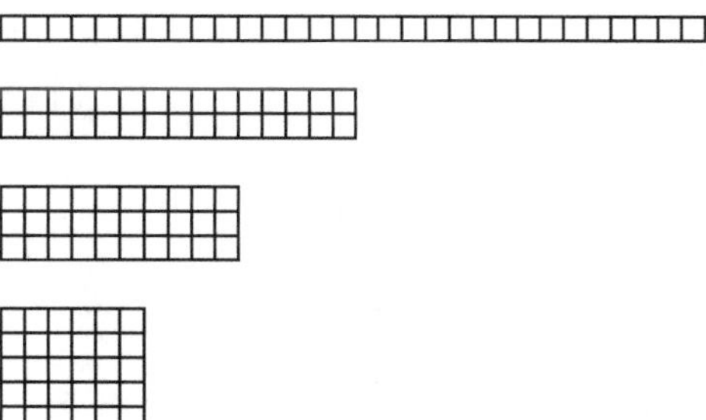

ACE ANSWERS 2

b.

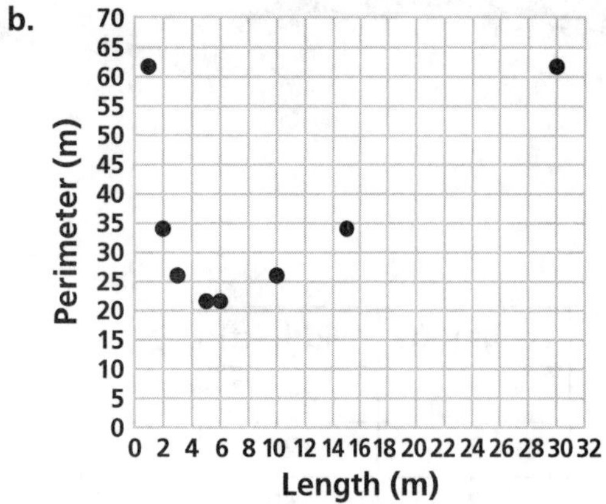

c. On the table, look for the greatest (least) number in the perimeter column. The dimensions will be next to this entry in the length and width columns. On the graph, look for the highest (lowest) points. Then read left to the perimeter axis to get the perimeter. The dimensions will be the x-values of the 2 points.

4. a.

Length (m)	Width (m)	Area (m²)	Perimeter (m)
1	20	20	42
2	10	20	24
4	5	20	18
5	4	20	18
10	2	20	24
20	1	20	42

b.

Perimeter (m)

70 65 60 55 50 45 40 35 30 25 20 15 10 5 0

0 2 4 6 8 10 12 14 16 18 20 22 24 26 28 30 32

Length (m)

5. a.

Length (m)	Width (m)	Area (m²)	Perimeter (m)
1	64	64	130
2	32	64	68
4	16	64	40
8	8	64	32
16	4	64	40
32	2	64	68
64	1	64	130

(Figure 1)

Figure 1

b.

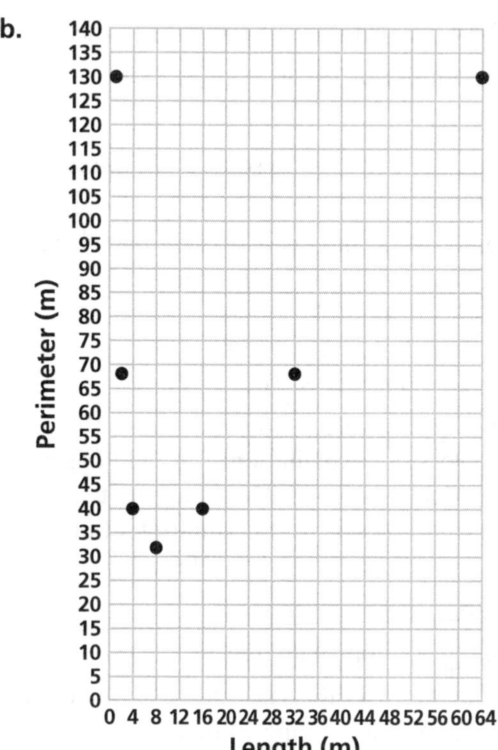

6. a. 32 m, 14 m

b. It is a 1 m-by-28 m rectangle. It is long and skinny.

c. It is a 4 m-by-7 m rectangle. It is more compact, or closer to a square.

d. The fixed area is 28 m^2. This is the area of the two rectangles in parts (b) and (c).

7. The area is the same because she just shifted one part of the rectangle to another part of it. The perimeter is longer because the distance around the new shape is longer than the original rectangle.

8. 18-cm lengths to make a square with an area of 324 cm^2.

9. a. 24 m^2, 12 m

b. It is a 7 m-by-7 m square.

c. This rectangle is long and skinny; 1 m by 13 m.

d. The fixed perimeter is 28 m. This is the perimeter of the two rectangles in parts (b) and (c).

10. a.

Length (m)	Width (m)	Area (m^2)	Perimeter (m)
1	3	3	8
2	2	4	8
3	1	3	8

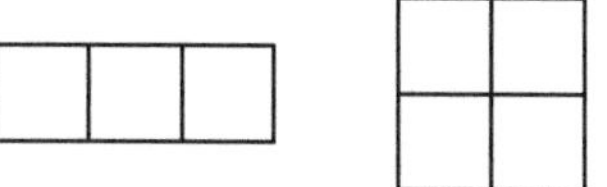

b.

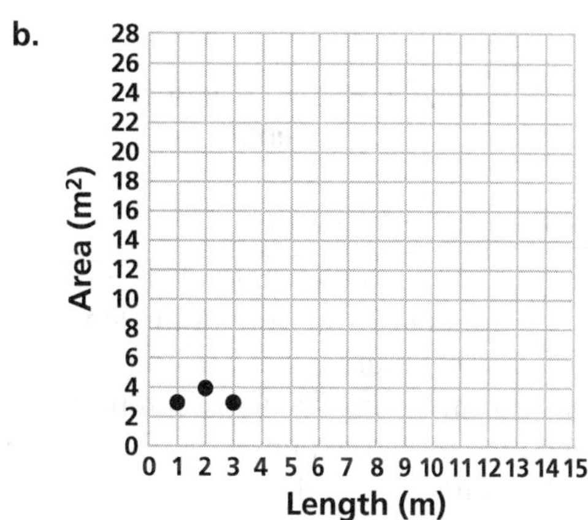

c. On the table, look for the greatest (least) number in the area column. The dimensions will be next to this entry in the length and width columns. On the graph, look for the highest (lowest) point. Then read down to the length axis to get the length. Divide the area by the length to get the width.

11. a.

Length	Width	Area	Perimeter
1	9	9	20
2	8	16	20
3	7	21	20
4	6	24	20
5	5	25	20
6	4	24	20
7	3	21	20
8	2	16	20
9	1	9	20

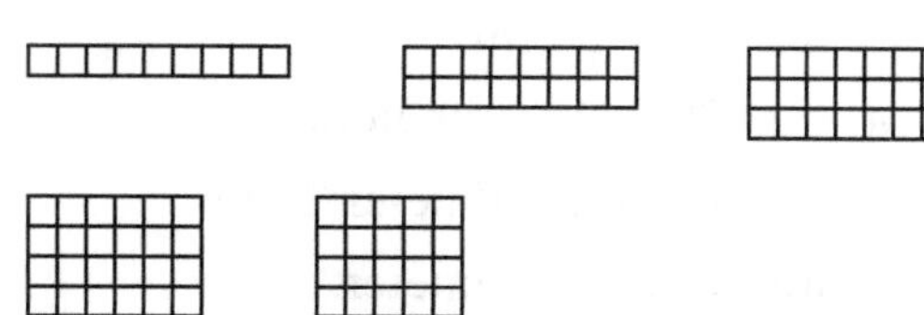

b. 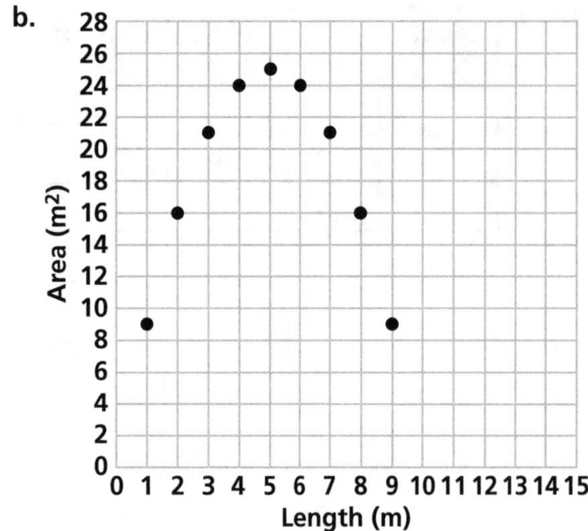

c. See Exercise 10, part (c).

12. There are no such rectangles. This is because we need to double the sum of the length and width. If length and width are both whole numbers, their sum is a whole number. Doubling any whole number gives an even number. Fifteen is odd.

13. No; there are always many different possible perimeters for rectangles with given areas.

14. a. $P = 28$ m; $A = 48$ m^2

b. One possible answer: A 4 m-by-12 m rectangle whose perimeter is 32 m.

c. One possible answer: A rectangle whose dimensions are 6 by 10 and $A = 60$ m^2.

15. A

Connections

16. a. 10 m

b. 6.5 m + 6.5 m + 10 m + 10 m = 33 m

c. \$129.99 × 33 = \$4,289.67

17. F

18. a. dimensions: 6 cm by 2 cm, area: 12 cm^2, perimeter: 16 cm

b. dimensions: $3\frac{1}{2}$ cm by $3\frac{1}{2}$ cm, area: $12\frac{1}{4}$ cm^2, perimeter: 14 cm

c. dimensions: 4 cm by 4 cm, area: 16 cm^2, perimeter: 16 cm

19. a. area: 30 cm^2, perimeter: 26 cm

b. area: 64 in.^{2}, perimeter: 32 in.

c. area: 48 in.^{2}, perimeter: 52 in.

20. Yes; the rectangle in Exercise 17 has perimeter of $19\frac{2}{3}$ m.

21. C

22. No; the 6 m-by-6 m square has the maximum area.

23. a. Sarah would need 142 feet or $47\frac{1}{3}$ yd of fence. Possible explanations:
$30 + 41 + 30 + 41 = 142$;
$2 \times (30 + 41) = 142$;
$2 \times 30 + 2 \times 41 = 142$

b. Sarah would need to purchase 10 boxes. Possible explanation: The field has an area of $30 \times 41 = 1{,}230$ square feet, and dividing this by 125 square feet per box of seed gives 9.84 boxes of seed.

c–d. Answers will vary.

e. $\frac{25}{246}$, or approximately $\frac{1}{10}$

24. The 36 card tables should be arranged in a straight line, seating 74 people.

25. a. 1 by 60, 2 by 30, 3 by 20, 4 by 15, 5 by 12, and 6 by 10.

b. 1 by 61

c. 1 by 62 and 2 by 31

d. The factors of a number and the dimensions of the rectangles that can be made from that number of tiles are the same. For example, the factors of 62 are 1, 2, 31, and 62.

26. 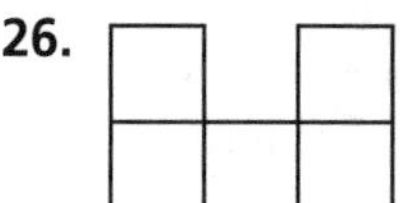

NOTE: This question asks students to think about how removing tiles affects perimeter. The ideas for removing tiles work in reverse of adding tiles.

Case 1: You can remove a tile that is touching one edge of a figure. This eliminates three exposed sides and adds one, decreasing the perimeter by 2 units.

Case 2: You can remove a tile from a corner where it is touching two tiles. This will both remove two exposed sides and expose two sides, leaving the perimeter unchanged.

Case 3: You can remove a tile from a space where it is surrounded by three tiles. This will remove one exposed side and add three exposed sides, increasing the perimeter by 2 units.

It is interesting to think about these ideas as they relate to area. Adding tiles, which increases area, does not always increase the perimeter. Similarly, removing tiles or decreasing the area does not always decrease the perimeter.

Extensions

27. a. The rectangle has dimensions $4\frac{1}{2}$ cm by $6\frac{1}{2}$ cm. The perimeter is 22 cm. The area is $29\frac{1}{4}$ cm^2. (If students use the square as 1 unit, the rectangle has dimensions $3\frac{1}{4}$ units by $2\frac{1}{4}$ units; the perimeter is 11 units; the area is $7\frac{5}{16}$ square units.)

b. Answers will vary. Possible answer: a 9 cm-by-2 cm rectangle. The area of this rectangle is 18 cm^2. (Or a 5 unit-by-$\frac{1}{2}$ unit rectangle with an area of $2\frac{1}{2}$ square units.)

28. a.

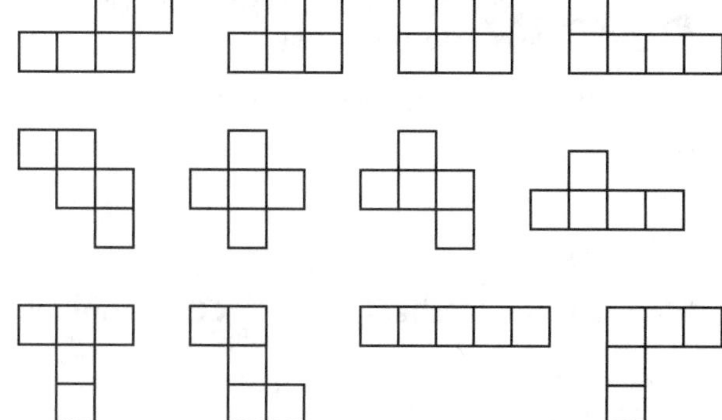

b. Possible answer: I conducted a systematic search.

c. This pentomino has the smallest perimeter, 10 units, because four of the tiles have two edges joined. All of the other pentominos have a perimeter of 12 units.

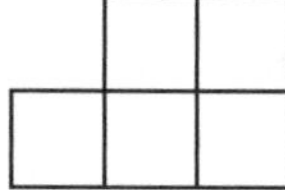

29. You may want to ask students to write their answers as fractions because the patterns are more obvious.

a. $\frac{1}{4}$ m

b. Rectangle; side lengths are $\frac{1}{4}$ m, $\frac{1}{8}$ m, $\frac{1}{4}$ m, $\frac{1}{8}$ m; perimeter $= \frac{3}{4}$ m.

c. A rectangle; side lengths are $\frac{1}{4}$ m, $\frac{3}{16}$ m, $\frac{1}{4}$ m, $\frac{3}{16}$ m; perimeter $= \frac{7}{8}$ m.

d. A rectangle; side lengths are $\frac{1}{4}$ m, $\frac{7}{32}$ m, $\frac{1}{4}$ m, $\frac{7}{32}$ m; perimeter $= \frac{15}{16}$ m.

e. perimeter $= \frac{31}{32}$ m

Possible Answers to Mathematical Reflections

1. a. The most square-like rectangle with a fixed area will have the smallest perimeter. It will be the most compact and have the fewest number of exposed edges.

b. The "skinniest" rectangle will have the largest perimeter. The tiles for the skinny rectangle only touch on one or two edges, so lots of edges will be exposed. If the dimensions of a rectangle are restricted to whole numbers and the area is 12 square units, then the greatest perimeter would be from a 1-by-12 rectangle. If the dimensions are not restricted, then there is no largest perimeter.

2. a. The longest, thinnest rectangle with a fixed perimeter will have the smallest area. This is the rectangle with two sides that are 1 unit long. If the dimensions of a rectangle are restricted to whole numbers and the perimeter is 12 units, then the least area would be from a 1 unit-by-5 unit rectangle. If the dimensions are not restricted, then there is no least area.

b. The rectangle that is the most like a square will have the greatest area. This square-like rectangle is compact or has a lot of tiles in the middle of the figure that are not part of the edge so they don't increase the perimeter, but they do increase the area.

Investigation 3 Measuring Triangles

Mathematical and Problem-Solving Goals

- Develop and employ reasonable strategies for estimating the area of a triangle
- Find relationships between rectangles and triangles and use these to develop techniques for finding the area of a triangle
- Distinguish among base, height, and side lengths of triangles
- Understand that depending upon how you position a given triangle, it has more than one base and height, but only one area
- Explore how triangles with the same base and height can look different but have the same area
- Apply techniques for finding the areas and perimeters of rectangles and triangles to a variety of problem situations

In this investigation, students deepen their understanding of area and perimeter by finding the areas and perimeters of triangles. The primary goal is for students to use their knowledge of rectangles to develop, understand, and use the formula for finding the area of a triangle. Students also understand and develop the ability to identify the base and height of a triangle.

There is a developmental sequence to these problems beginning with shapes on a grid and moving to descriptions of shapes without reference to a grid. In Investigation 4 students will use their knowledge of triangles to study area and perimeters of parallelograms.

Mathematics Background

For background on measuring perimeter and area, see page 4.

Summary of Problems

Problem 3.1 Triangles on Grids

Students estimate the areas and perimeters of triangles on a grid.

Problem 3.2 More Triangles

Students change the orientation of triangles to better understand base and height and how these are related to the area of a triangle.

Problem 3.3 What's the Area?

Students study triangles with common bases and heights to derive a formula for the area of a triangle.

Problem 3.4 Designing Triangles Under Constraints

Students draw triangles satisfying given restrictions.

	Suggested Pacing	Materials for Students	Materials for Teachers	ACE Assignments
All	4 days	Calculators, student notebooks, centimeter grid paper, centimeter rulers	Transparency of centimeter grid paper, transparent centimeter ruler, blank transparencies and transparency markers (all optional)	
3.1	$1\frac{1}{2}$ days	Labsheets 3.1 (2 per student), 3ACE 1–6, 3ACE 26–31	Transparencies 3.1A, 3.1B, 3.1C, 3.1D	1–6, 26–31
3.2	1 day	Labsheet 3.2A (one per student), scissors, cutouts from a transparency copy of Labsheet 3.2B (optional—see Explore section)	Transparencies 3.1A, 3.2A, 3.2B, Shape T from CMP Shapes Set (optional)	7–20, 32–34
3.3	1 day		Transparency 3.3	21, 22, 35–38
3.4	1 day			23–25, 39, 40
MR	$\frac{1}{2}$ day			

3.1 Triangles on Grids

Goals

- Develop and employ reasonable strategies for finding the area of a triangle
- Find relationships between rectangles and triangles
- Use these relationships to develop techniques for finding the area of a triangle

This section may take $1\frac{1}{2}$ days. The first day will use a complete Launch-Explore-Summarize sequence for Question A and launching Question B. In Question A, students will find the area and perimeter of six different triangles. Developing and using the formula for the area of a triangle is not the goal.

Next the students will use the same six triangles to complete Questions B and C. This time they will explore the relationship between area of a triangle and area of the smallest rectangle that surrounds it. Students will work with right and acute triangles in this problem. At the end of Problem 3.1, students should be able to verbalize that the area of a triangle is half the area of a rectangle when the rectangle is the smallest possible rectangle that can surround the triangle. This will be a first look at the relationship between the area of a rectangle and the area of a triangle. This relationship along with base, height, orientation, and obtuse triangles will be explored in the other problems in this investigation.

Day 1: Question A

Launch 3.1

Begin the problem by using the Getting Ready to introduce students to cm^2 notation. This notation will be used in future units.

Have students lay their paper over the diagram and copy the centimeter square, or give them a piece of centimeter grid paper. Talk about each question in the Getting Ready. The first question should not pose much difficulty. It suggests to students that a square can be divided into two congruent triangles.

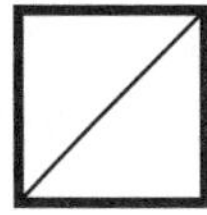

This idea is developed throughout this problem. Spend most of your time focusing on the second question.

Suggested Questions

- *What is the area of each triangle?* (The area of each triangle is $\frac{1}{2}$ cm^2.)
- *Would the perimeter of one of the triangles be greater than, less than, or equal to 3 cm?* (The perimeter is greater than 3 cm. The diagonal is longer than 1 cm, so the perimeter of each triangle is longer than 3 cm.
  $1 + 1 +$ more than $1 =$ more than 3.)

The above question provides an opportunity to address a common mistake students make when finding the length of the diagonal side of a right triangle. Students often mistake the length of the diagonal to be the same as the other sides. By having students measure the diagonal of this triangle, they will discover that the diagonal is longer than either of the two sides that form the right angle. In this case, the diagonal is longer than 1 cm. This makes the perimeter of the triangle greater than 3 cm. Since students will be measuring the lengths with a centimeter ruler, be sure they know how to measure accurately to the nearest millimeter.

If you feel students need another example, have them draw a rectangle that is two square centimeters, insert the diagonal, and answer the two Getting Ready questions. Also discuss labels for area and perimeter using the cm^2 notation for area.

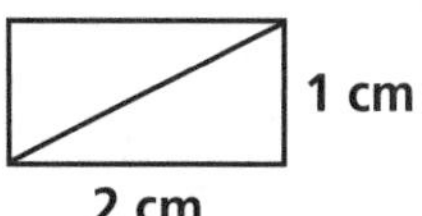

INVESTIGATION 3

Explain to students that they will be working on Question A only and then stopping to discuss their findings. Explain to the students that they will be asked to find the perimeters and areas of six triangles that are not covered with whole squares. Because students have already counted to find the areas of rectangles and then developed a formula, they might ask you to tell them the formula for triangles. Suggest that they think of strategies for finding the area of triangles while they work on the problems in this Investigation. Encourage students to look for patterns that would lead to a formula, as they did with rectangles.

Give students a copy of Labsheet 3.1. Have students work in pairs to find the perimeters and areas of the triangles.

Day 1: Question A

Explore 3.1

As you circulate, remind students to record their findings and explain how they arrived at their answers.

For Question A, part (1), be sure that students are measuring the length of the diagonal (or slanted) sides of triangles with a centimeter ruler so that they get an accurate measure for perimeter. Students can also mark the length of a slanted side on the edge of a sheet of paper and compare it to the centimeter grid on which the triangles are drawn. If students have perimeters that seem unreasonable, challenge them to measure again and compare. Check to see if students are lining up the ruler correctly and reading the measurement accurately.

Day 1: Question A

Summarize 3.1

Ask students for the measures they found for each figure, and record their answers on the board. Continue to collect answers (even if you have several different areas proposed for the same figure) until all the answers that groups found are recorded. Transparency 3.1C is provided for students to come up to the overhead projector and show their work.

Figure	Perimeter (cm)	Area (cm^2)
A	about 18.8	15
B	about 29.2	35
C	about 19.5	12
D	about 24.2	27
E	about 21.2	21
F	about 23	24

Suggested Questions Focus the class's attention on the chart.

- *How did you find these perimeter measurements?* (At this point, most students will understand that perimeter is the length around a figure and that they need to measure the three edges of a triangle and add the results. If there are disagreements about the perimeter, you might want to add three more columns to your table, collect the measures of the lengths of the sides, and resolve the perimeter differences. If other students agree with the side lengths reported, then perhaps students totaled incorrectly. Have students come up to the overhead and measure the side lengths where there is disagreement.)
- *How did you find these area measurements?* (Here are three possible ways that students might find the areas of the triangles in Question A.

  Students may count the number of whole square centimeters and then estimate how many partial square centimeters there are.

  Students may enclose the triangle in a rectangle twice as large as the triangle, find the area of the rectangle, and then divide that by 2.

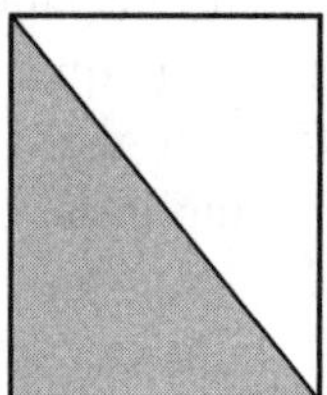

Students may chop off half of the height of the triangle and rearrange it to make a rectangle for which they can find the area. Some students describe this as making a rectangle as wide as the triangle but with half the height.

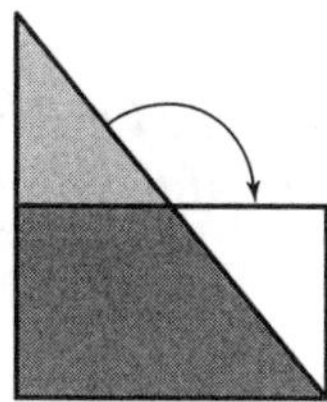

In the case of triangles D–F, they may enclose the triangle in a rectangle, find the area of the rectangle, and subtract the area of the two corner right triangles. They may also subdivide the triangles into rectangles and right triangles.)

Suggested Questions As students offer their methods for finding the areas of the triangles, ask other students if they agree with the methods.

- *Do you agree with what Tinesha did? Why?*
- *Did anyone use another approach?*
- *How did you find the area?* (Students will likely have found the area by counting. Ask whether they tried any other strategies. Again, we are not looking for the formula for finding the area of a triangle at this point, but the following questions could be used to start students thinking about other strategies.)
- *Which of the triangles are right triangles?* (triangles A, B, and C)
- *How do you think right triangles are related to rectangles?*
- *How could you get a right triangle from a rectangle?*

If students have no ideas, demonstrate with two sheets of paper that are the same size. Fold one sheet on the diagonal, and cut along the fold.

- *What shapes do I have now?* (two right triangles)
- *How do the two right triangles compare in size and shape?* (Lay one triangle on top of the other to show that they are the same size and shape.)
- *What measures of the right triangles are the same as measures of the original rectangle?*

Hold up the uncut sheet of paper so students can compare the two figures. They should notice that the length and width of the original rectangle are now two edges of the right triangle.

- *Will the areas of the rectangle and the right triangle be the same?* (no)
- *How do they compare?* (The right triangle is half the original rectangle, so the area of the right triangle is half the area of the rectangle.)
- *How might knowing this relationship help you to find the area of any right triangle?* (Some students may be able to verbalize that the area of a right triangle is half the area of a rectangle whose length and width are equal to the lengths of the two sides of the triangle that form the right angle. It is not important that all students be able to verbalize this relationship at this time. You just want them to think about how their knowledge of rectangles might help them to find the area of triangles.)

Use the relationship between a right triangle and a rectangle to launch Questions B and C.

Day 1: Questions B and C

Launch 3.1

Students will need Labsheet 3.1, which they completed when working on Question A. They will also need a new copy of Labsheet 3.1.

Read Questions B and C. Make sure students understand that they need the smallest rectangle that fits around the triangle. You might want to draw a right triangle and an isosceles triangle and talk about how the smallest rectangle will have the same base and height as the triangle.

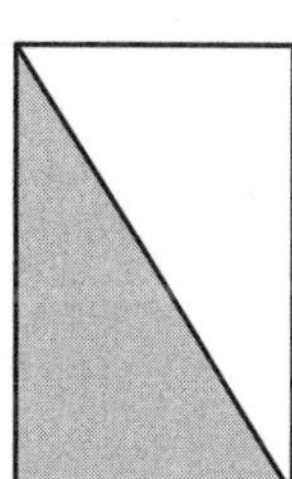

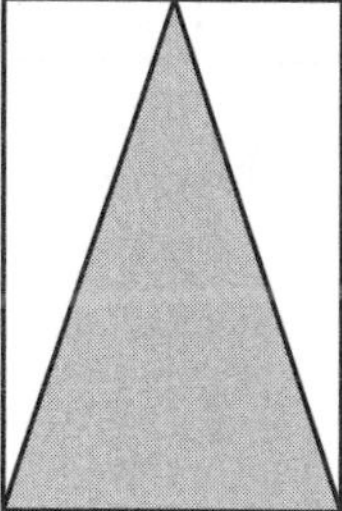

Students can continue to work in pairs.

INVESTIGATION 3

Day 2: Questions B and C

Explore 3.1

As students work, check to be sure they are using the smallest rectangles. Listen to how students are describing the relationship between the areas of the rectangle and the areas of the triangles.

Suggested Question For students who finish quickly and can correctly identify the relationship between the triangle and the smallest enclosing rectangle, ask:

- *Does this relationship occur with perimeter?* (No. This is because at most two of the sides of the rectangle are also sides of the triangle. There is at least one additional side, of a different length, in the triangle.)

Day 2: Questions B and C

Summarize 3.1

Ask students for the measures they recorded in their table and record them in a table at the board. Transparency 3.1D is provided for students to come up to the overhead projector and show their work. If students offer two different answers for a problem, stop and talk about how they arrived at those answers.

Design	Area of Rectangle (cm^2)	Area of Triangle (cm^2)
A	30	15
B	70	35
C	24	12
D	54	27
E	42	21
F	48	24

Suggested Questions Talk about the comparisons students made when they compared the areas of the rectangles and triangles.

- *How are the areas of the triangle and smallest enclosing rectangle related?* (The area of the smallest rectangle is twice the area of the triangle.)
- *Will the perimeter of the smallest rectangle be twice the length of the triangle's perimeter?* (No.)

Move to Question C.

- *How could we write a rule to find the area of a triangle?*

At this point students can offer a rule using words. For example, "If you find the area of the smallest enclosing rectangle and divide it by 2, you will get the area of the triangle."

Help them connect their rule for a triangle to the formula they developed in Investigation 1 for area of a rectangle. For example, with Triangle A on Labsheet 3.1,

- *So, if you multiply the length and the width of the smallest enclosing rectangle, you will get the area of the rectangle?* (Yes)
- *How are the measurements for length and width of the rectangle related to the triangle?* (They are as high and as wide as the triangle.)

Using these words, you would find the area of a triangle by multiplying the length and width of the smallest enclosing rectangle and dividing by two or $(l \times w) \div 2$. Talk briefly with them about how you do not use the labels *length* and *width.*

- *In a triangle these parts are called base and height. In the next problem we will learn about base and height, and modify our rule for finding area of a triangle to be more like the one that mathematicians use.*

3.1 Triangles on Grids (Day 1)

At a Glance

PACING 1 day

Mathematical Goals

- Develop and employ reasonable strategies for finding the area of a triangle
- Find relationships between rectangles and triangles

Launch

Question A

Use the Getting Ready to introduce students to cm^2 notation. Have students lay their paper over the diagram and copy the centimeter square. Talk about each question.

If you feel students need another example, have them draw a rectangle that is 2 square centimeters, insert the diagonal, and answer the two Getting Ready questions. Also discuss labels for area and perimeter using the cm^2 notation for area.

Explain to students that they will be working on Question A only and then stopping to discuss their findings. Suggest that they think of strategies for finding the area of triangles while they work on the problems in this Investigation. Encourage students to look for patterns that would lead to a formula, as they did with rectangles.

Have students work in pairs.

Materials

- Transparencies 3.1A, 3.1B

Explore

Question A

Remind students to record their findings and explain how they arrived at their answers.

Be sure that students measure the length of the diagonal sides of triangles with a ruler so that they get an accurate measure for perimeter. Check to see if students line up the ruler correctly and read the measurement accurately.

Materials

- Labsheet 3.1

Summarize

Question A

Record students' answers on the board. Focus the class's attention on the chart.

- *How did you measure the perimeter?*

Have students come up to the overhead and measure the side lengths where there is disagreement.

- *How did you measure the area?*

Materials

- Transparency 3.1C
- Student notebooks

continued on next page

Summarize

continued

As students explain their methods for finding the areas of the triangles, ask other students if they agree with the methods.

- *Which of the triangles are right triangles?*
- *How do you think right triangles are related to rectangles?*
- *How could you get a right triangle from a rectangle?*

Ask students to think about how their knowledge of rectangles might help them to find the area of triangles.

Launch

Questions B and C

Students will need Labsheet 3.1 from Question A. They may also need a new copy of Labsheet 3.1.

Read Questions B and C. Make sure students understand that the smallest rectangle is supposed to fit around the triangle. You might want to draw a right triangle and an isosceles triangle and talk about how the smallest rectangle will have the same base and height as the triangle.

Materials

- Transparency 3.1B
- Labsheet 3.1 (one fresh copy per student, optional)

ACE Assignment Guide for Problem 3.1 (Day 1)

Core 1–6
Labsheet 3ACE Exercises 1–6 is provided if Exercises 1–6 are assigned.

Adapted For suggestions about adapting ACE exercises, see the CMP *Special Needs Handbook.*

Answers to Problem 3.1 (Day 1)

A. 1. Triangle A: about 18.8 cm
Triangle B: about 29.2 cm
Triangle C: about 19.5 cm
Triangle D: about 24.2 cm
Triangle E: about 21.2 cm
Triangle F: about 23 cm

2. Strategies will vary but should include that the length of a diagonal side was measured with a centimeter ruler.

3. Triangle A: 15 cm^2
Triangle B: 35 cm^2
Triangle C: 12 cm^2
Triangle D: 27 cm^2
Triangle E: 21 cm^2
Triangle F: 24 cm^2

4. Strategies will vary but may include cutting and rearranging the triangle into a rectangle, or surrounding a triangle by a rectangle, then finding the area of the rectangle and dividing it by 2.

3.1 Triangles on Grids (Day 2)

At a Glance

PACING $\frac{1}{2}$ day

Mathematical Goals

- Find relationships between rectangles and triangles
- Use these relationships to develop techniques for finding the area of a triangle

Explore

Questions B and C

As students work, check to be sure they are using the smallest rectangles. Listen to how students are describing the relationship between the areas of the rectangle and the areas of the triangles.

For students who finish quickly and can correctly identify the relationship between the triangle and the smallest enclosing rectangle, ask:

- *Is the same relationship true with perimeter?*

Summarize

Questions B and C

Record students' measures in a table at the board. Discuss how they arrived at those answers.

- *How are the areas of the triangle and smallest rectangle related?*
- *Will the perimeter of the smallest enclosing rectangle be twice the length of the triangle's perimeter?*

Move to Question C.

- *How could we write a rule to find the area of a triangle?*

Help students connect their rule for a triangle to the formula they developed in Investigation 1 for area of a rectangle.

- *How are the measurements for length and width of the rectangle related to the triangle?*

Talk briefly about how triangles do not use the labels *length* and *width*, but rather *base* and *height*.

Materials

- Transparencies 3.1C, 3.1D
- Student notebooks

Vocabulary

- base
- height

ACE Assignment Guide for Problem 3.1 (Day 2)

Core 26–31
Labsheet 3ACE Exercises 26–31 is provided if Exercises 26–31 are assigned.

Adapted For suggestions about adapting ACE exercises, see the CMP *Special Needs Handbook.*

Answers to Problem 3.1 (Day 2)

B. 1.

Design	Area of Rectangle (cm^2)	Area of Triangle (cm^2)
A	30	15
B	70	35
C	24	12
D	54	27
E	42	21
F	48	24

2. The area of a rectangle is twice the area of a triangle or the area of the triangle is half the area of the rectangle.

C. Possible answer: $(b \times h) \div 2$ (NOTE: $(\ell \times w) \div 2$ is acceptable at this time.)

3.2 More Triangles

Goals

- Distinguish among base, height, and side lengths of triangles
- Understand that depending upon how you position a given triangle, it has more than one base and height, but only one area

In this section students are introduced to the conventions of base and height as they apply to triangles. Using these conventions, they will explore how changing the position or orientation of a triangle affects the base, height, and area of a triangle. This exploration will also lead to an efficient rule for finding the area of any triangle.

When working with area and perimeter of triangles, there are some important differences from rectangles. In particular, the terms *length* and *width* are ambiguous for triangles. The length of a rectangle is always the length of one of the rectangle's sides and likewise for the width. For a triangle, the base is the length of one of the triangle's sides, but the height is not necessarily the same length as a side. When calculating area of a triangle, the product of the base and height is divided by 2 because a triangle has half the number of square units that a rectangle with corresponding base and height (length and width) has.

Launch 3.2

Discuss the overview of base and height in the introduction in the student edition. The *height* of a triangle is the perpendicular distance from the vertex to the base. In the first triangle shown, the height falls inside the figure. In the right triangle, the height is one of the sides. For the third triangle, the height falls outside the figure.

You may want to use the triangles from Problem 3.1 to help students understand base and height. Place Transparency 3.1A of the triangles on the overhead projector.

Suggested Question Ask:

- *What are the base and height of Triangle A?*

If someone tells you 6 units for height and 5 units for base (which is correct), ask him or her to explain why. If no one figures this out, explain that height is the perpendicular distance from the side you have identified as the base to the vertex opposite the base.

Check for understanding by having students find the base and height of some other triangles. Be sure to have students identify side lengths on triangles where the sides are not the height (e.g., Triangle D on Labsheet 3.1).

Suggested Questions Return to the ideas raised at the end of the second summary discussion of Problem 3.1.

- *How do the base and height identified for each triangle correspond to the length and width of the rectangles you used to surround the triangles in Problem 3.1?* (Help students see that when they multiply the length and width of the smallest enclosing rectangle, this is numerically equivalent to multiplying the base and the height on the triangle. Talk briefly with students about why triangles do not use the labels *length* and *width* and what base and height measure.)
- *How do your words for describing the method of finding area relate to the symbolic representation for area of a triangle?* [Using their words, to find the area of a triangle, you multiply the length (number of square units in one row) and width (the number of rows) of the smallest enclosing rectangle and divide by two, or $(\ell \times w) \div 2$. With a triangle, these parts are called the base and the height. This leads to the formula $(b \times h) \div 2$.]
- *How does the height of a triangle relate to the height of a rectangle?* (The height of the triangle is the same as the width of the rectangle. Note that the height of the triangle may not be the length of a side of the triangle. For example, the height of Triangle D on Labsheet 3.1 is inside the triangle, but it has the same measure as the height of the rectangle surrounding it.)

Next, discuss the second part of the introduction on orientation. As you discuss how orientation changes where the base and height fall, it helps to model what students will be doing in the problem. In the problem, they will cut out a triangle, place it on grid paper (aligning a side with the grid), trace it, and label the base and height. They will then place the same triangle in a different position on grid paper (aligning a side with the grid), trace it, and label the base and height.

Now read the problem with the students and be sure they understand what they are to do. Be sure to read Questions C and D pointing out that they should think about these two questions while they work on Questions A and B. Provide students with Labsheet 3.2A, centimeter grid paper, and centimeter rulers to use to make accurate measurements for the base and height.

Have students work in pairs, each making his or her own drawings.

Explore 3.2

Encourage each pair to compare their measurements and discuss how to approach the problems. Students need to be careful when they cut out and trace their triangles onto grid paper.

If students are way off in their measurements, check to see if their drawings are accurate and whether they are using the ruler or counting the grid correctly.

As you circulate, remind students to label their drawings so that they are easy to refer to during the summary. If you are short on time, start the summary once students have finished Questions A and B and discuss Questions C and D as a class.

Meeting Special Needs

Labsheet 3.2B has several shaded copies of each triangle. These are provided so that you can copy them onto a transparency and cut them out for students who struggle to transfer the triangles onto grid paper or to visualize the grid beneath them. The shading on this labsheet is light enough to allow the grid lines to show through.

Summarize 3.2

Have a student or student pair come up to the overhead projector to show how they placed Triangle 1 on grid paper, where they think base and height are, and how they found the area.

Suggested Questions Ask other students who used this orientation if they used a different approach to find the area.

- *Did anyone find the area of this triangle a different way?*

Once you have discussed various ways to find the area of the triangle in one orientation, look at a second orientation of Triangle 1. Have another student or student pair come up and show how they placed the triangle, where they think the base and height are, and how they found the area. Again ask:

- *Did anyone use a different orientation or place the triangle on the grid a different way?*

Even though the problem asks students to use two orientations, there are three possible orientations that can emerge across the work the class does. As students present the different orientations, make a table to keep track of the base, height, and area.

Triangle 1

Base (cm)	Height (cm)	Area (cm^2)
7 (longest side)	3	$10\frac{1}{2}$
4 (shortest side)	$\approx 5\frac{1}{4}$	$\approx 10\frac{1}{2}$
$\approx 5\frac{1}{4}$ (other side)	4	$\approx 10\frac{1}{2}$

Ask questions that prompt students to talk about base and height in terms of what is being measured. When 7 cm is given for the base, ask students what the 7 cm represents.

- *What is the 7 cm you found for the base a measure of?* (the length of the horizontal side of the triangle)
- *What does the 3 cm you found for height represent?* (the vertical distance between the base and the vertex of the triangle)

Once all three orientations are presented ask Question C:

- *Does changing the base of the triangle change the area of the triangle? (No) Why? (The shape does not change, just the position in which it is placed.)*
- *If the measurements are slightly different, ask why.* (measurement error)
- *How can there be three different ways to find the same area?* (The area does not change when the shape is turned. Since there are three sides of a triangle, there are potentially three bases. Each base is associated with a unique height.)

Have students present the measurements they collected for Triangle 2. Since Triangle 2 is an isosceles triangle, there are only two different sets of measurements.

Triangle 2

Base (cm)	Height (cm)	Area (cm²)
6 (longest side)	4	12
5 (shortest side)	$\approx 4\frac{4}{5}$	$\approx$12

- *Why does this triangle have two sets of measurements when Triangle 1 had three?* (It is an isosceles triangle. Two of the sides (bases) are the same length and they each have the same corresponding height measurements.)

If you have time it would be interesting to use Shape T, a right triangle, from the Shapes Set or any cut-out right triangle. With right triangles, the base and height can fall on the sides of the triangle. Rather than measure, show students the triangle and tell them the short side is 5 cm long. Give a chart with the base, height, and area measurements and ask students to tell you which way to place the triangle onto the centimeter grid paper.

Base (cm)	Height (cm)	Area (cm²)
$\approx 9\frac{1}{2}$ (longest side)	$\approx 4\frac{1}{4}$	$\approx 20\frac{3}{16}$
5 (shortest side)	8	20
8 (other side)	5	20

Suggested Questions Discuss Question D.

- *Are there advantages or disadvantages to choosing a particular base and its corresponding height to find the area of a triangle?*

Students may offer different views. There is no "best" answer to this problem. Ask them about the different types of triangles (right, isosceles, obtuse, equilateral). Students might offer the following ideas:

It is easier to find the area when the height falls inside the rectangle.

It is easier to find the position that gives the nicest measurements, such as whole-number measurements.

With a right triangle it is easier to use the position where the sides are the base and height.

With an obtuse triangle (like Triangle 1) it may be easier to turn the triangle so the vertex is above the base.

3.2 More Triangles

At a Glance

PACING 1 day

Mathematical Goals

- Distinguish among base, height, and side lengths of triangles
- Understand that depending upon how you position a given triangle, it has more than one base and height, but only one area

Launch

Discuss the overview of base and height in the introduction in the Student Edition. Check for understanding by having students find the base and height of some other triangles.

Return to the ideas raised at the end of Problem 3.1. Talk about how the base and height they identify for each triangle correspond to the length and width of the rectangles they used to enclose the triangles in Problem 3.1.

Help students understand how their words are related to the symbolic representation for area of a triangle.

Discuss the second part of the introduction on orientation. Model what students will do in the problem.

Read the problem with the students. Have students work in pairs.

Materials

- Transparencies 3.1A, 3.2A, 3.2B
- Labsheet 3.2A (one per student)
- scissors
- cut-outs from a transparency copy of Labsheet 3.2B (optional—see Explore section)

Explore

Pairs can compare their measurements and discuss how to approach the problems.

Check students' drawings and measurements as they work. Remind students to label their drawings so that they are easy to refer to during the summary.

Summarize

Discuss the various ways to orient Triangle 1, as well as the area calculations that result from each.

- *Did anyone find the area of this triangle a different way?*
- *Did anyone use a different orientation or place the triangle on the grid a different way?*

As students present the different orientations, make a table to keep track of the base, height, and area. Once all three orientations are presented, ask Question C:

- *Does changing the base of the triangle change the area of the triangle?*
- *Why not? Why are these three triangle area measurements slightly different?*
- *How can there be three different ways to find the same area?*

Materials

- Student notebooks

continued on next page

Summarize

continued

Repeat with Triangle 2. If you have time, use Shape T from the Shapes Set to repeat the conversation.

Finish by discussing the advantages to different orientations.

- *Are there advantages and disadvantages to choosing a particular base and its corresponding height to find the area of a triangle?*

ACE Assignment Guide for Problem 3.2

Core 7–10, 13–17

Other *Applications* 11, 12, 18–20; *Connections* 32–34; unassigned choices from previous problems

Adapted For suggestions about adapting Exercise 17 and other ACE exercises, see the CMP *Special Needs Handbook*.

Answers to Problem 3.2

A. **1.** Possible choices for positioning and labeling Triangle 1 shown below.

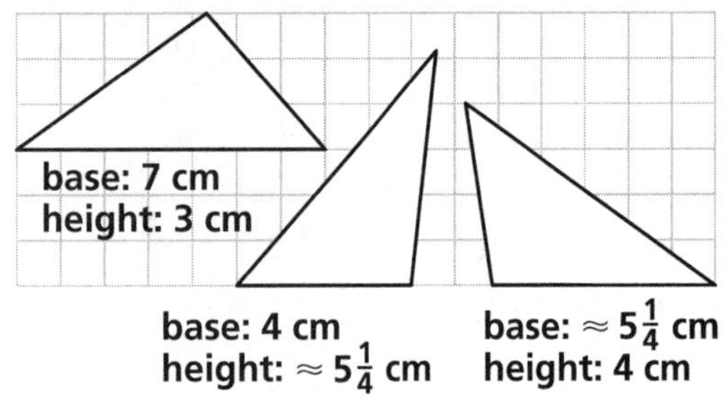

Possible choices for positioning and labeling Triangle 2 are shown below.

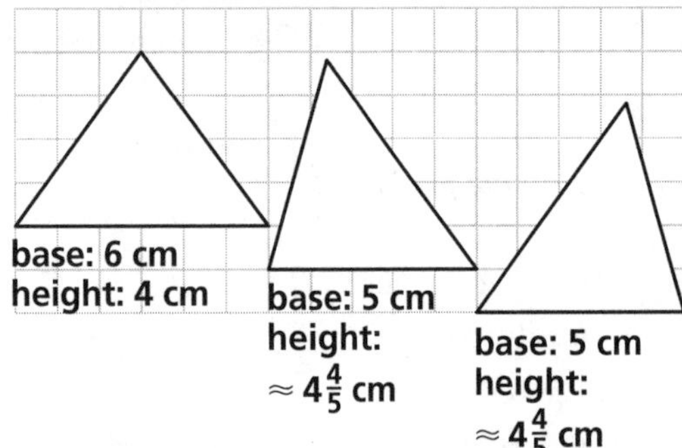

2. The following are based on approximate measurements. This is why the area of each triangle varies. Some students may count the squares. Some may imbed it in a rectangle and subtract off excess area. Some may use the height-base relationship.

Triangle 1

Base (cm)	Height (cm)	Area (cm²)
7 (longest side)	3	$10\frac{1}{2}$
4 (shortest side)	≈ $5\frac{1}{4}$	≈ $10\frac{1}{2}$
≈ $5\frac{1}{4}$(other side)	4	≈ $10\frac{1}{2}$

Triangle 2

Base (cm)	Height (cm)	Area (cm²)
6 (longest side)	4	12
5 (shortest side)	≈ $4\frac{4}{5}$	≈ 12
5 (other side)	≈ $4\frac{4}{5}$	≈ 12

B. **1.** See answers to Question A, part (1).

2. See answers to Question A, part (2).

C. No, the area of a shape does not change when it is repositioned. The base and height measurements may change but they will still lead to the same area. However, the area we calculate might be slightly different because of the approximations we make when we measure the base and height.

D. Students' answers may vary. Here are two possibilities. See summary for others.

Possibility 1: It is easier to find the area when the height falls inside the rectangle.

Possibility 2: It is easier to find the position that gives the nicest measurements, such as whole-number measurements.

3.3 What's the Area?

Goal

- Explore how triangles with the same base and height can look different but have the same area

In this problem students plot points on a coordinate grid as they explore the idea that you can make many triangles with the same base and height. This infinite collection of triangles is referred to as a "triangle family."

Launch 3.3

Begin by discussing the introduction to Problem 3.3. Talk about what a "family" is and ask students to speculate about what a family of triangles might be. Review the characteristics of right, isosceles, and scalene triangles.

You may want to do Question A, part (1), with your students to be sure they understand how to plot points and sketch the triangle. Students will need centimeter grid paper.

Suggested Questions

- *Where can we place the third vertex in order to make a right triangle?* (One possible answer is to place the third vertex directly above either endpoint of the given segment. There are other possibilities.)

Form the triangle and ask some questions about the right triangle.

- *Where is the base of the triangle?* (It is the segment we started with.)
- *How long is the base of the triangle?* (6 cm)
- *Where is the height and how long is it?* (The height is the vertical side of the triangle. It is 4 cm.)
- *What is the area of this right triangle?* (12 cm^2)

Students will need a second sheet of grid paper to complete Question C.

Have students work in pairs or groups of three with each student completing their own work.

Explore 3.3

As students work, observe the strategies students use to find the area of each triangle.

Suggested Questions As students work on Question B, you might ask:

- *Do the triangles have anything besides area in common?* (base and height)
- *Why do these triangles have the same area?* (same base and height)
- *Do the triangles all have the same perimeter? Why not?*

At this point, students may not have an answer to the last two questions. It is okay to pose them for students to think about and return to them in the summary.

Summarize 3.3

Have students offer the various triangles they created. Ask a few students to talk about or demonstrate how they found the area of the different triangles that were formed.

Suggested Questions

- *What do all these triangles have in common?* (base, height, area)
- *How can the triangles have the same base and height as well as the same area, even though they look different?*

By changing the placement of the third vertex, the height stays the same while it rearranges the way the area is shaped. Students worked with a similar idea in Investigation 2 when they designed storm shelters. There are many ways to arrange an area of 24 units to make a rectangle. Some configurations are long and skinny while others are more square-like. Similarly, moving the placement of the third vertex of a triangle on a line parallel to the base keeps the base and height the same length and preserves the area.

Suggested Questions

- *Do these triangles all have the same perimeter?* (no)
- *Why?* (The side lengths get longer or shorter depending upon where the third coordinate is placed.)
- *What conditions give a longer perimeter? A shorter perimeter?* (The perimeter is shortest when the third vertex is centered over the base to make an isosceles triangle.)

If you have a geoboard you can demonstrate how the perimeter increases and decreases as the third coordinate is moved on a line parallel to the base.

- *What are some other coordinates that could be used as the third vertex of a triangle that belongs in this family?*
- *How many different triangles do you think you can make that belong to this family?* (an infinite number)

If students have trouble seeing this, ask them to visualize sliding a point (representing the triangle's vertex for height) on a line 4 cm above and parallel to the base from above one end of the base to the other (Figure 1). The areas of the triangles will be the same, but the perimeters will be different.

Note that the perimeters of these triangles do not vary widely. The shortest perimeter is 10 units, while the longest is just over 11 units. If we continue to slide the third vertex to the right (or the left) on a line parallel to the base, so that it is no longer directly above the base, the perimeter can increase without limit.

If you have time, ask a few students to share the triangle families they created on grid paper. As they share their triangle families, also ask them to describe their triangles by giving the base, height, and area.

Check for Understanding

Sketch some triangles and label a base and corresponding height.

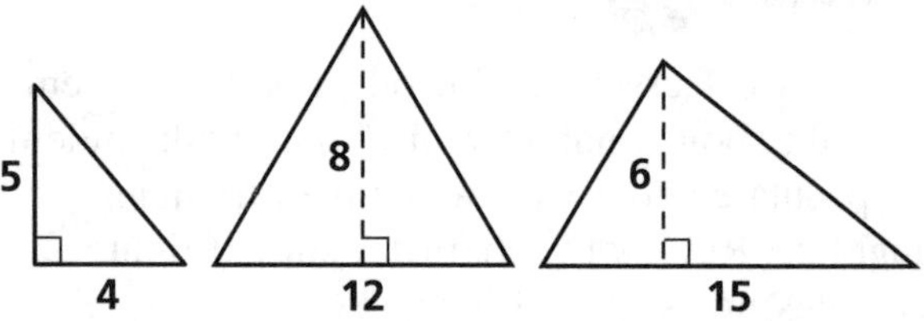

Suggested Question

- *What is the area of each triangle?* (10 square units, 48 square units, 45 square units)

Figure 1

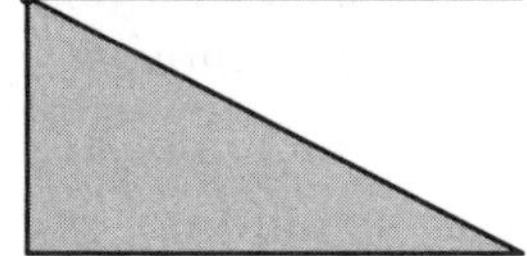

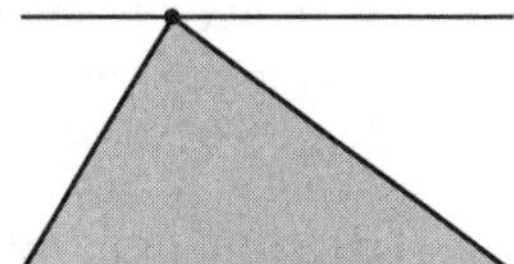

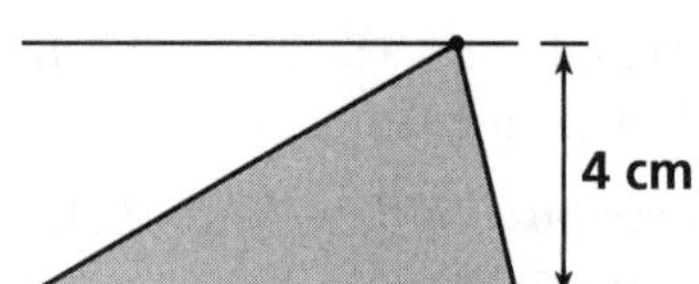

3.3 What's the Area?

At a Glance

PACING 1 day

Mathematical Goal

- Explore how triangles with the same base and height can look different but have the same area

Launch

Read the introduction to Problem 3.3. Discuss what a "family" is. Review the terms *right, isosceles,* and *scalene.*

Do Question A, part (1), with your students. Students will need centimeter grid paper.

- *Where can we place the third vertex in order to make a right triangle?*

Form the triangle and ask some questions about the right triangle.

- *Where is the base of the triangle?*
- *How long is the base of the triangle?*
- *Where is the height and how long is it?*
- *What is the area of this right triangle?*

Give students a second sheet of grid paper to complete Question C.

Have students work individually and discuss in pairs.

Materials

- Transparency 3.3
- Centimeter grid paper
- Grid Paper Transparency

Explore

As students work, observe the strategies students use to find the area of each triangle. As students work on Question B, you might ask:

- *Do the triangles have anything besides area in common?*
- *Why do these triangles have the same area?*
- *Do the triangles all have the same perimeter? Why not?*

Summarize

Have students offer the various triangles they created.

- *What do all these triangles have in common?*
- *How can the triangles have the same base and height as well as the same area, even though they look different?*
- *Do these triangles all have the same perimeter? Why?*
- *What conditions give a longer perimeter? A shorter perimeter?*

Demonstrate how the perimeter increases and decreases as the third coordinate is moved on a line parallel to the base.

- *What are some other coordinates that could be used as the third vertex of a triangle that belongs in this family?*
- *How many different triangles do you think you can make that belong to this family?*

Materials

- Student notebooks

continued on next page

Summarize

continued

Ask students to visualize sliding a point from above one end of the base to the other on a line 4 cm above and parallel to the base. If you have time, ask a few students to share the triangle families they created on grid paper. Ask them to describe their triangles by stating the base, height, and area.

ACE Assignment Guide for Problem 3.3

Core 21, 22

Other *Connections* 35–38; unassigned choices from previous problems

Adapted For suggestions about adapting ACE exercises, see the CMP *Special Needs Handbook*

Connecting to Prior Units 35–38: *Bits and Pieces I*

Answers to Problem 3.3

A. 1–2. Possible triangles:

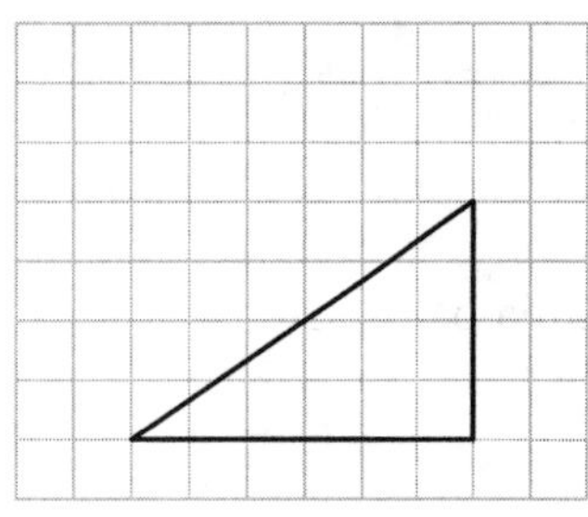

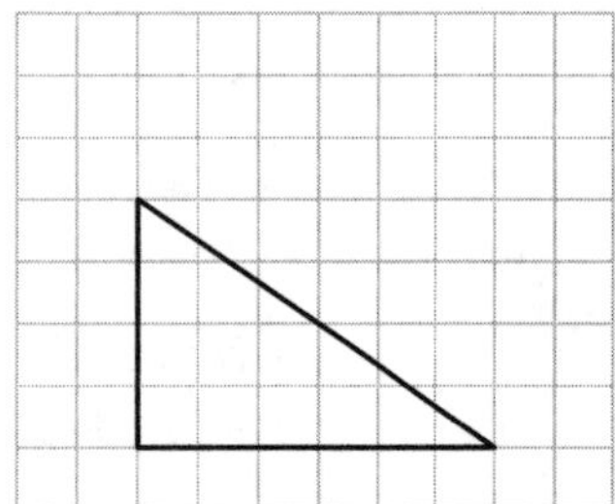

3. There is one possibility:

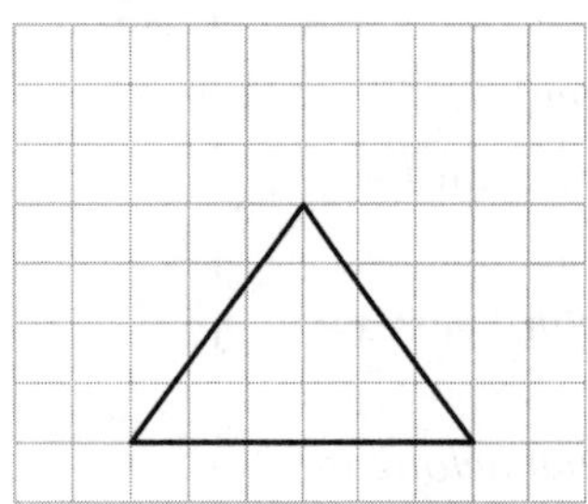

4. Any triangle other than those above. For example:

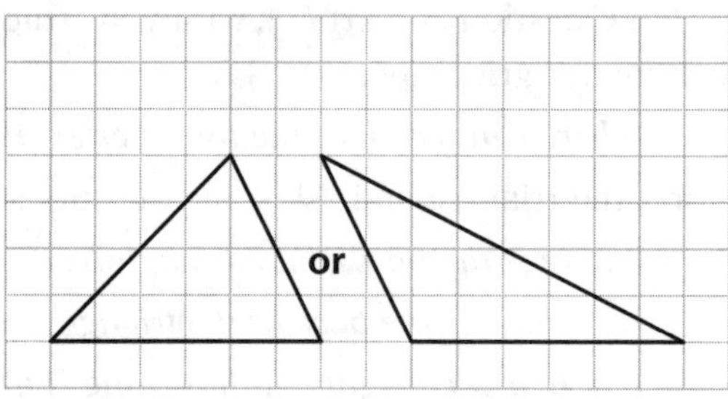

5. 12 cm^2

B. 1. The four triangles have the same base, height, and area.

2. Because they have the same base, height and area.

C. Answers will vary. Here is one possibility of a triangle family that has a base of 3, height of 5, and an area of $7\frac{1}{2}$ cm^2.

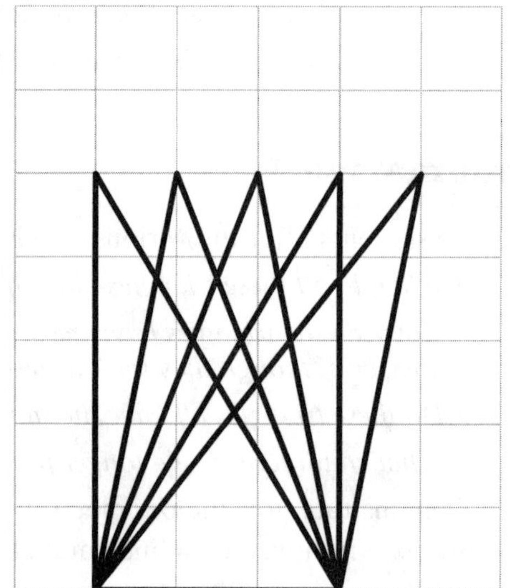

3.4 Designing Triangles Under Constraints

Goal

- Apply techniques for finding the areas and perimeters of rectangles and triangles to a variety of problem situations

In this problem, students are asked to construct triangles with given measurements, areas, or angles. In each case, they are asked whether they can draw a different triangle for the same constraints and to determine whether the areas or perimeters of the two triangles differ.

At this point in Investigation 3, students have developed strategies for finding the area and perimeter of triangles, and have explored how orientation and the position of the base and height affect area and perimeter. This problem will provide a context for students to use these ideas and for you to assess how they are reasoning at this point in time.

Launch 3.4

Explain to students that they are going to design triangles with given conditions. Students may be given the base, height, area, side lengths, or angles.

Give the directions from Question A, part (1). Have a student come to the overhead projector and draw a triangle with a base of 5 cm and a height of 6 cm on centimeter grid paper. Have them label the base and height.

Suggested Questions When the class agrees this has been done successfully, ask them about the second instruction in the question.

- *You are now asked to try to draw a different triangle that is not congruent to the first triangle but has these same dimensions. What does "not congruent" mean?* (The second triangle cannot have the same shape as the first. If the new triangle is turned or flipped, it should not fit on top of the first triangle.)

Have several sheets of grid paper available; students will make mistakes. To save time and materials, you might suggest that they cross out or erase figures that don't meet the requirements rather than throwing away their paper.

Have students work in pairs. Each student should make his or her own drawings. Pairs can discuss how to approach each part, then check each other's drawings.

Explore 3.4

As you circulate, remind students to label their drawings so that they are easy to refer to during the summary.

Listening to Students

As you observe and interact with students, consider the following questions:

- *Do students use the terms* base *and* height *in their conversations?*
- *Do students struggle to identify the base and height?*
- *Do students make connections between what these problems are asking and previous problems they have worked on? (For example, students can use their knowledge of triangle families to answer Questions A and B.)*

In the summary be sure that students discuss some of the observations that you have made.

Summarize 3.4

Suggested Questions Start the summary by asking students what they have found when making these designs.

- *What kinds of constraints make drawing a triangle easy? What kinds of constraints make drawing a triangle difficult?*

Students may find it easiest to construct a triangle when all three side lengths or a base and height measurement are given. Other students may find it difficult to construct a triangle with a fixed area. If a student identifies a certain type of information as difficult, ask the other students whether they came up with strategies for drawing triangles under that kind of constraint.

- *Were there any questions for which you could only make one triangle to fit the constraints?*

If students say no, ask them to share what they found for Question C. If they give two different triangles, the second is probably simply a different orientation of the first. The idea that triangles with fixed side lengths are unique was a goal of the sixth-grade unit *Shapes and Designs*.

Have students share their responses to the question. Rather than giving approval as the teacher, ask students to decide if they agree or disagree. If they disagree, have them talk with other students and the class about why they disagree. After students agree on a solution, ask if anyone has a different solution.

When discussing Questions A and B, you want students to notice that fixing the base and height of a triangle does not limit the shape of the triangle but does fix the area.

Question D alludes to triangle similarity. Triangles with the same angle measures are said to be *similar*. Similarity is not an idea that your students will be familiar with, and it is not suggested that you discuss it at this time. The ideas of similarity are covered in the seventh-grade unit *Stretching and Shrinking*. Rather than focus on similarity, focus on the idea that you can make an infinite number of right triangles with a 30° angle by making the side length shorter or longer.

3.4 Designing Triangles Under Constraints

At a Glance

PACING 1 day

Mathematical Goal

- Apply techniques for finding the areas and perimeters of rectangles and triangles to a variety of problem situations

Launch

Explain to students that they are going to design triangles with given conditions. Read Question A aloud. Have a student come to the overhead projector and draw a triangle with a base of 5 cm and a height of 6 cm on centimeter grid paper. Have them label the base and height. When the class agrees this has been done successfully, ask them about the second instruction in the question.

Suggest that they cross out or erase figures that don't meet the requirements rather than throwing away their paper.

Have students work individually and discuss in groups.

Explore

Remind students to label their drawings so that they are easy to refer to during the summary. Consider the following as you listen to their conversations:

- Do students use the terms *base* and *height* in their conversations?
- Do students struggle to identify the base and height?
- Do students make connections between what these problems are asking and previous problems they have worked on?

Summarize

Start the summary by asking students what they have found when making these designs.

- *What kinds of constraints make drawing a triangle easy? What kinds of constraints make drawing a triangle difficult?*

Ask students whether they found strategies for drawing triangles under particular constraints they describe as difficult.

- *Were there any questions for which you could only make one triangle to fit the constraints?*

Have students share their responses to the question. Ask students to decide if they agree with each other. If not, have them talk about why they disagree. After students agree on a solution, ask if anyone has a different solution.

Materials

- Student notebooks

ACE Assignment Guide for Problem 3.4

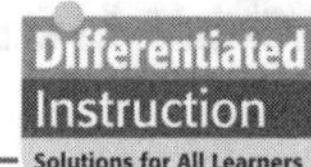

Core 23–25

Other *Extensions* 39, 40; unassigned choices from previous problems

Adapted For suggestions about adapting ACE exercises, see the CMP *Special Needs Handbook*.

Answers to Problem 3.4

A. Drawings will vary. Students may recognize that this question is making reference to the idea of "triangle families" in Problem 3.3. You can draw many triangles (actually, an infinite number) with the same base and height. The areas of the triangles will be the same, but the perimeters will be different. Possible drawings:

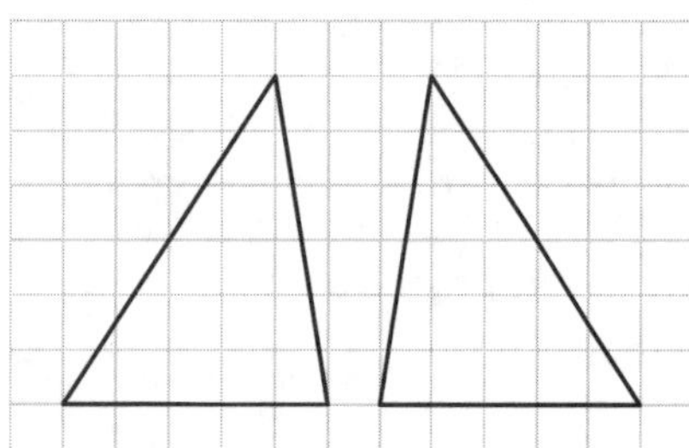

B. Drawings will vary. Drawings will be of a triangle with base 6 units and height 5 units, a triangle with base 10 units and height 3 units, and a triangle with base 15 units and height 2 units. The perimeters will all be different. Note that any triangle from Question A will satisfy this constraint.

C. Only one triangle is possible. In the sixth-grade unit *Shapes and Designs,* students learned that at most one triangle is possible from three given side lengths. Of course, this triangle may be oriented in different ways.

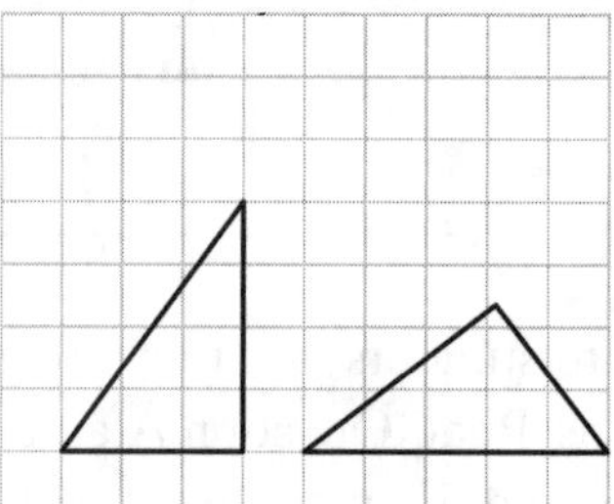

D. Drawings will vary. You can draw an infinite number of right triangles with a 30° angle. The triangles will have different areas and different perimeters, but they will all have the same angle measures and the same shape. Possible drawings:

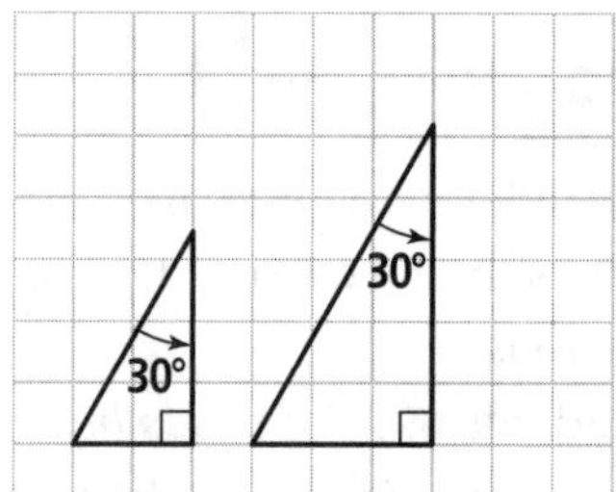

Investigation 3

ACE Assignment Choices

Problem 3.1

Core Day 1: 1–6; Day 2: 26–31

Problem 3.2

Core 7–10, 13–17

Other *Applications* 11, 12, 18–20; *Connections* 32–34; unassigned choices from previous problems

Problem 3.3

Core 21, 22

Other *Connections* 35–38; unassigned choices from previous problems

Problem 3.4

Core 23–25

Other *Extensions* 39, 40; unassigned choices from previous problems

Adapted For suggestions about adapting Exercise 17 and other ACE exercises, see the CMP *Special Needs Handbook.*

Connecting to Prior Units 35–38: *Bits and Pieces I*

Applications

1. $A = (5 \times 5) \div 2 = 12\frac{1}{2}\text{ cm}^2$
   $P \approx 5 + 5 + 7 = 17$ cm. Possible explanations: I found the area by counting the number of square cm covering the figure, by using the rule, or by finding half of the area of the smallest rectangle that surrounds the triangle. I found the perimeter by measuring around the edge of the triangle with a string and comparing the length marked off on the string to the units on the grid.
2. $A = (7 \times 6) \div 2 = 21\text{ cm}^2$,
   $P \approx 7 + 7\frac{1}{4} + 6\frac{3}{4} = 21$ cm
3. $A = (3 \times 7) \div 2 = 10\frac{1}{2}\text{ cm}^2$,
   $P \approx 3 + 7\frac{1}{4} + 7\frac{1}{4} = 17\frac{1}{2}$ cm
4. $A = (4 \times 7) \div 2 = 14\text{ cm}^2$,
   $P \approx 7\frac{1}{4} + 7\frac{1}{4} + 4 = 18\frac{1}{2}$ cm. Possible explanations: I found the area by counting the number of square cm covering the figure, or by using the rule. I found the perimeter by measuring around the edge of the triangle with a string and comparing the length marked off on the string to the cm on the grid.
5. $A = (7 \times 8) \div 2 = 28\text{ cm}^2$,
   $P \approx 7 + 8\frac{1}{2} + 9\frac{1}{4} = 24\frac{3}{4}$ cm. Possible explanations: I found the area by counting the number of square cm covering the triangle, or by using the rule. I found the perimeter by measuring around the edge of the triangle with a string and comparing the length marked off on the string to the cm on the grid.
6. $A = (2 \times 8) \div 2 = 8\text{ cm}^2$,
   $P \approx 2 + 8 + 8\frac{1}{4} = 18\frac{1}{4}$ cm
7. **a.** 39 cm^2
   b. 7.5 cm^2
   c. 40 m^2
   d. 35 ft^2
8. Vashon is correct because no matter which side of the triangle he chooses for the base, as long as he chooses the corresponding height, the area will be the same.
9. **a.** Based on the simplest orientation for each triangle:

	Base (cm)	Height (cm)	Area (cm²)
A	5	6	15
B	10	7	35
C	3	8	12
D	9	6	27
E	6	7	21
F	6	8	24

   b. The areas should be the same. Any differences should be small and related to different approximations in measuring.

10. Talisa is correct because it does not matter which side of the triangle you use as the base, as long as you choose the appropriate corresponding height. For example, a right triangle with a base of 4 units and a height of 5 units will have an area of 10 square units, which is the same if the base was 5 and the height was 4 units.

11. a. Possible answer:

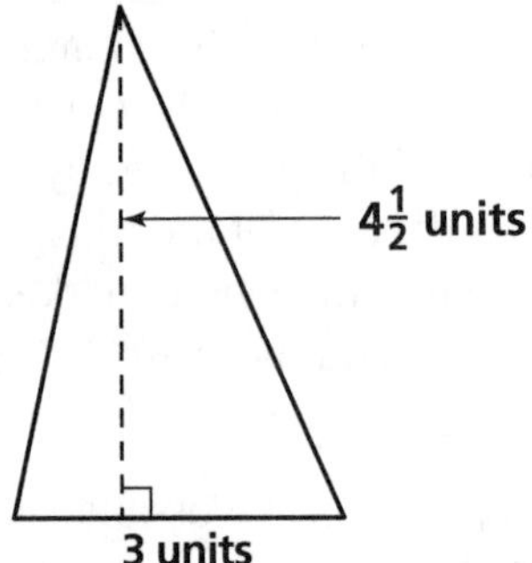

b. $6\frac{3}{4}$ square units

12. The height is $3\frac{1}{5}$ m because

$\frac{1}{2} \times 2\frac{1}{2} \times 3\frac{1}{5} = 4$; or, $h = \dfrac{4}{\frac{1}{2} \times 2\frac{1}{2}}$.

13. $A = 28$ cm^2, $P = 22$ cm

14. $A = 120$ cm^2, $P = 60$ cm

15. $A = 60$ cm^2, $P = 36$ cm

16. $A = 7\frac{1}{32}$ in.^{2}, $P = 14\frac{1}{4}$ in.

17. Keisha is incorrect because these triangles are the same size and shape (congruent) and therefore have the same area. Also they both have an area of $(3 \times 4) \div 2 = 6$ cm^2.

18. $A = 24$ cm^2

19. $A = 24$ cm^2

20. $A = 24$ cm^2

21. Marlika is correct. It is the base and height of a triangle that determine its area, not the size of its angles.

22. D

23. The triangles have the same area. Some possible triangles:

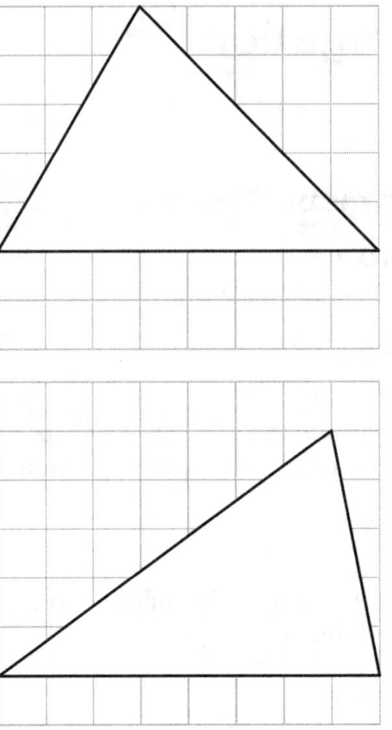

24. These triangles have the same area but not the same perimeter. Some possible triangles:

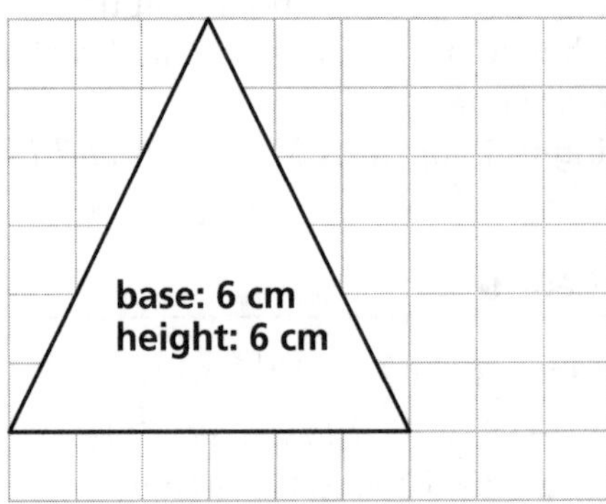

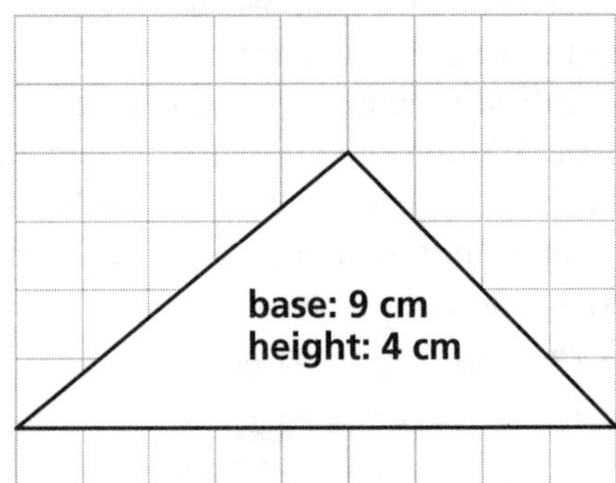

25. Only one triangle (although it may be oriented multiple ways):

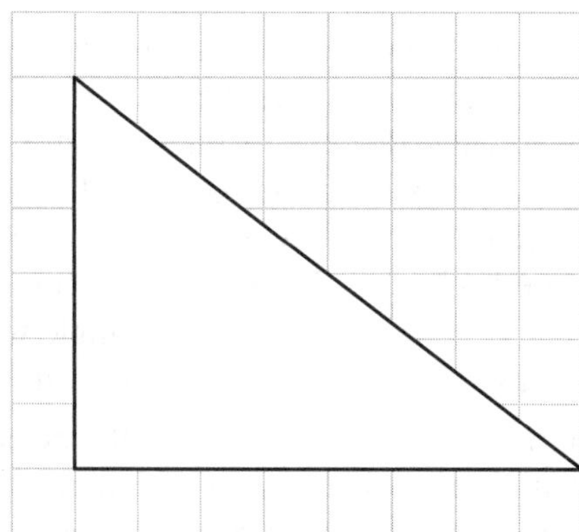

With these side lengths, the only possible triangle is a right triangle. The Pythagorean Theorem will justify this for students in the eighth-grade unit *Looking for Pythagoras.*

Connections

26. $A = 28 \text{ cm}^2$; $P \approx 22.6$ cm

27. $A = 28 \text{ cm}^2$; $P \approx 23$ cm
(Divide shape into a 5-by-4 rectangle with two triangles on either side. The two triangles can come together to make a 2-by-4 rectangle. So, $20 \text{ cm}^2 + 8 \text{ cm}^2 = 28 \text{ cm}^2$. I found perimeter by measuring around the edge of the shape with a string and measuring it with a centimeter ruler.)

28. $A = 6 \text{ cm}^2$; $P \approx 11\frac{1}{2}$ cm

29. $A = 27 \text{ cm}^2$; $P \approx 24\frac{1}{2}$ cm

30. $A = 31\frac{1}{2} \text{ cm}^2$; $P \approx 26$ cm
(Base = 9 cm and height = 7 cm, so
$A = \frac{1}{2}(9)(7) = 31\frac{1}{2} \text{ cm}^2$.
I found perimeter by measuring around the edge of the triangle with a string and measuring it with a centimeter ruler.)

31. $A = 15 \text{ cm}^2$; $P \approx 19$ cm
(Base = 5 cm and height = 6 cm, so
$A = \frac{1}{2}(5)(6) = 15 \text{ cm}^2$.
I found perimeter by measuring around the edge of the triangle with a string and measuring it with a centimeter ruler.)

32. a.

b. You would need to measure the base and height of each triangle in the sail to find its area, then add the areas of the triangles to find the area of the cloth.

33. G

34. The four isosceles triangles each have areas of $(42 \times 28) \div 2 = 588 \text{ cm}^2$, and the square base has an area of $42 \times 42 = 1{,}764 \text{ cm}^2$. Therefore, you would need $588 \times 4 + 1{,}764$ or $4{,}116 \text{ cm}^2$ of glass.

35. Answers will vary. Students may divide the squares into tenths, and then mark off $\frac{1}{10}$, $\frac{2}{10}$, $\frac{3}{10}$, and $\frac{4}{10}$.

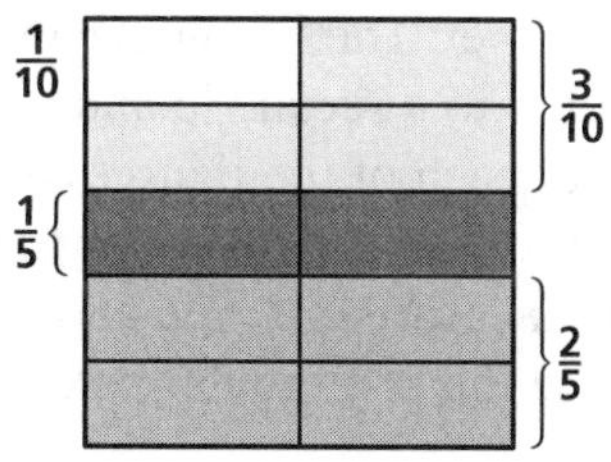

36. Answers will vary. Two possibilities:

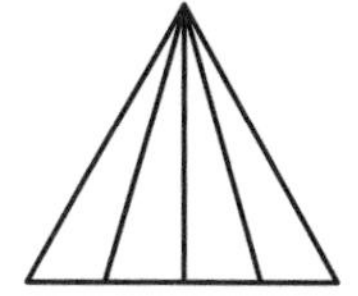

37. Answers will vary. Students may divide the rectangle into twelfths and mark off $\frac{4}{12}$, $\frac{2}{12}$, $\frac{3}{12}$, and $\frac{3}{12}$.

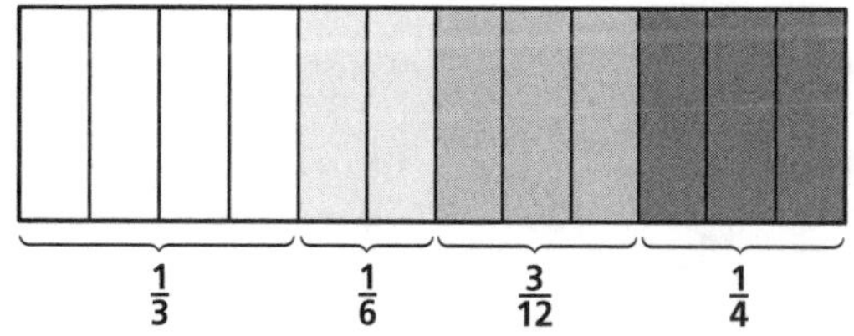

38. Answers will vary. Students may divide the rectangle into sixteenths and mark off $\frac{1}{16}$, $\frac{8}{16}$, $\frac{3}{16}$, and $\frac{4}{16}$.

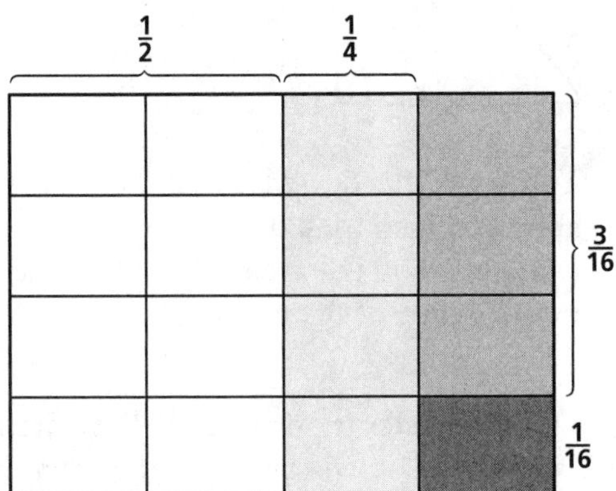

Extensions

39. Only Question C represents a situation where the triangles are large enough to fold up to meet at a point above the base to make a pyramid.

40. Possible answer: The hexagon can be subdivided into a rectangle and two triangles. The area of each of the figures can be found and then the results added. For the perimeter you could measure one side and multiply it by six, because this is a regular hexagon.

Possible Answers to Mathematical Reflections

1. To find the area of a triangle, measure the base (any one of its sides) and its height (the perpendicular distance from the vertex opposite the base to the base), multiply these measurements, and divide the answer by 2. This method works because the area of a triangle is half the area of a rectangle with the same base and height (length and width).

2. To find the perimeter of a triangle measure the length of each side and add these measurements together. Some triangles have shortcuts. For example, with an equilateral triangle all the sides are the same length so you can measure one side and multiply by three to find the perimeter.

3. When you find the perimeter of triangles and rectangles you are finding the sum of the measures of all of the edges. Each shape has special shortcuts you can use to find perimeter, but the result will be the length of the total distance around the shape. Finding the area of rectangles and triangles is related. The area of a triangle is half of the area of the smallest rectangle that will enclose the triangle. With a triangle you measure the base and height, multiply them, and divide the product by two to find the area. With a rectangle you measure and multiply the length and width. You do not divide by 2.

Investigation 4 Measuring Parallelograms

Mathematical and Problem-Solving Goals

- Develop and employ reasonable strategies for finding the areas and perimeters of parallelograms
- Find area relationships between rectangles, triangles, and parallelograms
- Use relationships between parallelograms and triangles to develop techniques for finding the areas of parallelograms
- Distinguish among the base, height, and side lengths of a parallelogram
- Understand that a parallelogram may be positioned in more than one way, and thus may have more than one base-height pair, but only one area
- Apply techniques for finding the areas and perimeters of parallelograms to a variety of problem situations

In this investigation, students continue to deepen their understanding of area and perimeter by finding the areas and perimeters of parallelograms. The primary goal is for students to develop, use, and understand formulas for finding areas and perimeters of parallelograms.

Summary of Problems

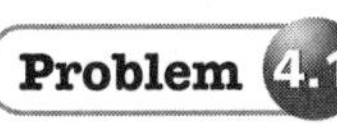

Problem 4.1 Finding Measures of Parallelograms

Students estimate the areas and perimeters of parallelograms drawn on grid paper.

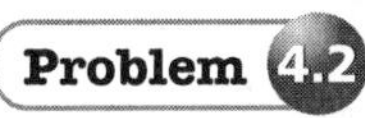

Problem 4.2 Parallelograms from Triangles

By relating parallelograms to triangles, students develop a rule for finding the area of a parallelogram.

Problem 4.3 Designing Parallelograms Under Constraints

Students draw parallelograms satisfying certain given conditions.

Problem 4.4 Parks, Hotels, and Quilts

Students apply their understanding of area and perimeter of rectangles, triangles, and parallelograms.

	Suggested Pacing	Materials for Students	Materials for Teachers	ACE Assignments
All	5 days	Calculators, student notebooks, centimeter grid paper, centimeter rulers	Transparency of centimeter grid paper (optional), blank transparencies and transparency markers (optional)	
4.1	1 day	Labsheet 4.1 (one per student), centimeter ruler	Transparencies 4.1A, 4.1B	1–8, 32
4.2	$1\frac{1}{2}$ days	Labsheet 4.1 (a second copy for each student), Labsheet 4.2A (one per student), scissors, cut-out copies of shapes from transparency of Labsheet 4.2B (optional)	Transparency 4.2	9–21, 33–35
4.3	1 day			22–31, 38, 39
4.4	1 day		Transparencies 4.4A, 4.4B (optional)	36, 37
MR	$\frac{1}{2}$ day			

4.1 Finding Measures of Parallelograms

Goal

- Develop and employ reasonable strategies for finding the areas and perimeters of parallelograms

Students will find the area and perimeter of six different parallelograms. The purpose is to have students develop and employ reasonable strategies for finding the area of these parallelograms: counting, estimating, and talking about ways to rearrange and use parts of grid squares.

Launch 4.1

Begin by discussing the Getting Ready in the introduction to Problem 4.1. Rather than show students where the base and height are on the third parallelogram, it is left open to see if students can apply what they know about bases and heights of triangles to parallelograms.

Suggested Questions

- *Where are the base and the height on a triangle?* (The base is the length of one of the sides of the figure and the height for that base is the perpendicular distance from the base to an opposite vertex.)
- *What can measures of the base and height tell you?* (Measures of the lengths of the base and height can tell you the number of square units in a row and the number of rows with that many square units. The base of a parallelogram is one side of the parallelogram. It could be any of the four sides. The height of a parallelogram is any perpendicular from the base to the side parallel to the base. The height of a parallelogram depends on the side that is chosen for the base.)

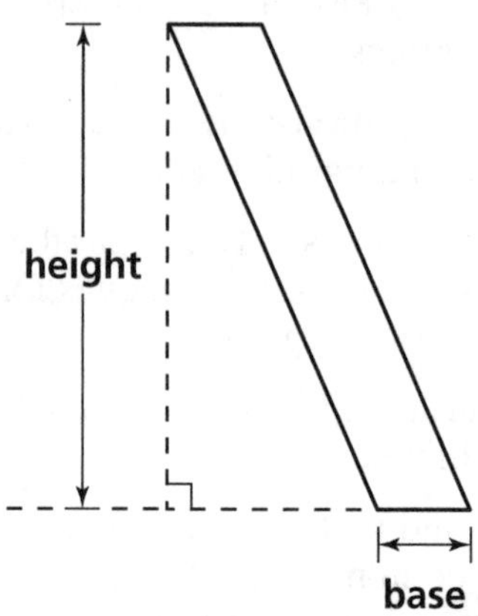

- *Do height and base mean the same as they did for triangle?* (The base and height have the same meaning when used with parallelograms as they did when used with triangles. You can think of the height as the distance a rock would fall if you dropped it from a point at the top of a parallelogram perpendicular down to the line the base is on.)

Have students come to the overhead projector and show where they think the base and height are on the parallelograms on Transparency 4.1B.

- *Where would the base and height be on each parallelogram?* (Unlike triangles, parallelograms have multiple places where the line representing the height for a given base can be positioned. Using the first parallelogram in the Getting Ready, the diagram below shows three possible places where the height can be drawn if the bottom side is used as the base.)

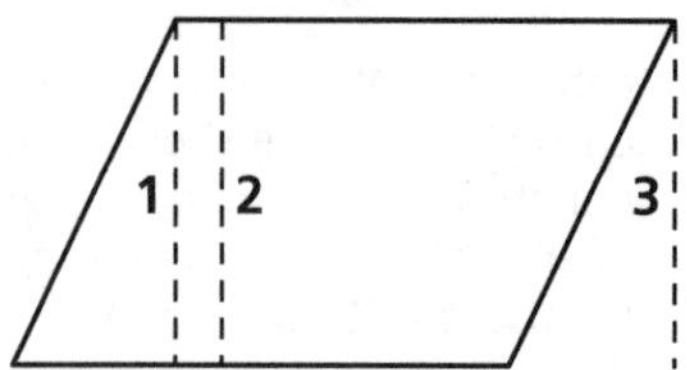

- *With triangles, you could label different bases and heights if you placed the triangle in different positions. How can I change the position of the parallelograms in the Getting Ready and label a different base and height for each one?* (Turn the parallelogram and use the short side for the base as shown in the diagram below.)

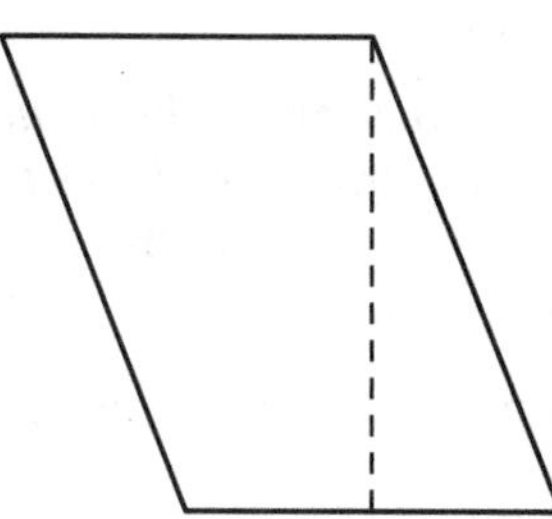

Read Questions A and B of Problem 4.1 to students. Provide them with a copy of Labsheet 4.1. Have students work in pairs.

Explore 4.1

As you circulate, remind students to record their findings and describe their strategies.

Be sure students are measuring the length of the diagonal sides of triangles with a centimeter ruler so that they get an accurate measure for perimeter. If students have perimeters that seem incorrect, have them measure a second time with a centimeter ruler. Check to see if students are lining up the ruler correctly and reading the measurement accurately.

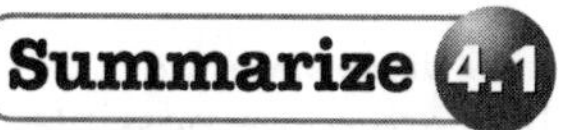

Ask students for the measures they found for each figure, and record their answers on the board.

Figure	Perimeter (cm)	Area (cm²)
A	about $12\frac{1}{2}$	8
B	about $12\frac{1}{5}$	8
C	about 21	24
D	about 24	35
E	16	$15\frac{3}{4}$
F	about $21\frac{4}{5}$	18

Suggested Questions Focus the class's attention on the chart.

- *How did you find these perimeter measurements?* (At this point, most students will understand that perimeter is the length around a figure. Since parallelograms have opposite sides congruent, like rectangles, there are several formulas that can be used to find the perimeter. Possible answers include: add the lengths of the sides; add the lengths of the two sides that form an angle and double; or double one side length, double the other side length, and total.)

As students describe their methods, record them in words and ask:

- *How could I write this method for finding perimeter of a parallelogram as a rule with symbols?* (Example answer: perimeter of parallelogram = length of side a + length of side a + length of side b + length of side b or $P = a + a + b + b$.)

Now move to discussing area.

- *How did you find the area measurements for the parallelograms?* (Here are some possible ways that students might find the areas of the parallelograms:

  Students may count the number of whole square centimeters and then estimate how many partial square centimeters there are.

  Students may cut off part of the parallelogram and then rearrange the parts to form a rectangle, and find the area of the rectangle.

  Some students may notice that the area of the parallelograms in the table for Question A are approximately equal to the base times the height.

  Some students may draw a diagonal and use the two congruent triangles to find the area.

  If students offer the formula $b \times h$ for area, ask them to explain why this makes sense. If they cannot explain why the formula works, you can write it up on the board and put a question mark by it. Explain that this is an idea for the class to continue to think about.)

Remember, developing a formal rule for finding the area of a parallelogram is not the goal for this problem.

- *Parallelogram A and B have the same area, but different perimeters. Does this make sense?* (Two shapes can have the same area and different perimeters.)

Use this summary to launch the next problem.

4.1 Finding Measures of Parallelograms

At a Glance

PACING 1 day

Mathematical Goal

- Develop and employ reasonable strategies for finding the areas and perimeters of parallelograms

Launch

Discuss the Getting Ready in the introduction.

- *Where are the base and the height on a triangle?*
- *What can measures of the base and height tell you?*

Explain that base and height have the same meaning when used with parallelograms as when used with triangles.

- *With triangles, you could label different bases and heights on one triangle if you placed the triangle in different positions. How can I change the position of the parallelograms in the Getting Ready and label a different base and height for each one?*

Read Questions A and B of Problem 4.1 with the students. Provide a copy of Labsheet 4.1.

Have students work in pairs.

Materials

- Transparencies 4.1A and 4.1B
- Labsheet 4.1

Vocabulary

- base
- height

Explore

Remind students to record their findings and describe their strategies.

Check how students are measuring as they work.

Summarize

Ask students for the measures they found for each figure, and record their answers on the board. Focus the class's attention on the table.

- *How did you find these perimeter measurements?*

As students describe their methods, record them in words and ask:

- *How could I write this method for finding perimeter of a parallelogram as a rule with symbols?*

Now move to discussing area.

- *How did you find the area measurements for the parallelograms?*
- *Parallelograms A and B have the same area, but different perimeters. Does this make sense?*

Materials

- Student notebooks

ACE Assignment Guide for Problem 4.1

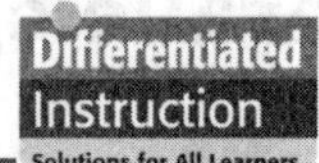

Core 1–8
Other *Connections* 32
Labsheet 4ACE Exercises 1–7 is provided if Exercises 1–7 are assigned.

Adapted For suggestions about adapting ACE exercises, see the CMP *Special Needs Handbook.*
Connecting to Prior Units 32: *Bits and Pieces I*

Answers to Problem 4.1

A. **1.** Figure A: about $12\frac{1}{2}$ cm
Figure B: about $12\frac{1}{5}$ cm
Figure C: about 21 cm
Figure D: about 24 cm
Figure E: 16 cm
Figure F: about $21\frac{4}{5}$ cm

2. Possible answers include: add the lengths of the sides, add the lengths of the two sides that form an angle and double, or double one side length, double the other side length and total.

B. **1.** Figure A: 8 cm^2
Figure B: 8 cm^2
Figure C: 24 cm^2
Figure D: 35 cm^2
Figure E: $15\frac{3}{4}$ cm^2
Figure F: 18 cm^2

2. Possible answers include: count the number of whole square centimeters and estimate how many partial square centimeters there are; or cut off part of the parallelogram by cutting perpendicular to the base, rearranging to make a rectangle, and then finding the area of the rectangle.

4.2 Parallelograms From Triangles

Goals

- Find area relationships between rectangles, triangles, and parallelograms
- Use relationships between parallelograms and triangles to develop techniques for finding the areas of parallelograms
- Distinguish among the base, height, and side lengths of a parallelogram
- Understand that a parallelogram may be positioned in more than one way, and thus may have more than one base-height pair, but only one area

Students will use the same six parallelograms as they did in Problem 4.1. This time they will explore the relationships between the base, height, and area of parallelograms and the base, height, and area of triangles. By the end of Problem 4.2, students should develop a rule for finding the area of a parallelogram.

Launch 4.2

Students will need Labsheet 4.1. They will also need a new copy of Labsheet 4.1.

Read Questions A and B. Make sure students understand how to draw the diagonal in Question B, part (2). You might want to model this with parallelogram A on Labsheet 4.2A.

Suggested Questions

- *How are the two triangles that are formed alike?* (They have the same area, base, and height. They are congruent.)
- *How can you find the area of each triangle?* (Multiply the base and height and divide by 2. You only have to find the area of one triangle since they are congruent.)
- *Do the base and height differ if you use the triangles formed when using the diagonal that slants the opposite way (i.e., from upper left to lower right)?* (No; the base and height of the two triangles are the same.)

Record the measures for parallelogram A into the table. Also take a minute and talk about what the base and height measures represent. Let students work in pairs.

Explore 4.2

As students work, observe and be sure they understand the problem and are filling in the table correctly. Listen to how students are describing the relationship between the bases, heights, and areas of the parallelograms and the bases, heights, and areas of the triangles.

Summarize 4.2

Begin by having students give the measures they found and recorded for base, height, and area of parallelogram F. Have students talk about how, just as with triangles, we can position parallelograms in two ways, giving two possible bases, each with its own height. The essential point is that however we orient the figure, the area remains constant. Move to a discussion of the relationship between the areas of the parallelograms and the triangles.

Suggested Questions Discuss Question B, parts (3) and (4).

- *How is the area of a parallelogram related to the area of a triangle?* (The area of the triangle is half the area of the parallelogram.)
- *How are the bases and heights of the rectangle and parallelogram related?* (They are the same.)
- *If the bases and heights are the same, why is the area of the parallelogram twice as large as the area of the triangle?* (When you find the area of a triangle, multiplying the base and height will give the area of the smallest surrounding rectangle, so you divide it by two because a triangle is half of a rectangle.)
- *A triangle is half of a rectangle when you draw a diagonal in the rectangle. In this problem you used half of a parallelogram. When you draw a diagonal in the parallelogram, what shape is half of the parallelogram?* (triangle)

Ask students to share the rules they wrote for finding the area of a parallelogram.

- *How did you use* b *and* h *to write a rule for finding the area of a parallelogram?* ($b \times h =$ area of a parallelogram)

As rules are offered, ask students whether they agree. Using the parallelograms on their labsheet, have them show that their rule works by identifying the base and height and comparing their solution with the formula to the solutions from Problem 4.1. You might want to have a transparency with several original gridded parallelograms drawn for students to work with. Once students are sure their rule will work on gridded shapes, have them show how to use it on the non-gridded parallelogram in Question C, part (2).

- *If the area of a parallelogram can be found by multiplying the base and height, where are the base and height on this parallelogram?*
- *How did you find the length of the base and height?* (Measure the base and height with a ruler. The base is 6 cm and the height is 3 cm.)
- *What is the area?* (18 cm^2)
- *How can we check to see if this is correct?* (You can place a centimeter grid on the figure and count the number of centimeter squares.)
- *Why can't you multiply the two edge lengths like you do when finding the area of a rectangle?* (With a rectangle, the edge lengths are also the base and height or how many square units across and how many layers of those units there are. The length of the diagonal edge on a parallelogram is how long the edge is, but it does not tell how many rows have the number of square units represented by the base.)

Some students may suggest that you cut the parallelogram along the height and rearrange it to create a rectangle. Then find the area of the rectangle. This is a good strategy to use with most of the parallelograms in this problem.

Depending upon your students and the ideas they offer, you might want to have a discussion with them about the relationship between area of parallelograms and area of rectangles. The point is not to discredit their idea, after all it does make sense in most cases, but to show that it has limitations and a rule that works for all cases is more powerful. (NOTE: The answer for ACE Exercise 37 in this investigation includes a sample cutting of the parallelogram below.) Draw the following parallelogram and ask:

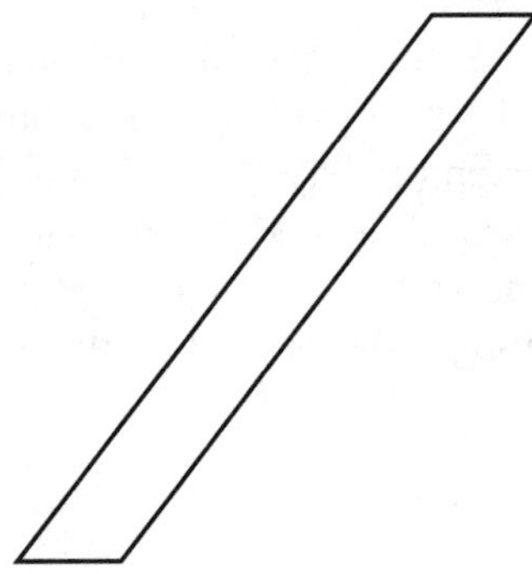

- *Without reorienting the figure, is there is a way to make a cut perpendicular to the base and rearrange it into a rectangle?* (no)
- *Can you divide it into two triangles?* (yes)

For all parallelograms, you can create a rectangle and find the area of the rectangle as a way to find the area of the parallelogram, but some parallelograms require changing the side that will be the base. Using what you know about finding the area of a triangle, you can find the area of every parallelogram without changing the base and height.

4.2 Parallelograms From Triangles

At a Glance

PACING $1\frac{1}{2}$ days

Mathematical Goals

- Find area relationships between rectangles, triangles, and parallelograms
- Use relationships between parallelograms and triangles to develop techniques for finding the areas of parallelograms
- Distinguish among the base, height, and side lengths of a parallelogram
- Understand that a parallelogram may be positioned in more than one way, and thus may have more than one base-height pair, but only one area

Launch

Read Questions A and B. Make sure students understand how to draw the diagonal in Question B, part (2). Model this with parallelogram A.

- *How are the two triangles that are formed alike?*
- *How can you find the area of each triangle?*
- *Do the measures differ if you use the triangles formed when using the diagonal that slants the opposite way?*

Record the measures for parallelogram A into the table. Also take a minute and talk about what the base and height measures represent. Use the diagram to make clear what base and height are measuring.

Materials
- Transparency 4.2
- Labsheet 4.1 (a fresh copy for each student)
- Labsheet 4.2A (one per student)

Vocabulary
- diagonal

Explore

As students work, observe and be sure they understand the problem and are filling in the table correctly. Listen to how students are describing the relationship between the bases, heights, and areas of the parallelograms and the bases, heights, and areas of the triangles.

Materials
- Scissors, cut-out transparent shapes from Labsheet 4.2B (optional)

Summarize

Have students give the measures they found for base, height, and area of parallelogram F. Have students talk about how, just as with triangles, we can position parallelograms in two ways, giving two possible bases, each with its own height.

Discuss relationships between areas of parallelograms and triangles.

- *How is the area of a parallelogram related to the area of a triangle?*
- *How are the bases and heights of the rectangle and parallelogram related?*
- *If the bases and heights are the same, why is the area of the parallelogram twice as large as the area of the triangle?*
- *A triangle is half of a rectangle when you draw a diagonal in the rectangle. In this problem you used half of a parallelogram. When you draw a diagonal in the parallelogram, what shape is half of the parallelogram?*

Materials
- Student notebooks

continued on next page

Summarize
continued

Have students share their rules for finding the area of a parallelogram.

- *How did you use* b *and* h *to write a rule for finding the area of a parallelogram?*

As rules are offered, ask students whether they agree. Explore some other questions about the areas of parallelograms, for example:

- *Why can't you multiply the two edge lengths like you do when finding the area of a rectangle?*

ACE Assignment Guide for Problem 4.2

Core 9–17

Other *Applications* 18–21; *Connections* 33–35; unassigned choices from previous problems

Adapted For suggestions about adapting ACE exercises, see the CMP *Special Needs Handbook.*

Connecting to Prior Units 33–35: *Shapes and Designs*

Answers to Problem 4.2

A. 1.

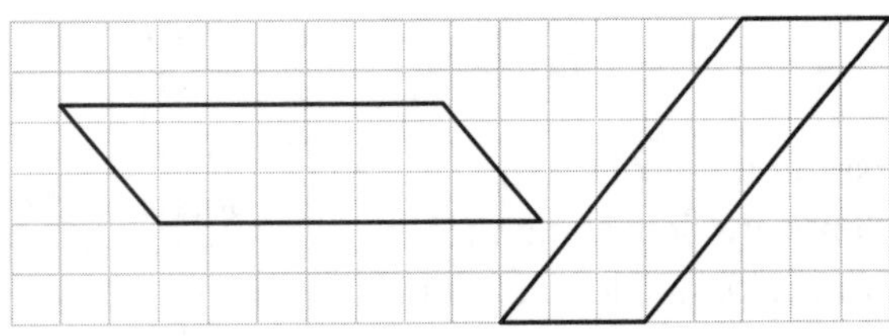

2. Left: base ≈ 7.8 cm, height ≈ 2.3 cm
Right: base = 3 cm, height = 6 cm

3. In each case, the base times the height is (approximately) equal to the area of the parallelogram: 18 cm^2.

B. 1.

Parallelograms			
Figure	Area (cm^2)	Height (cm)	Base (cm)
A	8	2	4
B	8	4	2
C	24	4	6
D	35	7	5
E	$15\frac{3}{4}$	$3\frac{1}{2}$	$4\frac{1}{2}$
F	18	6	3
Triangles			
Figure	Area (cm^2)	Height (cm)	Base (cm)
A	4	2	4
B	4	4	2
C	12	4	6
D	$17\frac{1}{2}$	7	5
E	$7\frac{7}{8}$	$3\frac{1}{2}$	$4\frac{1}{2}$
F	9	6	3

2. See table with answer for Question C, part (1).

3. The areas of the parallelograms are twice the area of the triangles.

4. The triangles have the same bases and heights as the parallelograms.

C. 1. area of a parallelogram = $b \times h$. Students may see this as $2 \times (\frac{1}{2} \times b \times h)$.

2. 18 cm^2; b = 6 cm and h = 3 cm

4.3 Designing Parallelograms Under Constraints

Goals

- Distinguish among the base, height, and side lengths of a parallelogram
- Understand that a parallelogram may be positioned in more than one way, and thus may have more than one base-height pair, but only one area
- Apply techniques for finding the areas and perimeters of parallelograms to a variety of problem situations

In this problem, students are asked to construct rectangles and parallelograms with given measurements. In each case, they are asked whether they can draw a different rectangle or parallelogram with the same constraints and to determine whether the area or perimeter of the two figures differ.

Launch 4.3

Describe the problem to the students. Explain to students that they are going to construct rectangles and parallelograms satisfying measurements that are given. Students may be given edge lengths, height, or area.

Review base and height, which were introduced in Problem 4.1. Read Question C aloud. Ask students if they understand what is meant by "a height of 4 cm." If they don't, refer them to figure A on Labsheet 4.1. Review with them that the lengths of the edges are 4 and about $2\frac{1}{4}$. Demonstrate that the height is 2 units. Because of the orientation of this parallelogram, it is easy to measure the vertical distance between the two sides of 4 units. We could measure the perpendicular distance between the two shorter sides, but it would require measuring with a ruler. If students need more practice, have them identify the height of the other parallelograms on Labsheet 4.1.

Suggested Question Choose a student to come to the overhead projector and ask:

- *Draw a parallelogram with a base of 7 cm and a height of 4 cm on a centimeter grid.* (When the class agrees this was done successfully, have students work in pairs on the rest of the problem.)

Have several sheets of grid paper available because students will make mistakes. To save time and materials, you might suggest that they cross out or erase figures that don't meet the requirements rather than immediately throwing away their paper.

Let students work in groups of 2 to 4.

Explore 4.3

Each student should make his or her own drawings. Groups can discuss how to approach each part, then check each other's drawings. As you circulate, remind students to label their drawings so that they are easy to refer to during the summary.

For pairs that finish early, you may want to pose additional questions.

Going Further

- *Find three rectangles, each with an area of 18 square units and with at least one edge that is not a whole-number length.*
- *Can you construct a rectangle with an area of 18 square units and a perimeter larger than the perimeter of the 1 unit-by-18 unit rectangle or smaller than the perimeter of the 3 unit-by-6 unit rectangle?*

Summarize 4.3

Suggested Questions Start the summary by asking students to think about the problem in general.

- *What kinds of constraints make drawing a figure easy? What kinds of constraints make drawing a figure difficult?* (Students might offer that it is easiest to construct a rectangle when the dimensions are given, and a parallelogram when the base and height are given. Some students may say that it was difficult to construct a parallelogram with a fixed area.)

If a student identifies a certain type of information as difficult, ask the other students whether they came up with strategies for drawing parallelograms under that kind of constraint.

- *Were there any questions for which you could make only one figure that fits the constraints?* (If students say no, ask them to share what they found for Question B. If they give two different rectangles, the second is probably simply a different orientation of the first. By now most of your students should agree that these rectangles are really the same: they have the same dimensions, area, and perimeter.)
- *For which parallelograms was it possible to make more than one shape?* (Continue to have students share their responses to the parts of the problem. After one student gives an answer, ask if anyone has a different answer. You want students to see the variety of responses possible for Questions A, C, D, and E. The discussion should help students understand that fixing the length of the sides or the height of a nonrectangular parallelogram does not limit the figure to one shape as it does for rectangles.)
- *Which measures are important for determining area and perimeter of parallelograms? Of triangles?* (With rectangles, length and width represent two ideas: both the linear measure of the sides and the number of square units that can fit along the base and number of rows that have that number of square units needed to match the height. Like triangles, parallelograms distinguish between these two measures by using different names. With perimeter the measures represent the length of the sides. Base and height are used to describe and count the number of square units in the parallelogram.)

Question C is the case where base and height are held constant. Students explored a similar situation with triangles in Investigation 3. There are several parallelograms that can be created with the same base and height. These parallelograms form a "family" with the same base, height and area.

When students present their solutions to Question C, ask:

- *Do these parallelograms have the same area?* (yes)
- *Why?* (The measures of base and height tell you the number of square units in a row and the number of rows with that number of square units it takes to cover the parallelogram. Each parallelogram has 7 cm^2 in the row that matches the length of the base and 4 rows of 7 cm^2 to match the height.)
- *Do the parallelograms have the same perimeter?* (no)
- *Why?* (Perimeter represents how long the sides are. The measure of the slanted side length changes as you shift the position of the two sides that are 7 cm long.)

Question D presents a situation where edge lengths are fixed.

- *What is the same and what is different with this set of parallelograms?* (The parallelograms have the same perimeter and different areas.)
- *Why does the area change?* (You can keep the side lengths at 6 cm and slant them in different ways to make a new shape.)

4.3 Designing Parallelograms Under Constraints

At a Glance

PACING 1 day

Mathematical Goals

- Distinguish among the base, height, and side lengths of a parallelogram
- Understand that a parallelogram may be positioned in more than one way, and thus may have more than one base-height pair, but only one area
- Apply techniques for finding the areas and perimeters of parallelograms to a variety of problem situations

Launch

Explain to students that they are going to construct rectangles and parallelograms satisfying measurements that are given.

Review base and height. Read Question C aloud.

Choose a student to come to the overhead projector and draw a parallelogram with a base of 7 cm and a height of 4 cm on a centimeter grid. When the class agrees this was done successfully, have students work in small groups on the rest of the problem. Have students work individually and then discuss with the group.

Explore

As you circulate, remind students to label their drawings so that they are easy to refer to during the summary.

For groups that finish early, you may want to pose additional questions.

- *Find three rectangles, each with an area of 18 square units and with at least one edge that is not a whole-number length.*
- *Can you construct a rectangle with an area of 18 square units and a perimeter larger than the perimeter of the 1 unit-by-18 unit rectangle or smaller than the perimeter of the 3 unit-by-6 unit rectangle?*

Summarize

Ask students to think about the problem in general.

- *What kinds of constraints make drawing a figure easy? What kinds of constraints make drawing a figure difficult?*
- *Were there any questions for which you could make only one figure that fits the constraints?*

Ask them to share what they found for Question B. Continue to have students share their responses to the parts of the problem. After one student gives an answer, ask if anyone has a different answer.

Materials

- Student notebooks

continued on next page

Summarize

continued

Help students understand that fixing the length of the sides or the height of a nonrectangular parallelogram does not limit the figure to one shape as it does for rectangles.

When students present their solutions to Question C, ask:

- *Do these parallelograms have the same area? Why?*
- *Do the parallelograms have the same perimeter? Why?*

Question D presents a situation where edge lengths are fixed.

- *What is the same and what is different with this set of parallelograms?*
- *Why does the area change?*

ACE Assignment Guide for Problem 4.3

Core 22–27

Other *Applications* 28–31; *Extensions* 38, 39; unassigned choices from previous problems Labsheet 4ACE Exercise 39 is provided if Exercise 39 is assigned.

Adapted For suggestions about adapting Exercise 31 and other ACE exercises, see the CMP *Special Needs Handbook*.

Answers to Problem 4.3

A. Drawings will vary. The most common drawings will be 1 unit-by-18 unit, 2 unit-by-9 unit, and 3 unit-by-6 unit rectangles. The rectangles do not have the same perimeter.

B. It is not possible to draw two different rectangles. Some students may draw the same rectangle twice with different orientations.

C. Drawings will vary. All the parallelograms will have an area of 28 cm^2. A geoboard is an excellent tool for demonstrating that you can keep the same base and height, but move the side parallel to the base to get different parallelograms with the same area.

D. Drawings will vary. The areas of the parallelograms can vary from almost 0 up to 36 cm^2.

E. Drawings will vary. The base times the height of all the parallelograms will be 30 cm^2. The perimeters of the parallelograms will vary.

Parks, Hotels, and Quilts

Goal

- Apply techniques for finding the areas and perimeters of parallelograms to a variety of problem situations

In this problem, students apply their understanding of area and perimeter of rectangles, triangles, and parallelograms to some interesting situations.

Launch 4.4

Read the problem with the students and answer any questions they might have about contexts of each part.

Talk with students about the pyramid in Question B. If you have a square pyramid that you can show students, it will help them understand what a pyramid is and what shape the faces are. Show them where the equilateral triangle in the problem is located. Be sure students understand that the problem is about one triangular face of the pyramid, not the entire pyramid.

As you talk with students about this problem, you might find the following facts about the pyramid interesting to share with your students:

- The Luxor Hotel is one of the world's largest hotels.
- Its atrium is the world's largest, measuring 29 million cubic feet. Nine Boeing 747 airplanes could fit into it.
- The four faces are made out of glass.
- Altogether, the four faces of glass cover 13 acres.
- It cost $700 million to build.
- It was constructed in 18 months.
- 150,000 cubic yards of concrete were used.
- There are 4,455 rooms and 36 stories.
- A specially designed window-washing device takes 64 hours to clean the sides of the pyramid.

Have students work in pairs or groups of three.

Explore 4.4

Listening to Students

As you observe and interact with students, consider the following questions:

- *Can students make sense of situations where area is needed and where perimeter is needed?*
- *Do they understand and correctly label solutions with measures of area or perimeter?*

If students struggle with these ideas, spend time talking about them in the summary.

Summarize 4.4

Have students share their approaches to the problems. If students disagree with someone's solution or reasoning, have them explain why.

For each problem, ask students to talk about how they decided if the problem was about area or perimeter. Also have conversations about the labels that are used and why.

4.4 Parks, Hotels, and Quilts

At a Glance

PACING 1 day

Mathematical Goal

- Apply techniques for finding the areas and perimeters of parallelograms to a variety of problem situations

Launch

Read the problem with the students and answer any questions they might have about contexts of each part.

Talk with students about the pyramid in Question B. Show students a square pyramid to help them understand what the faces are. Show them where the equilateral triangle is located on the pyramid.

Have students work in pairs or groups of three.

Materials

- Transparencies 4.4A, 4.4B (optional)

Explore

Pay attention to the following issues as students work:

- Can students make sense of situations where area is needed and where perimeter is needed?
- Do they understand and correctly label solutions with measures of area or perimeter?

If students struggle with these ideas, spend time talking about them in the summary.

Summarize

Have students share their approaches to the problems. If students disagree with someone's solution or reasoning, have them explain why.

For each problem, ask students to talk about how they decided if the problem was about area or perimeter. Also have a conversation about the labels that are used and why.

Materials

- Student notebooks

ACE Assignment Guide for Problem 4.4

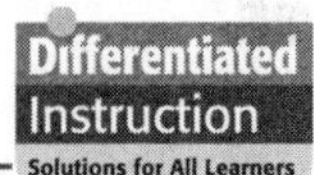

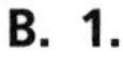

Core 36

Other *Extensions* 37; unassigned choices from previous problems

Adapted For suggestions about adapting ACE exercises, see the CMP *Special Needs Handbook.*

Connecting to Prior Units 36: *Shapes and Designs*

Answers to Problem 4.4

A. 1. $\frac{4}{9}$ of the park will be used for skateboarding $(\frac{2}{3}\ell \times \frac{2}{3}w = \frac{4}{9}(\ell \times w) = \frac{4}{9}A)$.

2. The dimensions of the playground area are 20 ft by 70 ft, giving an area of 1,400 ft^2 and a perimeter of 180 ft.

B. 1.

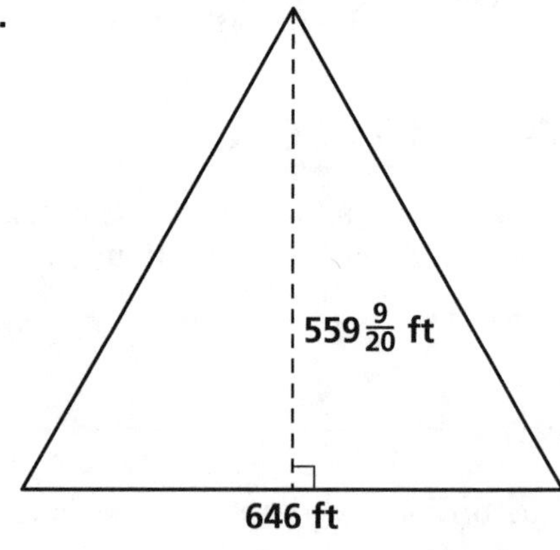

2. $A \approx 646 \times 559\frac{1}{2} \div 2$, or about $180,718\frac{1}{2}\ \text{ft}^2$ of glass

3. 1,938 ft of lights

C. 1. 10 in.^2 of fabric for each nonsquare parallelogram and 4 in.^2 of fabric for each square.

2. 16 in.^2 of fabric for all of the squares together

3. 44 in.^2 of white fabric will be visible. $100 - (40 + 16) = 100 - 56 = 44$.

Investigation 4

ACE Assignment Choices

Problem 4.1

Core 1–8
Other *Connections* 32

Problem 4.2

Core 9–17
Other *Applications* 18–21; *Connections* 33–35; unassigned choices from previous problems

Problem 4.3

Core 22–27
Other *Connections* 28–31; *Extensions* 38, 39; unassigned choices from previous problems

Problem 4.4

Core 36
Other *Extensions* 37; unassigned choices from previous problems

Adapted For suggestions about adapting Exercise 31 and other ACE exercises, see the CMP *Special Needs Handbook*.
Connecting to Prior Units 32: *Bits and Pieces I*, 33–36: *Shapes and Designs*

Applications

1. area $= 20$ cm^2 (base $= 5$ cm, height $= 4$ cm), perimeter $= 20$ cm
(Dimensions are 5 cm by about 5 cm.)

2. area $= 9$ cm^2 (base $= 3$ cm, height $= 3$ cm), perimeter $\approx 12\frac{1}{2}$ cm
(Dimensions are 3 cm by about $3\frac{1}{4}$ cm.)
Explanations will vary.

3. area $= 30$ cm^2 (base $= 6$ cm, height $= 5$ cm), perimeter ≈ 25 cm
(Dimensions are 6 cm by about $6\frac{1}{2}$ cm.)

4. area $= 8$ cm^2 (base $= 2$ cm, height $= 4$ cm), perimeter $=$ about $15\frac{2}{5}$ cm
(Dimensions are 2 cm by about $5\frac{7}{10}$ cm.)

5. area $= 6$ cm^2 (base $= 6$ cm, height $= 1$ cm), perimeter $\approx 20\frac{1}{5}$ cm
(Dimensions are 6 cm by about $4\frac{1}{10}$ cm.)

6. area $= 8$ cm^2, perimeter $=$ about $11\frac{1}{5}$ cm
(Dimensions are about $2\frac{4}{5}$ cm by $2\frac{4}{5}$ cm.)

For the Teacher: Explaining ACE Exercise 6

The area of this square can be found easily. The length of the sides, from the Pythagorean Theorem, are $\sqrt{8} \approx 2.8284271$. We don't expect students will know this, but some families who help their children may offer this as an answer. Some students may say that the length of the sides is 3 cm, and thus the perimeter is 12 cm. Although this is close, you will want to discuss why it is not possible for the length to be 3 cm. If it were, the area would be 9 cm^2, and they can easily see from the drawing that this is not the case. The figure can be split into 4 pieces.

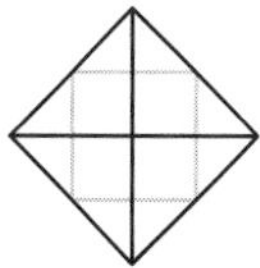

These pieces can be rearranged to form a rectangle with an area 8 cm^2.

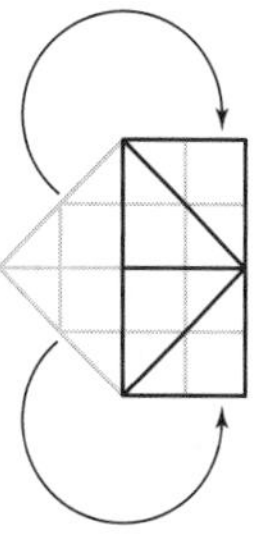

7. area $= 20$ cm^2 (base $= 5$ cm, height $= 4$ cm), perimeter ≈ 19 cm
(Dimensions are 5 cm by about $4\frac{1}{2}$ cm.)
Explanations will vary.

8. a. The base is 4 units. The height is 5 units, and the area of each parallelogram is 20 square units.

   b. The bases, heights, and areas are the same.

   c. They are a family, because the bases, heights, and areas are the same.

9. $A = 24 \text{ cm}^2$, $P = 20$ cm

10. $A = 24 \text{ cm}^2$, $P = 22$ cm

11. $A = 30 \text{ cm}^2$, $P = 30$ cm

12. $A = 29\frac{3}{4} \text{ cm}^2$, $P = 25\frac{7}{10}$ cm

13. $A = 72 \text{ in.}^2$, $P = 35$ in.

14–19.

Exercise	Approximate Area (cm²)	Approximate Perimeter (cm)
14	8 ($b = 2, h = 4$)	12
15	4.5 ($b = 3, h = 3$)	$10\frac{1}{4}$
16	15 ($b = 5, h = 3$)	$16\frac{4}{5}$
17	18 ($b = 4.5, h = 4$)	$17\frac{1}{5}$
18	3 ($b = 3, h = 2$)	$12\frac{3}{10}$
19	18 (15 + 3)	18

20. a. The area of Tennessee is approximately 41,800 mi².

   b. The estimate is about the same as the actual area.

21. These parallelograms all have the same area because the first two have a base of 4 and a height of 3, and the last parallelogram has a base of 3 and a height of 4. Since area is base times height, the areas are all the same.

For Exercises 22–27, answers will vary. Possible answers are listed.

22. a–b.

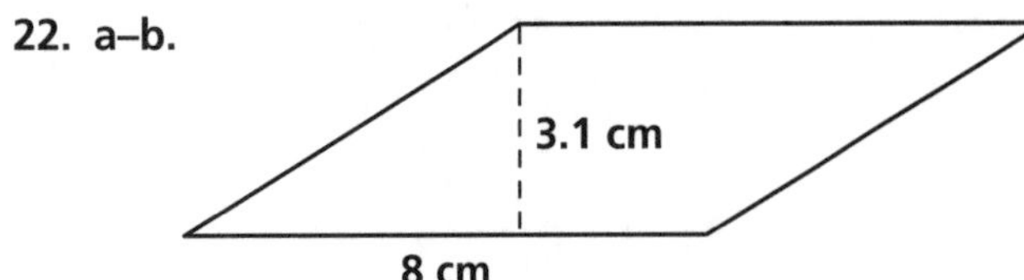

   c. Yes, you can draw more than one parallelogram with base 8, and perimeter 28. Visualize pressing on the top side to lower it without changing the lengths of the sides.

23. a–b.

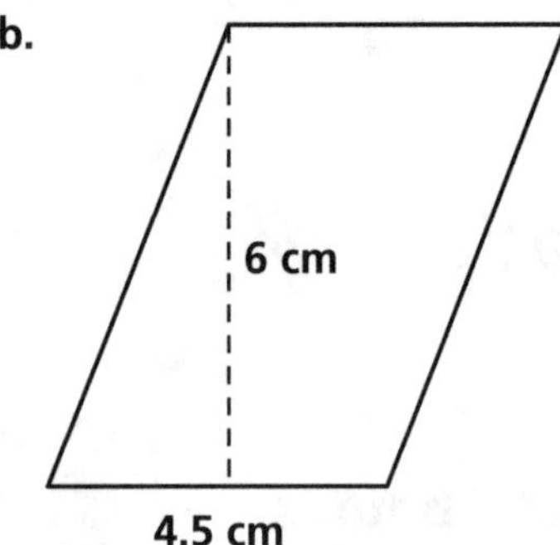

   c. Yes, you can draw more than one parallelogram with base $4\frac{1}{2}$ and area 27. You just slide the top vertices over, keeping the same base and height. The area remains the same, but the perimeter changes.

24. a–b.

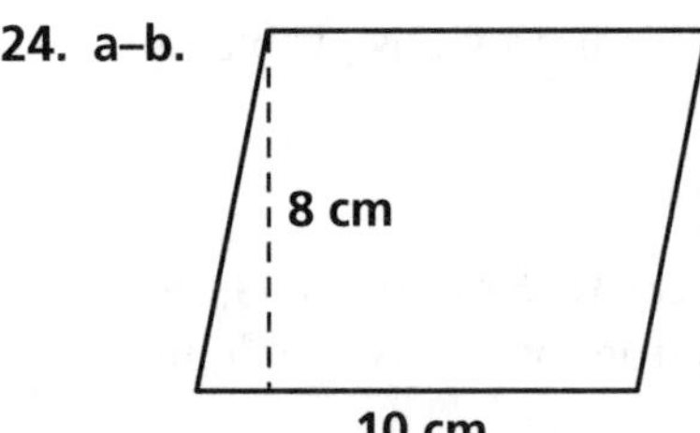

   c. Yes, you can draw more than one parallelogram with base 10, and height 8. You just slide the top vertices over, keeping the same base and height. The area remains the same, but the perimeter changes.

25. a–b.

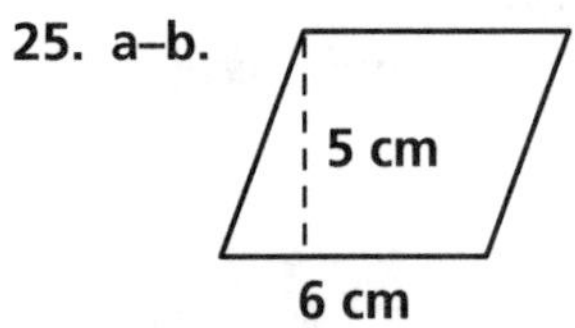

   c. Yes, you could draw more than one parallelogram with a base of 6 and area of 30. You would have a height of 5, and slide the top vertices over.

26. a–b.

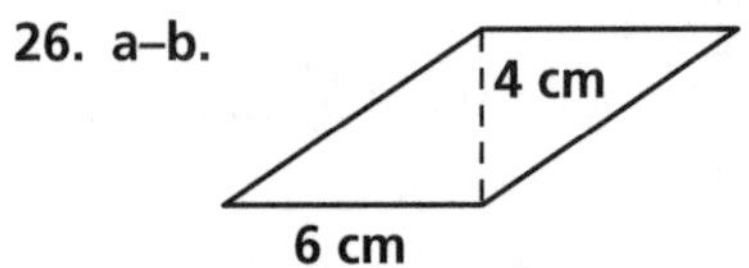

   c. Yes, you could have some of these combinations: $b = 1, h = 24; b = 2, h = 12; b = 3, h = 8; b = 4, h = 6$. They would all have an area of 24 cm².

27. a–b.

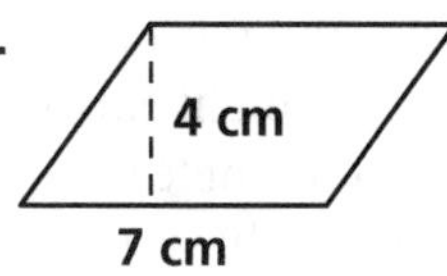

c. Yes, you could have some of these side lengths: $b = 1, s = 11; b = 2, s = 10;$ $b = 3, s = 9, b = 4, s = 8; b = 5, s = 7,$ $b = 6, s = 6$, where b = base length, and s = nonbase side length. They would all have a perimeter of 24.

28. a. There are three parallelograms. Each consists of two small triangles.

b. 8 square units

29. a. 4 ft^2

b. 24 ft^2

30. Mr. Lee would need 72 tiles. Possible methods: $24 \div 3 = 8$ tiles along the length, $18 \div 2 = 9$ tiles along the width, $8 \times 9 = 72$ tiles, or $18 \div 3 = 6$ tiles along the length, $24 \div 2 = 12$ tiles along the width, $6 \times 12 = 72$ tiles, or $24 \times 18 = 432$ ft^2 is the area for the whole ceiling divided by the area for 1 tile, which is 6 ft^2 to find the total number of tiles, 72.

31. They will have the area of the lot minus the area of the house left for grass. $20{,}000 - 2{,}250 = 17{,}750$ ft^2.

Connections

32. D

33. a. The angles will change, area will decrease, and perimeter will stay the same.

b. Opposite sides have equal length and are parallel. Opposite angles have equal measure.

34. J

35. Answers will vary. Possible examples: two sheets of notebook paper, or two speed limit signs.

36. a. 240 rectangular floor pieces are needed. One possible method: $120 \div 5 = 24$ pieces along the length, $40 \div 4 = 10$ pieces along the width, $24 \times 10 = 240$ pieces.

b. 240 tiles × \$20 per tile = \$4,800 for the floor. If you have 30 bumper cars × \$10 per car = \$300. The total cost is \$5,100.

Extensions

37. a. Possible answer:

It may take several cuttings, but every parallelogram can be rearranged to make a rectangle with the same base and height as the original.

b. Possible answer:

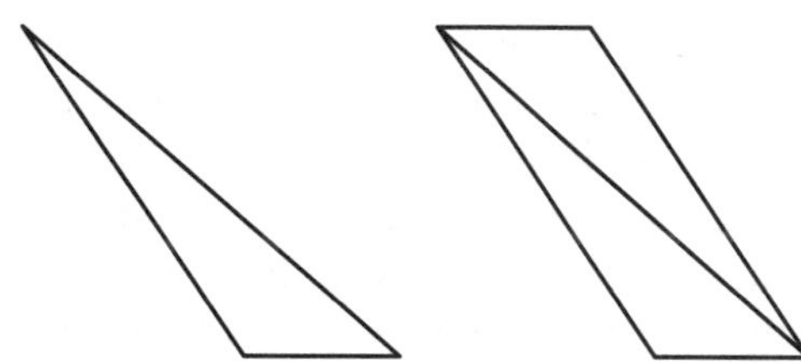

Every triangle can be put together with a copy of itself to create a parallelogram. The area of the parallelogram is the base times the height so the area of each triangle is half of that.

38. $A = 42$ in.^{2}, $P = 26\frac{6}{10}$ in., or $26\frac{3}{5}$ in.

39. a. and c.

Trapezoid	Approximate Area (cm^2)	Approximate Perimeter (cm)
I	5	$9\frac{1}{4}$
II	7	$12\frac{1}{10}$
III	$10\frac{1}{2}$	$13\frac{4}{5}$
IV	6	$10\frac{1}{2}$
V	$3\frac{1}{2}$	$10\frac{13}{20}$
VI	9	$14\frac{1}{10}$

b. Most students will find the area of the trapezoids by dividing them into a rectangle and one or two triangles, finding the area of these and adding the areas. You may want to challenge some of your top students to modify the method used for parallelograms. They may come up with the formula:

$\text{area} = \frac{1}{2} \times (\text{base} + \text{top}) \times \text{height}$.

d. The perimeter was found measuring the length of each side in centimeters and adding them.

Possible Answers to Mathematical Reflections

1. If the parallelogram is a rectangle, multiply the length and width. If the parallelogram is nonrectangular, multiply the base and height. In either case, you measure the number of square units in one row (length for rectangle and base for parallelogram) and multiply by the number of rows with that many square units to match the height (width for rectangle and height for parallelogram).
2. If a rectangle, triangle, and parallelogram have the same base and height (also called length and width on a rectangle) the rectangle and the parallelogram will have the same area. With a rectangle and a parallelogram, you multiply the base (number of square units in a row) by the height (number of rows) to find the area. Two congruent triangles can be formed by drawing a diagonal in a rectangle and a parallelogram. As long as they all have the same base and height, the area of the triangle will be half of the area of the rectangle and parallelogram or $(b \times h) \div 2$.
3. Perimeter is the sum of the lengths of the sides of a shape. With any shape you can measure each side and find the sum. Since the opposite sides of any parallelogram (rectangular and nonrectangular) are congruent you could add the length of two adjacent sides and double the amount. This works because the sum of two adjacent sides is the distance halfway around the shape. If you double this you will get the distance all the way around.
4. While there are shortcuts that you can use for various cases of these shapes, when you find the perimeter of any shape you are finding the total length of the sides or the distance around the figure.

Measuring Irregular Shapes and Circles

Mathematical and Problem-Solving Goals

- Develop counting techniques for estimating areas and perimeters of irregular figures
- Use ideas about area and perimeter to solve practical problems
- Continue to develop a conceptual understanding of area and perimeter
- Discover that it takes slightly more than three diameters to equal the circumference of a circle
- Use this discovery to develop a formula for the circumference of a circle
- Develop strategies for organizing and comparing data
- Develop techniques for estimating the area of a circle
- Discover that it takes slightly more than three radius squares to equal the area of the circle
- Use this discovery to develop a formula for the area of a circle

Summary of Problems

Problem 5.1 Measuring Lakes

Students estimate the area and perimeter of irregular shapes.

Problem 5.2 Surrounding a Circle

Students measure and compare the circumferences and diameters of several circular objects. This leads to deriving the formula for the circumference of a circle.

Problem 5.3 Pricing Pizzas

Students estimate the areas of three different sized circular pizzas. By making a table, they evaluate the pricing scheme for the pizzas.

Problem 5.4 "Squaring" a Circle

Students cover circles with *radius squares* in order to derive the formula for the area of a circle.

Note for the Teacher Students will be working with decimal multiplication, which they will not learn formally until *Bits and Pieces III*. However, they have had some experience with decimals, and they can use estimation strategies. You may choose to use calculators if desired.

	Suggested Pacing	Materials for Students	Materials for Teachers	ACE Assignments
All	5 days	Calculators, student notebooks, string, scissors, centimeter rulers, tape measure (optional)	Blank transparencies and transparency markers (optional)	
5.1	1 day	Labsheet 5.1 (1 per student), transparencies of centimeter grid paper	Transparency 5.1, transparency of half-centimeter grid paper	1–4, 47
5.2	1 day	Several circular objects, tape measure or string, scissors	Transparencies 5.2A, 5.2B	5–14, 39, 40, 48, 49
5.3	1 day	Labsheets 5.3A, 5.3B (1 of each per student); scissors, glue and construction paper (optional)	Transparency 5.3, string (one piece at least 18 cm long)	15
5.4	$1\frac{1}{2}$ days	Labsheet 5.4 (1 per student, on colored paper), centimeter grid paper (2–3 per student), scissors, glue and construction paper (optional)	Transparencies 5.4A, 5.4B	16–38, 41–46
MR	$\frac{1}{2}$ day			

5.1 Measuring Lakes

Goals

- Develop counting techniques for estimating areas and perimeters of irregular figures
- Use ideas about area and perimeter to solve practical problems
- Continue to develop a conceptual understanding of area and perimeter

In this problem, students estimate the area and perimeter of two lakes: Loon Lake and Ghost Lake. Using their estimates they make decisions about how best to use the lakes and the surrounding land. Similar to the work in Investigations 1 and 2 of this unit, students will have to take into account the shape of the lake as well as the actual measurements for area and perimeter.

The last part will ask students to think about methods that could be used to find a more accurate measure of area. It is not expected that all students actually carry out these methods, but it is worth discussing them. For more on this, see the discussion beginning on p. 8 about estimating perimeter and area of irregular figures. There is no need to spend a lot of time on these issues in this lesson. Instead, the goal is to have students develop estimation strategies and to have them consider ways to make their estimates better.

Note: Launch the unit project. For more information, see page 16.

Launch 5.1

Begin the problem by asking students to offer ideas about how the area of the surface of a lake and the length of the shoreline might be measured. Once students offer some ideas, read the introduction to the problem.

Hand out Labsheet 5.1. Help students understand the measures and scale in Question A. The diagram of the lakes has been covered with a centimeter grid on Labsheet 5.1. (The diagram in the Student Edition has been shrunk, so it is not on a centimeter grid. If you do not use Labsheet 5.1, adjust the following questions accordingly.)

Suggested Questions Ask students to explain what the scale in the bottom right corner of the diagram means.

- *What does the scale tell you?* (This picture is measured in centimeters. The actual measurements will be 100 m in length for each centimeter in the diagram.)
- *On this map, what might you measure in centimeters?* (perimeter, the length of the shoreline, the distance across a lake)
- *If 1 cm = 100 m, how many square meters will 1 cm² represent?*

Students may struggle to answer this last question. Use diagrams and questions like the following to help them:

- *If I draw a square centimeter, what are the actual dimensions of the square this square represents?* (It is 100 m by 100 m.)

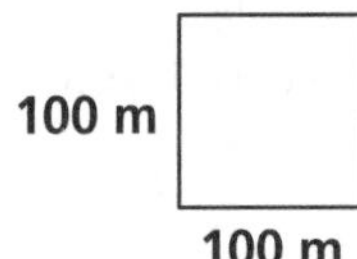

- *How can you find the area of a square?* (Multiply the length and width to get 10,000 m².)
- *In a 100 m-by-100 m area, there are 10,000 m². Each square centimeter represents a 100 m-by-100 m or 10,000 m² area. In the area section of your table you will need to record the number of square centimeters and then use them to convert that to square meters.*

It is okay if students struggle with understanding why the conversion from square centimeters to square meters works. They will formally explore this concept in the seventh-grade unit *Stretching and Shrinking*.

Question B asks students to explain which lake is larger. Have students look at the two lakes and, without counting, make a prediction for which lake they think is larger.

- *Without counting or measuring, which lake do you think is larger? Why?*

Listen to see if students interpret *larger* to mean a larger area or a larger perimeter. Do not try to work this out now. Allow students to discuss it briefly and then let them work on the problem.

This problem can be done in pairs or groups of three.

Explore 5.1

Hand out Labsheet 5.1 and have string and rulers available for students to use for measuring. (Caution: String is better than yarn for this problem because yarn can stretch, leading to incorrect measurements.)

Listening to Students

As you observe and interact with students, consider the following questions:

- *Are there estimates that do not make sense that need to be discussed in the summary?*
- *Do students use other methods besides counting each square when finding area?*
- *What are the variety of methods students use to find area that would be useful or interesting to talk about in the summary?*
- *Do some estimation techniques give overestimates and others underestimates? How does this affect the way students answer Question D?*
- *Are students able to convert from centimeters to meters and square centimeters to square meters?*

Be sure to discuss some of your observations in the summary.

Summarize 5.1

Have students offer various estimates for Question A. If there are outliers that appear to be measuring errors, ask the student who recorded the value how he or she made the measurement. Discuss whether this method is reasonable.

Suggested Questions Begin a discussion of strategies that students used to find perimeter and area.

- *Explain how you found the perimeter of the lakes.*
- *Did anyone have another way to find the perimeter?*
- *Why are the measurements slightly different?*

Use similar questions to talk about strategies for finding area.

- *Explain strategies you used to find area.*
- *Did anyone do it another way?*
- *What did you do with the parts of squares?*

Move to Question B. Students may have different interpretations of what *larger* means. Some may use perimeter and others may use area to decide which is larger. Both approaches can be correct.

Talk with students about how the term *larger* is ambiguous in this question. Without a context it is difficult to know how to answer. While Ghost Lake is larger in perimeter because it is long and thin, Loon Lake has a slightly larger area.

Question C is intended to help students think about how the uses of a lake depend on its shape and its area and perimeter. Be sure to have students provide a reason for their decision. Focus on getting students to talk about how the shape of the lake matters.

- *What if you did not have a picture of the lakes and you were only given measures for area and perimeter? How would that affect your answers in Question C?*
- *How is the park planners' problem similar to what you thought about when you decided what size pen would be best for a dog or what bumper-car plan was the best one to buy?*

Close the problem by talking about Question D. Listen to students' ideas, letting students decide if an idea makes sense and why. If the idea to use a smaller grid is not offered, ask:

- *If we used a smaller grid to measure the lakes, the numbers would be changed. Would the number of square units of area get larger or smaller?* (Larger; since the units are smaller, you will need more.)
- *If your count with smaller units is greater, does that mean the area is larger?*

This question is tied to the work students did with equivalent fractions. When you have a smaller unit, you need more of those units to make the same amount. For example, if I cut my cake into fourths and you cut your cake into eighths, you have to eat more eighths to eat as much cake as I eat in fourths.

- *How would using a smaller grid make the area measurement more precise or more accurate?*

It will help to lay a transparency of half-centimeter grid paper over Transparency 5.1; the lakes as they appear in the problem. Take a few minutes to talk with students about how the smaller grid paper lets you count more accurately in places where you had to estimate before. Count the number of whole square centimeter units that fit in one of the lakes. Then count the number of the whole square quarter-centimeter units that can be counted when using the half-centimeter grid.

Help students understand that when you use the half-centimeter grid, four small squares equals 1 cm^2. If you want to compare the measurements, you have to change one of the units to use the same scale when reporting the area.

- *If 29 whole square centimeters fit inside Loon Lake, and 151 of the smaller squares fit into Loon Lake, how can I compare the two measurements, since they use different size units?* (Divide the number of smaller units by 4 or multiply the number of larger units by 4.)
- *Which grid gives a closer measurement?* (the grid with smaller units)

Students do not need to master this conversion, but it is important for them to start to think about how to compare measures that are related but use different-sized units.

5.1 Measuring Lakes

At a Glance

PACING 1 day

Mathematical Goals

- Develop techniques for estimating areas and perimeters of irregular figures
- Use ideas about area and perimeter to solve practical problems
- Continue to develop a conceptual understanding of area and perimeter

Launch

Ask students how the area of the surface of a lake and the length of the shoreline might be measured. Once students offer some ideas, read the introduction to the problem.

Help students understand the scale and the measures found for Question A. Ask students to think about the scale in the bottom right corner of the diagram.

- *What does the scale tell you?*
- *On this map, what might you measure in centimeters?*
- *If 1 cm = 100 m, how many square meters will 1 cm^2 represent?*

Students may struggle to answer this last question. Use questions like the following to help them:

- *If I draw a square centimeter, what are the actual dimensions of the square this square represents?*
- *How can you find the area of a square?*

Have students look at the two lakes and predict which lake is larger.

- *Without counting or measuring, which lake do you think is larger? Why?*

Have students work in pairs or groups of three.

Explore

Hand out Labsheet 5.1 and have string and rulers available for students to use for measuring. Here are some questions to ask yourself as you observe students working:

- Are there estimates that do not make sense that need to be discussed in the summary?
- What is the variety of methods students use to find area that would be useful or interesting to talk about in the summary?

Materials

- Labsheet 5.1
- String
- Rulers

Summarize

Have students offer various estimates for Question A. Begin a discussion of strategies that students used to find perimeter and area.

Materials

- Transparency 5.1
- Student notebooks

continued on next page

Summarize

continued

- *Explain how you found the perimeter of the lakes.*
- *Did anyone have another way to find the perimeter?*
- *Why are the measurements slightly different?*

Use similar questions to talk about strategies for finding the area.

- *Explain strategies you used to find the area.*
- *Did anyone do it another way?*
- *What did you do with the parts of squares?*

Discuss Question B briefly. Question C is intended to help students think about how the size of a lake depends upon its shape and what it is being used for. Be sure to have students provide a reason for their decision. Focus on getting students to talk about how the shape of the lake matters.

Close the problem by talking about Question D.

ACE Assignment Guide for Problem 5.1

Core 1, 3, 47

Other *Applications* 2, 4

Labsheets 5ACE Exercises 1–2 and 5ACE Exercises 3–4 are provided if Exercises 1–4 are assigned.

Adapted For suggestions about adapting ACE exercises, see the CMP *Special Needs Handbook*.

Answers to Problem 5.1

A. **Lake Size Estimates**

Estimates	Loon Lake	Ghost Lake
Perimeter (units)	25–26	45–50
Perimeter (m)	2,500–2,600	4,500–5,000
Area (units^2)	38–42	34–37
Area (m^2)	380,000–420,000	340,000–370,000

B. Answers will vary depending upon how "larger" is interpreted. If you use perimeter, Ghost Lake is larger. If you use area, Loon Lake is larger.

C. **1.** Ghost Lake

2. Loon Lake

3. Ghost Lake

4. Loon Lake is better for swimming, boating, and fishing and Ghost Lake will make the better nature preserve.

D. **1.** Answers will vary depending upon the strategy used for estimating area.

2. Answers will vary but one possibility is to use a grid with smaller units.

5.2 Surrounding a Circle

Goals

- Discover that it takes slightly more than three diameters to equal the circumference of a circle
- Use this discovery to develop a formula for circumference of a circle
- Develop strategies for organizing and comparing data

In this problem, students measure the diameters and circumferences of several circles, organize their data in a table, and look for patterns.

Launch 5.2

Begin by looking at the introduction to the problem where the terms diameter, radius, area and circumference are discussed. Students may be familiar with these terms but review them to be sure students understand them.

Use the Getting Ready about pizza restaurants to provide a context for knowing when circumference can be useful.

Suggested Question

- *How do pizza makers determine the price of a pizza? Do you think a large pizza is usually the best buy?* (Answers will vary. Many students will suggest that price is based on the diameter of the pizza. Students may not consider that there is a difference between basing the price on the diameter, on the circumference, and on the area, though they may raise all three possibilities. In fact, there is a big difference. If the price is based on the diameter of the pizza, then if a large pizza has a diameter that is twice the diameter of a small, the price will be twice as much, but the pizza would have four times the area. It is not expected that students know this. The study of area change in similar figures is in the seventh-grade unit *Stretching and Shrinking.*)

Describe the problem to the class. Emphasize that they are looking for patterns leading to a shortcut for finding the circumference of a circle.

- *At the beginning of this unit we found that there was a relationship between area of a triangle and area of a parallelogram. Mathematicians have found a relationship between diameter and circumference of a circle. By collecting data, you are going to try to figure out what that relationship is.*

Supply students with several circular objects, such as soda cans, pizza pans, round cake pans, wastebaskets, coins, and compact discs, or have them use objects they have brought from home. You might want to have sets of objects for pairs of students to measure and share with other groups. Set aside a few extra circular objects for groups to test their ideas for finding circumference.

Students can work in pairs to make the measurements but should record the data individually.

Explore 5.2

Observe to make sure students are accurately measuring the circumference and the diameter.

Suggested Questions For students who struggle with Question B, you might suggest they compare their actual lengths of string as well as the values in their table.

- *Look at the string you cut for a circle and compare diameter and circumference lengths. What do you notice? How are they related?*
- *How much bigger is the circumference than the diameter?*
- *If you know the diameter, can you predict the circumference?*
- *Does this happen with all your circles?*
- *If you know how long the circumference is, how can you predict the length of the diameter?*

Do not feel all students must complete both parts of Question B before moving on to the summary. What you want students to notice is that the relationship between diameter and circumference is multiplicative and that the circumference is always a bit more than three times the diameter. It is okay if all students do not come to this conclusion during the explore. This will come out in the summary. A discussion of pi and a more precise value will also be introduced in the summary.

Summarize 5.2

One way to start the summary is to have a group who used string display the data they collected for one object and tape the lengths of string they cut for diameter and circumference up on the board. Have them tape the string lengths so they line up at the top and hang down. If students used measuring tape you can have them draw the length of the circumference and diameter on the board.

Suggested Question

- *What patterns did you find when you compared the circumference and diameter?* (For each unit of diameter, the circumference increases by the same amount, a little more than 3 units. This can be seen in the table by comparing the diameter and circumference measures. This can be proven if students take the length of string they cut for diameter and use it to measure along the circumference.)

Some students may talk about the difference between the two amounts. If so, ask them to estimate the circumference of circles with diameters that are not displayed, perhaps for a circle much larger than those previously measured. This relationship will not hold.

After students have verbalized the relationship between diameter and circumference, have them test the idea on a few new objects. Measure the diameter of an object and have the class predict its circumference. Also measure the circumference of an object and ask the class to predict the diameter.

After a few examples, push for a more exact numeral than "a little more than 3." You might find the ratio of the circumference to the diameter for all the circular objects measured (which should be close to 3.1 or 3.2) and then introduce the number π (pi). (For our purposes, 3.14 is close enough, although you will want to tell students that this is a rounded number. For the curious student, the value of π to ten decimal places is 3.1415926535.)

After students have used π to find the circumferences of a few circles, have them test circles they have already found circumferences for. Then, have them work backward by finding the diameter of a circle when the circumference is given.

- *If the circumference of a circle is 100 in., what is its diameter?* (about 31.8 or 32 in.)

Going Further

- *Make a graph of the data in your table. Describe the shape of the graph.*

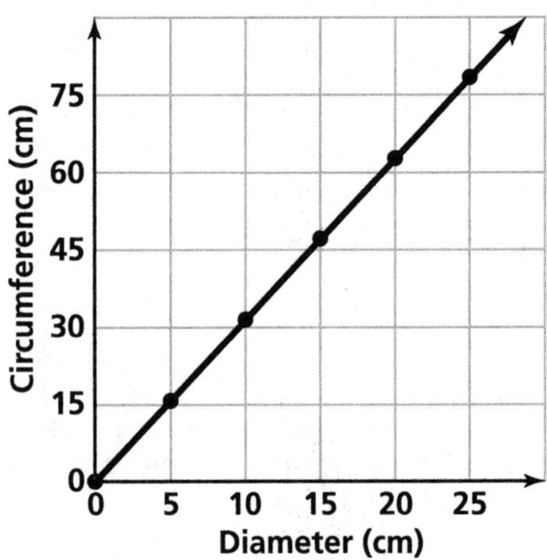

(The points lie on a straight line. Note the slope of the line is π.)

5.2 Surrounding a Lake

At a Glance

PACING 1 day

Mathematical Goals

- Discover that it takes slightly more than three diameters to equal the circumference of a circle
- Use this discovery to develop a formula for circumference of a circle
- Develop strategies for organizing and comparing data

Launch

Discuss the terms *diameter*, *radius*, *area*, and *circumference*. Use the Getting Ready about pizza restaurants to provide a context for knowing when the circumference can be useful.

Read the problem with the class. Emphasize that students are looking for patterns leading to a shortcut for finding the circumference of a circle.

- *By collecting data, you are going to try and figure out what the relationship is between the diameter of a circle and its circumference.*

Supply students with several circular objects, such as soda cans, pizza pans, round cake pans, wastebaskets, coins, and compact discs, or have them use objects they have brought from home. You might want to have sets of objects for pairs of students to measure and share with other groups. Set aside a few extra circular objects for groups to test their ideas for finding circumference.

Have students collect data in pairs and record individually.

Materials

- Transparencies 5.2A, 5.2B
- Several circular objects of different sizes
- Tape measures or string
- Rulers
- Scissors

Vocabulary

- center
- diameter
- radius
- circumference

Explore

Observe to make sure students are measuring accurately.

For students who struggle with Question B, suggest they compare their actual lengths of string as well as the values in their table.

- *Look at the string you cut for a circle and compare diameter and circumference lengths. What do you notice? How are they related?*
- *How much bigger is the circumference than the diameter?*
- *If you know the diameter, can you predict the circumference?*
- *Does this happen with all your circles?*

Summarize

Have a group who used string display the data they collected for one object and tape the lengths of string they cut for diameter and circumference up on the board. Ask students to share the patterns they found when they compared the circumference and diameter.

Materials

- Student notebooks

Vocabulary

- pi (π)

continued on next page

Summarize

continued

After students have verbalized the relationship between diameter and circumference, have them test the idea on a few new objects. Measure the diameter of an object and have the class predict its circumference. Also measure the circumference of an object and ask the class to predict the diameter.

After a few examples, push for a more exact numeral than "a little more than 3." Then introduce π (pi). Have students use π to find the circumferences of a few circles, then have them test circles they have already worked on. Finally, have them work backwards from the circumference to the diameter and vice versa.

ACE Assignment Guide for Problem 5.2

Core 5–11, 39

Other *Applications* 12–14; *Connections* 40; *Extensions* 48, 49; unassigned choices from previous problems

Adapted For suggestions about adapting ACE exercises, see the CMP *Special Needs Handbook*.

Answers to Problem 5.2

A. Answers will vary. The circumference for each object should be a little more than three times the diameter.

B. **1.** Possible answer: Add together three diameters and a bit more, or multiply the diameter by three and add a bit more.

2. Possible answer: divide the circumference by three and subtract a bit from the result.

5.3 Pricing Pizzas

Goals

- Develop techniques for estimating the area of a circle
- Develop strategies for organizing and comparing data
- Use ideas about area and perimeter to solve practical problems
- Continue to develop a conceptual understanding of area and perimeter

This problem asks students to think about how a pizza is priced relative to its diameter, radius, circumference, and area. Students are asked to find the measures for three different circular pizzas and to decide which measures are most closely related to price. Students will be able to use the formula they developed in Problem 5.2 to find circumference, but not area. Students are not expected to develop a rule for area in this problem but to see the need for a shortcut, or formula, for finding the area of a circle. Problem 5.4 will introduce a method for finding the area of a circle.

Launch 5.3

A review of how one finds the perimeter and area of other shapes might help students begin to think about strategies for finding the area of a circle.

- *We have found perimeters, circumferences, and areas for several shapes. Name a shape, and tell us how you can find the perimeter and area of that shape.* (On the board, record the name of the shape and the rules for finding its perimeter and area. Collect information until at least rectangles, parallelograms, triangles, and circles have been discussed.)

Rectangle
Perimeter: Add the lengths of the four sides, or add the lengths of two adjacent sides and multiply by 2. In symbols this is $P = \ell + w + \ell + w$, $P = 2 \times (\ell + w)$, or $P = 2\ell + 2w$.

Area: Multiply the length by the width. In symbols, this is $A = \ell \times w$.

Parallelogram
Perimeter: Add the lengths of the four sides, or add the lengths of two adjacent sides and multiply by 2. In symbols, this is $P = a + a + b + b$, $P = 2 \times a + 2 \times b$, or $P = 2 \times (a + b)$.

Area: Multiply the base by the height. In symbols, this is $A = b \times h$.

Triangle
Perimeter: Add the lengths of the three sides. In symbols, this is $P = a + b + c$.

Area: Multiply the base by the height and take half the result. In symbols, this is $A = \frac{1}{2} \times b \times h$.

Circle
Circumference: Multiply the diameter by π (approximately 3.14). In symbols, this is $C = \pi \times d$.)

It is not important for students to present the rules exactly as they are written here. What is important is that they have a correct formula that makes sense to them. The goal is for them to have efficient methods of finding area and perimeter and to be flexible enough to realize that their method and another's method may sound different but accomplish the same thing.

- *If we look at our list, we see that finding perimeters and areas for several shapes requires adding or multiplying the measures of the lengths of sides, distance between sides, or distance between a vertex and a side. For circles, we have no straight sides; only the circumference, the diameter, and the radius.*

Review what students have learned about radius, diameter, and circumference.

Suggested Questions Draw a circle and ask:

- *How can you find the length of this circle's diameter?* (Measure the distance across the circle from one point to another point, crossing through the center.)
- *What is the circle's radius? How did you find that?* (divided the diameter by 2)
- *What is the length of this circle's circumference? How did you find that?* (multiplied the diameter by π)
- *If a circle has a radius of 15 cm, what is the diameter?* (30 cm)
- *How did you find the diameter?* (doubled the radius)

- *What is the circumference of this circle?* (about 94.2 cm)

Describe Problem 5.3. Show students the three pizzas using Transparency 5.3. Read the questions.

- *You need to find the area in Question A. You know it can be found by counting and estimating the number of square units. It is fine to do that, but here you want to look for other methods where you do not have to count all the squares.*
- *Enter the radius, diameter, circumference, and area in a table like the one in Question B. Estimate the area, but try to find accurate measures for radius, diameter, and circumference.*
- *Question C asks you to describe the shortcuts that you found in Question A as rules. When looking at the data in your table, think about if you used the radius or diameter and how you could write a rule so someone else can use your shortcuts.*

Question C pushes students to articulate rules for finding area of a circle based on their work in Question A. Students are not expected to articulate the formal algorithm for finding area of a circle but to engage in thinking about efficient ways to find area of a circle. The formal algorithm will be developed in Problem 5.4.

- *The last question asks you to think about the best way to determine the cost of a pizza. The owner wants to charge \$6 for a small pizza. Use the data in the table to decide if the pizza owner should use area or circumference to price the medium and large pizzas.*

Have students work in pairs.

Explore 5.3

As you circulate, look to see if students are able to find the diameter and radius of each circle.

Encourage students to think about different methods and strategies for finding the area of the circles. As you circulate, check that they are prepared to share their answers and strategies.

Suggested Questions If students are struggling, ask questions that will help them save work by using the symmetry of a circle. For example:

- *Can you break the circle into equal parts so that you do not have to count every square?*
- *Suppose you enclose the circle in a square. How does the area of the circle compare to the square?*
- *You have methods for finding area of other shapes such as rectangles, triangles and parallelograms. Is there a way to use another shape to help you find the area of your circle?*

Students may want to cut and glue pieces of grid paper onto construction paper to show how they divided up a circle to get an accurate estimate. Gluing down pieces will help students to keep track of their work. Look for interesting strategies.

Summarize 5.3

On the board or overhead projector, record the measurements that students found for Question B. Answers for diameter, radius, and circumference should be accurate. Discuss any discrepancies.

Because students are estimating the area, the areas will vary but should be in a reasonable range. Have students share their measures and methods. Here are some strategies students have reported:

Find the area of the largest rectangle made from whole squares that you can get inside the circle. Then count and add the squares and parts of squares that are between the rectangle and circle.

Find the area of half of the circle, a semicircle, and double it.

Find the area of a quarter of the circle and multiply it by 4.

Surround the circle with a large square and find the area of the square. Then, find the area of the region outside of the circle, but inside of the large square, by counting the grid squares and parts of grid squares. Subtract this area from the area of the large square to get the area of the circle.

As students describe their strategies, ask them if they were able to express them as a rule in Question C. For example: (area of $\frac{1}{2}$ circle) $\times$ 2.

If a student offers the formula for area of a circle ($A = \pi r^2$), ask him or her to talk about the relationship between radius and area. If the student cannot explain why the formula is sensible, suggest that this idea be set aside until he or she can make sense of it.

5.3 Pricing Pizzas

At a Glance

PACING 1 day

Mathematical Goals

- Develop techniques for estimating the area of a circle
- Develop strategies for organizing and comparing data
- Use ideas about area and perimeter to solve practical problems
- Continue to develop a conceptual understanding of area and perimeter

Launch

Review how one finds the perimeter and area of other shapes. On the board, record the name of the shape and the rules for finding its perimeter and area. Collect information until at least rectangles, parallelograms, triangles, and circles have been discussed.

- *If we look at our list, we see that finding perimeters and areas for several shapes requires adding or multiplying the measures of the lengths of sides, distance between sides, or distance between a vertex and a side. For circles, we have no straight sides; only the circumference, the diameter, and the radius.*

Review what students have learned about radius, diameter, and circumference. Draw a circle and ask:

- *How can you find the length of this circle's diameter?*
- *What is the length of this circle's radius? How did you find that?*
- *What is the circle's circumference? How did you find that?*

Read the introduction to Problem 5.3. Show students the three pizzas and read the questions. Have students work in pairs.

Materials

- Transparency 5.3
- Labsheets 5.3A and 5.3B (1 of each per student)
- Scissors
- Glue
- Construction paper (optional)

Explore

Look to see if students are able to find the diameter and radius of each circle. Encourage students to think about different methods and strategies for finding the area of the circles. If students are struggling, ask questions that will help them cut down on the work by using the symmetry of a circle. For example:

- *Is there a way to break the circle into equal parts so that you do not have to count every square?*

Summarize

On the board, or overhead projector, record the measurements that students found for Question B. Discuss any discrepancies that exist.

Have students share their measures and their methods.

Materials

- Student notebooks

continued on next page

Summarize

continued

As students describe their strategies, ask them if they were able to express them as a rule in Question C. If a student offers the formula for area of a circle ($A = \pi r^2$), ask him or her to talk about the relationship between radius and area. If the student cannot explain why the formula is sensible, suggest that this idea be set aside until he or she can make sense of it.

Discuss answers to Question D.

ACE Assignment Guide for Problem 5.3

Core 15

Other unassigned choices from previous problems

Adapted For suggestions about adapting Exercise 15 and other ACE exercises, see the CMP *Special Needs Handbook*.

Answers to Problem 5.3

A. Strategies will vary. One example is to find the area of half of the circle and double it. Other possible strategies are listed in the summary of this problem.

B.

Size	Diameter (in.)	Radius (in.)	Circum. (in.)	Area. (in.^{2})
small	9	4.5	28.3	55–70
medium	12	6	37.7	105–120
large	15	7.5	47.1	170–185

C. possible answer: (area of a quarter of the circle) × 4

D. Answers will vary. Students might argue that area describes what you eat when you eat a pizza and the toppings are all over the pizza, not just on the edge or circumference.

Some may say that a medium pizza is about twice the area of a small and should cost twice as much. The large pizza is about three times the size of a small and should cost three times as much, or $18.

Others might say that the circumference and the diameter are closely related, with the circumference increasing about 10 in., for each 3-inch increase in diameter. Since the diameter and the circumference do not double when you compare the small and large, the price of the large should not be more than twice the small. The cost of a large should be about $12.

5.4 "Squaring" a Circle

Goals

- Discover that it takes slightly more than three radius squares to equal the area of the circle
- Use this discovery to develop a formula for area of a circle

In this problem, students make squares with sides the same length as the radius of a circle and then determine how many of these "radius squares" are needed to cover the circle. They will easily see that four is too many and three too few.

Answers involving pi were calculated using the π key on a calculator. If students use 3.14 for pi, their answers may vary slightly.

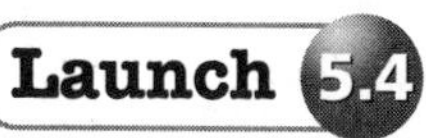

Launch 5.4

Describe Problem 5.4 to the class. You may want to demonstrate how to make the radius square for one of the circles. Demonstrate that four radius squares is too much because of the extra that overhangs the circle.

Suggested Questions Display Transparency 5.4B and ask this question:

- *Draw a square around a circle.*

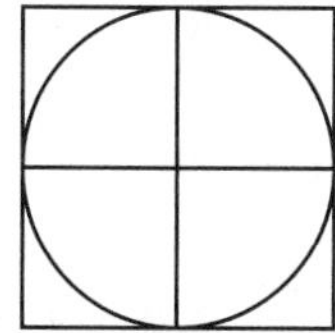

- *Draw two perpendicular diameters.*
- *How does the area of the circle compare to the square?* (It is less, or it is less than 4 radius squares.)

Challenge your students to come up with a more precise amount.

Students can work in pairs.

Explore 5.4

Students will need scissors, glue, and Labsheet 5.4. Also, have centimeter grid paper available for making radius squares. Have students cover their circles with radius squares, then work with a partner and compare answers. As you circulate, be sure they are recording their results in a table as suggested, which is organized to help them focus on the relationship between the area of the radius square and the area of the circle.

Also keep an eye out for how students are keeping track of how many radius squares fit into their circles. Make sure students are not losing track of the scraps of their squares as they piece things together.

Look for interesting strategies.

You might find it helpful if the labsheet and the grid paper are different colors. This will allow students to easily see what part of the circle they have and have not covered with radius squares.

Summarize 5.4

Have students share their strategies for finding the number of radius squares needed to cover a circle. Here are some strategies students have suggested:

- Put one radius square inside the circle. Then put as much of the second square inside as you can and trim off the edge. Put this trimmed piece inside the circle as well. Finally, cut a third square into lots of smaller pieces, and fit them where you can. When you have finished, you have fit three squares inside the circle and had a small amount of area uncovered.

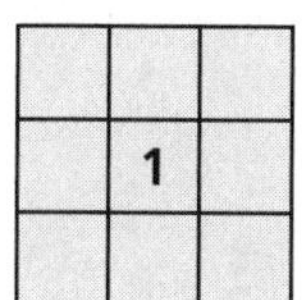

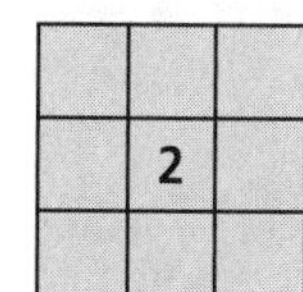

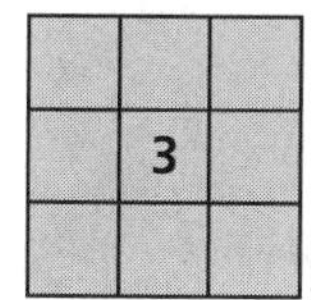

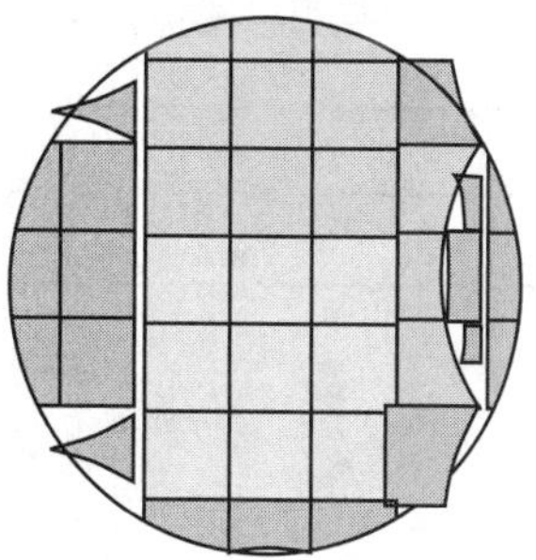

- Cover the circle with four radius squares. Then cut off the corners of the squares and figure out how much of a radius square the corners take up. This shows that it takes four radius squares minus almost a whole radius square to cover the circle. So it takes a little more than three radius squares to cover the circle.

- Use three radius squares to cover three quarters of the circle. Cut off the corners of the squares, and use them to fill in the fourth quarter. This shows that it takes a little more than three radius squares to cover the circle.

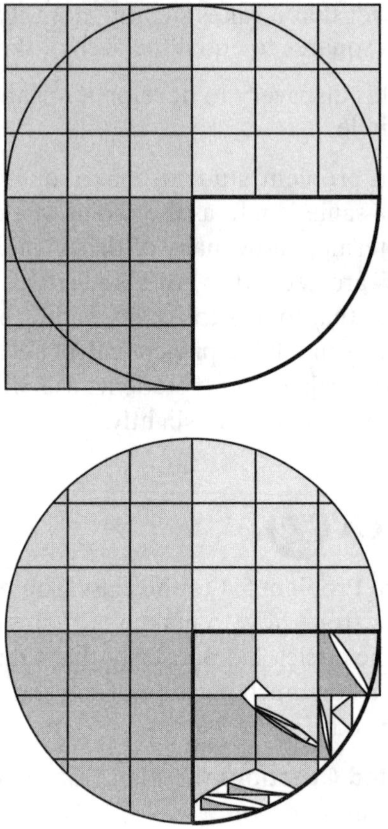

On the board or overhead, create a table like the one suggested in the Student Edition. Ask several groups of students to fill in the table for the three circles in the problem. Add the data from some of the other circular objects that students measured. (Figure 2)

Figure 2

Circle	Radius of Circle (units)	Area of Radius Square (square units)	Area of Circle (square units)	Number of Radius Squares Needed
1	6	36	about 113	a bit more than 3
2	4	16	about 50	a bit more than 3
3	3	9	about 28	a bit more than 3

Suggested Question

- *What patterns do you notice in the data?*

Students should be able to determine that it takes just over three radius squares to cover a circle. The answer, of course, is that it takes pi radius squares to cover a circle. You can help students formulate a way to describe finding the area of a circle.

The area of a circle is a little more than three times the area of a square that has the circle's radius as its side length.

The area of the radius square is found by multiplying the length by the width, which is the radius times the radius, $r \times r$ or r^2.

The area of a circle is thus a little more than $3 \times r \times r$ or a little more than $3r^2$.

- *Where have you seen "a bit more than 3" before?* (when finding circumference of circles)
- *What did "a bit more than 3" turn out to be?* (3.14, or pi)
- *If you use pi to calculate the area of the three circles, what do you get?* (about 113.10 cm^2, 50.27 cm^2, and 28.27 cm^2)
- *Are these areas close to what we figured before? Did anyone check our calculations by counting squares?*
- *If I have a circle with a radius of 10 cm, what do you think the area of that circle is?* (about 314 cm^2) *Explain how you got your answer.*
- *If I have a circle with a diameter of 10 cm, what is the area of that circle?* (about 78.5 cm^2) *Explain your answer.*
- *If I have a circle with a diameter of 10 cm, what is its circumference?* (about 31.4 cm)

Question D may be difficult for students, but it is worth asking.

- *If I know the area of a circle, how can I find the radius?*

Students may be able to see that they need to divide the area of the circle by 3.14. This will give the area of the radius square. They may struggle to figure how to determine the radius from that number. One strategy is to estimate using what they know about radius squares. Suppose the area of a radius square is 14.56. This is between a radius square with area of 9 where the radius of the circle is 3 and a radius square with area of 16 where the radius of the circle is 4. Since the area of the radius square, 14.56, is between 9 and 16, then the radius must be between 3 and 4.

5.4 "Squaring" a Circle

At a Glance

PACING $1\frac{1}{2}$ days

Mathematical Goals

- Discover that it takes slightly more than three radius squares to equal the area of the circle
- Use this discovery to develop a formula for area of a circle

Launch

Read Problem 5.4 with the class. You may want to demonstrate how to make the radius square for one of the circles. Demonstrate that four radius squares is too much because of the extra that overhangs the circle. Challenge your students to come up with a more precise amount.

Have students work in pairs.

Materials

- Transparency 5.4B

Explore

Be sure students are recording their results in a table as suggested, which is organized to help them focus on the relationship between the area of the radius square and the area of the circle.

Keep an eye out also for how students keep track of how many radius squares fit into their circles. Make sure students are not losing track of the scraps of their squares as they piece things together.

Materials

- Transparency 5.4A
- Scissors
- Glue
- Labsheet 5.4
- Centimeter grid paper

Summarize

Have students share their strategies for finding the number of radius squares needed to cover a circle.

On the board or overhead, create a table like the one suggested in the Student Edition. Ask several groups of students to fill in the table for the three circles in the problem. Add the data from some of the other circular objects that students measured.

- *What patterns do you notice in the data?*

Help students formulate a way to describe finding the area of a circle.

- *Where have you seen "a bit more than 3" before?*
- *What did "a bit more than 3" turn out to be?*
- *If you use 3.14 to calculate the area of the three circles, what do you get?*

Have students work more with the formula.

- *If I have a circle with a radius of 10 cm, what do you think the area of that circle is? Explain how you got your answer.*
- *If I have a circle with a diameter of 10 cm, what is the area of that circle? Explain your answer.*
- *If I know the area of a circle, how can I find the radius?*

Materials

- Student notebooks

Vocabulary

- pi (π)

ACE Assignment Guide for Problem 5.4

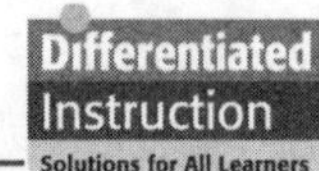

Core 22–32

Other *Applications* 16–21, 33–38; *Connections* 41–46; unassigned choices from previous problems

Adapted For suggestions about adapting ACE exercises, see the CMP *Special Needs Handbook*.

Connecting to Prior Units 41: *Bits and Pieces II*; 42: *Bits and Pieces II*, *Prime Time*; 43–46: *Bits and Pieces II*

Answers to Problem 5.4

A. (Figure 3)

B. Answers will vary but ideally students will notice that it takes a little more than three radius squares to cover any circle.

C. To find the area, take the radius of the circle and use it to find the area of the radius square. The area of the circle is the area of the radius square times pi, or 3.14. We can write this in symbols as $A = 3.14 \times r^2$.

D. To find the radius, divide the area by 3.14 to get the area of the radius square. Then find the number whose square is the area of the radius square. This is the same as finding the square root of the area of the radius square.

Figure 3

Circle	Radius of Circle (units)	Area of Radius Square (square units)	Area of Circle (square units)	Number of Radius Squares Needed
1	6	36	about 113	a bit more than 3
2	4	16	about 50	a bit more than 3
3	3	9	about 28	a bit more than 3

Investigation 5

ACE Assignment Choices

Problem 5.1

Core 1, 3, 47
Other *Applications* 2, 4

Problem 5.2

Core 5–11, 39
Other *Applications* 12–14, *Connections* 40; *Extensions* 48, 49; unassigned choices from previous problems

Problem 5.3

Core 15
Other unassigned choices from previous problems

Problem 5.4

Core 22–32
Other *Applications* 16–21, 33–38; *Connections* 41–46; unassigned choices from previous problems

Adapted For suggestions about adapting Exercise 15 and other ACE exercises, see the CMP *Special Needs Handbook*.
Connecting to Prior Units *Bits and Pieces II*; 42: *Bits and Pieces II*, *Prime Time*; 43–46: *Bits and Pieces II*

Applications

Answers involving pi were calculated using the π key on a calculator. If students use 3.14 for pi, their answers may vary slightly.

1. **a.** The area is about 97–100 square units.
   b. The perimeter is about 75–80 units.
   c. Twice the area of a hand plus a little more for the thickness of the hand would give a manufacturer some idea of how much material is needed for one glove. The perimeter would be a good estimate for the amount of thread needed to sew the two pieces together.
   d. The area would stay the same. However, our estimate might change slightly because of the number of whole and partial squares that the tracing would cover.
2. **a.** $\approx$ 31 cm^2
   b. $\approx$ 40 cm
   c. The amount of rubber in the sole is related to the area of the foot. The amount of thread required to stitch the sole to the rest of the shoe is related to the perimeter (although we would have to ignore the part of the perimeter between the toes!).
3. The developer can fit about 27 lots. The perimeter of the lake on the map is approximately 27 cm. Each centimeter on the map is equivalent to 100 ft on the real lake.
4. The lake covers approximately 250,000 ft^2 now. Therefore, the lake has been shrinking. It is now about half its original size.
5. diameter; 3 cm
6. diameter; 7.5 cm
7. circumference; $\approx$5 cm
8. radius; 2 cm
9.

Exercise	Diameter (cm)	Circumference (cm)
5	3	9.42
6	7.5	23.56
7	1.6	5.03
8	4	12.57

10. **a.** The diameters measure 3.3 cm.
    b. Diameters drawn in the same circle have equal measures.
    c. Since the circumference is a little more than 3 times the diameter, the circumference is a little more than 3 times 3.3, or about 10 cm.

11. a. All radii are 2 cm long.

b. All the radii drawn in the same circle will have the same measure.

c. Since the circumference is a little more than 3 times twice the radius, the circumference is a little more than 3 times 4, or more than 12 cm.

12. Terrell is correct. Students may say that the radius in a circle when doubled will equal the measurement of the diameter in the circle.

13. Enrique could divide the diameter by 2 (cutting the diameter into two radii), and find that each radius measures one-half of the length of the diameter.

14. C

15. a.

Size	Diameter (in.)	Radius (in.)	Circum. (in.)	Area. (in.^{2})
small	8	4	25.1	50.3
medium	10	5	31.4	78.5
large	12	6	37.7	113.1

One possible method: If you square the radius and multiply it by pi (or a little over 3), you will find the area of the circle.

b. It is a good estimate. Since the diameter is twice the radius, you can write Sam's expression as $\frac{3}{4}(2r)^2 = \frac{3}{4}(4r^2) = 3r^2$. Pi is a little more than 3, and since the area of a circle is πr^2, he is pretty close with $0.75 \times (\text{diameter})^2$.

16. Possible answer: The area of a compact disc tells you something about the storage space on the disc.

17. Possible answer: The circumference of a bicycle wheel tells you how far the bike travels in one revolution.

18. Possible answer: The diameter (and related cross-sectional area) of a pipe tells how much water can flow through the pipe.

19. Possible answer: The area of a lawn sprinkler's spray lets you estimate how much of your lawn will get watered at each location the device is used and thus will allow you to estimate how long it will take to water your lawn.

20. Possible answer: The circumference will help you estimate how many people can ride the wheel at the same time.

21. Answers will vary.

22. circumference $\approx$ 28.3 in., $A \approx$ 63.6 in.^{2}

23. radius = 13 in., circumference $\approx$ 81.7 in., $A \approx$ 530.9 in.^{2}

24. diameter = 80 ft, circumference $\approx$ 251.3 ft, $A \approx$ 5,026.5 ft^2

25. album: radius = 6 in., circumference $\approx$ 37.7 in., $A \approx$ 113.1 in.^{2}

compact disc: radius = $2\frac{5}{16}$ in., circumference $\approx$ 14.5 in., $A \approx$ 16.8 in.^{2}

26. The largest area for a rectangle is the 9 m-by-9 m square, with an area of 81 m^2. A circle with a circumference of 36 m would have a radius of about 5.73 m, and an area of about 103 m^2. Therefore the circle would give the dog the most area. A 17 m-by-1 m rectangle would give him the longest straight-line run.

27. $P = 50 + 50 + 24 + (24 \times \pi) \div 2 =$ 161.70 ft

$A = 50 \times 24 + (12^2 \times \pi) \div 2 =$ 1,426.2 ft^2

28. If r = 2 cm, $A \approx$ 12 cm^2, $C \approx$ 12 cm.

29. a 3 cm-by-5 cm rectangle: A = 15 cm^2, P = 16 cm

30. The area of the whole circle with a radius of 1.5 cm would be about 7 cm^2. This figure is half of that: about 3.5 cm^2, $P \approx$ 7.6 cm.

31. The area is half of the figure in Exercise 30: $A \approx$ 1.75 cm^2, $P \approx$ 5.3 cm.

32. This figure is a combination of the figures in Exercises 30 and 31: $A \approx$ 5.25 cm^2. $P \approx$ 10 cm.

33. If $b = h$ = 4 cm, $A \approx$ 8 cm^2, $P \approx$ 13 cm (isosceles triangle with lengths 4 cm, 4.5 cm and 4.5 cm)

34. G

35. C

36. a. 100 ft of fencing will enclose the patio.

b. $A \approx (8.5 \times 8.5 \times \pi)$ or 227.0 ft^2 of plastic. (The 1-ft overhang added 2 ft total to the diameter.)

c. The circumference tells you the amount of plastic tubing needed, 47.1 ft.

d. 600 – 176.7 ≈ 423.3 ft^2, which is the area of the pool subtracted from the area of the whole patio giving you the area of the ground covered with tiles.

37. a. The material required for the circle is $3 \times 3 \times \pi \approx 28.3$ ft^2. The rest of the flag needs: $36 - 28.3 = 7.7$ ft^2 of material.

b. For the material inside the triangle: $6 \times 6 \div 2 = 18$ ft^2. The rest of the flag needs $36 - 18 = 18$ ft^2 of material.

38. outer band: ≈ 113.10 $in.^2$
middle band: ≈ 87.96 $in.^2$
inner circle: ≈ 113.10 $in.^2$

Connections

39. a. The length of a belt is related to waist circumference.

b. The waist size of a pair of jeans is related to waist and hip circumference.

c. Hat size is related to head circumference.

d. Shirt size is related to neck, arm, and chest circumference.

40. a.

Diameter (in.)	Circumference (in.)
9	28.27
12	37.70
15	47.12
18	56.55
21	65.97

b.

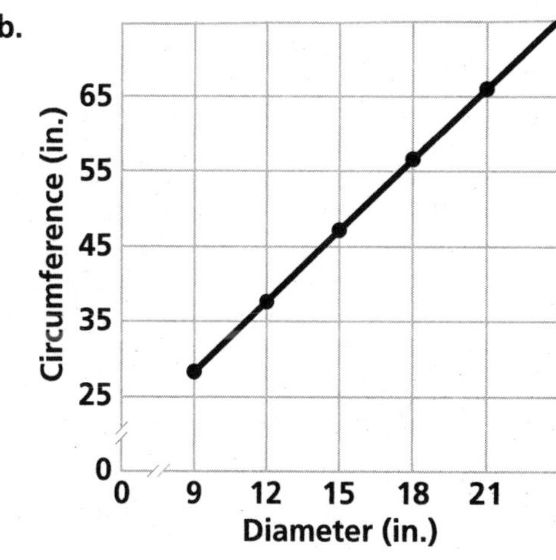

c. The graph is a straight line going diagonally upwards from the left to the right. This is because as the diameter increased by about 3 in., the circumference increased by about 9.42 or ($3 \times \pi$) in.

d. A circumference of about 3.14 in. less than the 21 in. diameter pizza: 62–63 in. is a good estimate for the diameter.

e. About 25–27 in. is a good estimate for the diameter.

41. 21; Possible answers: Doubling a radius to find the diameter, finding the area of a rectangle

42. 56.72; Possible answer: Finding the area of a circle

43. 55.66; Possible answer: Finding the area of a triangle

44. $3\frac{3}{5}$, or 3.6; Possible answer: Finding the area of a rectangle

45. 36; Possible answer: Finding the perimeter of a rectangle

46. 23.55; Possible answer: Finding the circumference of a circle

Extensions

47. Answers may vary. One possible answer is the surface area of a lawn to measure for fertilizer.

48. His head would move 38 more feet than his feet. Possible method: First find the circumference of Earth (which is the distance his feet moved):
$\pi \times 41{,}900{,}000 \approx 131{,}632{,}732$ ft, then the circumference of the circle made by his head $\pi \times 41{,}900{,}012 \approx 131{,}632{,}770$ ft. Finally, calculate the difference to determine how much farther his head moved than his feet:
$131{,}632{,}770 - 131{,}632{,}732 = 38$ ft.

49. a. The new rope is about 0.5 ft away from the surface of the earth. Possible answer: Subtract the radius of the earth from the radius of the circle made by the rope to find how far the new rope is from Earth. (Or, $131{,}632{,}735 \div \pi = 41{,}900{,}000.9$. So, the diameter is almost a foot longer, which means the new rope is about half a foot away from the surface of the earth.)

b. The new rope is about 0.5 in. away from the waist. You could use the same strategy as you did in part (a). An example is if someone's waist is 30 in. and radius is about 4.775 in. ($30 \div \pi \approx 9.55$ in., $9.55 \div 2 =$ 4.775 in.). Adding 3 in., the new waist is 33 in. with a new radius of $33 \div \pi \div 2$, or about 5.25 in. The difference is about 0.5 in. (5.25 – 4.775 is about 0.5 in.).

c. The results in parts (a) and (b) indicate that if you increase the circumference by 3 units, you increase the radius by about 0.5 units.

Possible Answers to Mathematical Reflections

1. The circumference of a circle is always a little bit more than 3 times the measure of its diameter. "A little bit more than 3" is a number called π and is about 3.14. If you want to find the circumference of a circle, you just multiply the diameter of the circle by π, or 3.14. If you are given the measure of the radius, multiply it by 2 to get the diameter of the circle. Then multiply the diameter by π.
2. If you make a square with sides the same length as the circle's radius, the area of the circle will be a little more than three times of these "radius" squares, which turns out to be the special number π (about 3.14). To find the area of a circle, you can find the area of a radius square and multiply it by π, or 3.14. You can write this as $A = \pi r^2$. This is a useful method, because the area of a circle is sometimes hard to find by covering it with a grid since there may be lots of parts of squares to count. If you are given the diameter of the circle, divide the diameter by 2 to get the radius. Use the radius to find the area of the radius square and then multiply the area of the radius square by pi, or 3.14.
3. If the shape is on grid paper, you can find the area by counting whole squares and fractional parts of squares. If the shape isn't on a grid, you can put a transparent grid over the shape and count squares. The smaller the grid paper the more accurate your area measurement will be. To find the perimeter, you can figure out what length string is needed to enclose the outside of the object, then measure the string with a ruler.
4. When you measure the area of a shape you are measuring the amount of space it covers. To find out how much space or area the shape has, you can cover the shape with square units (such as square centimeters or square inches) and see how many units cover the shape.
5. When you measure the perimeter of a shape or the circumference of a circle you are measuring the distance around the shape. This length or distance around a shape is measured in linear units such as centimeters or inches.

Answers to Looking Back and Looking Ahead

1. **a.** 36 square units

   b. First possible answer: Subdivide the hexagon into triangles, parallelograms, and rectangles and use the formulas for finding area of these figures. An example of subdivision is shown.

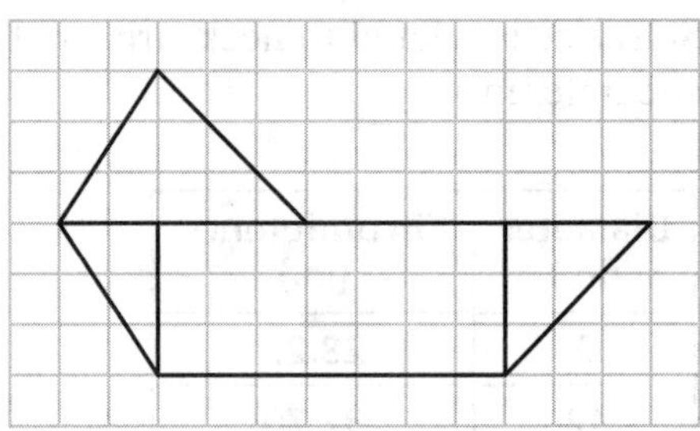

area of triangle = base × height ÷ 2: $5 \times 3 \div 2 = 7.5$ square units

area of the parallelogram = base × height: $7 \times 3 = 21$ square units

Since there are two triangles and one parallelogram, $7.5 + 7.5 + 21 = 36$.

Second possible answer: Rearrange the hexagon into a long rectangle and count the number of square units.

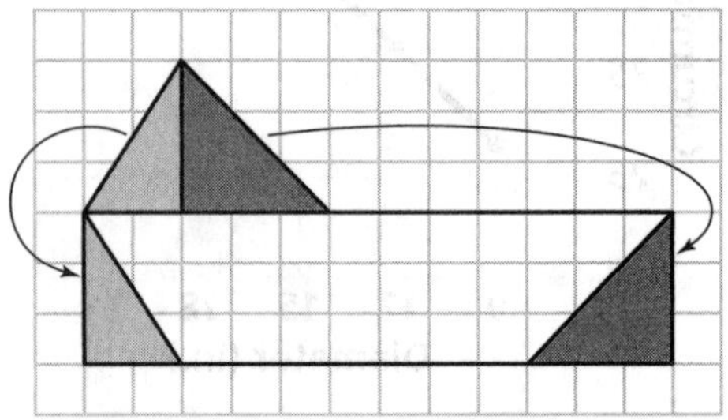

2. a. about 86 ft^2

area of the whole floor:
20 ft × 20 ft = 400 ft^2

area of quarter circle of carpet:
$0.25 \times \pi \times (20 \text{ ft})^2 \approx 314 \text{ ft}^2$

Subtract the area of quarter-circle of carpet from the area of the square floor area.

b. 86 ÷ 125 = 0.69, or 1 can of floor wax

c. 0.25 × circumference of circle or
$0.25 \times 2 \times \pi \times 20 \text{ ft} \approx 31.4 \text{ ft}$

3. a. Rectangle: area = length × width or base × height, measured in square units; perimeter = (length + width) × 2, measurement is a length such as inches

b. Triangle: area = base × height ÷ 2, measured in square units; perimeter = add the lengths of the three sides, measurement is a length such as inches

c. Parallelogram: area = base × height, measured in square units; perimeter = add the lengths of the four sides or add the lengths of two adjacent sides and double, measurement is a length such as inches

d. Circle: area = $\pi \times r^2$ or $\pi \times r \times r$, measured in square units; circumference = $\pi \times d$, measurement is a length such as inches

e. To estimate the area of an irregular figure, put a grid over the figure. Count the number of whole squares and combine partial squares together to make whole squares. The area is measured in square units. To estimate the perimeter, you can lay a piece of string along the edge of the shape. Then measure the length of the string using a ruler or grid. The measurement is a length such as inches.

4. a. Rectangle: Area is the number of square units covering the shape. The length of the base is the number of units along the base. The height tells how many rows of those units there are. If you multiply the number of units in a row (base) by the number of rows (height) you get the total square units covering the rectangle. Perimeter is the total length of the outside edges of a shape. You can add the length of the sides or since opposite sides are congruent, you can add two adjacent sides to get the distance halfway around and then double this for the total distance.

b. Triangle: The area of a triangle is half the area of a rectangle because if you multiply the base (square units along base) by the height (number of rows of square units), that gives you the area of the rectangle. Then divide it by 2 to get the area of the triangle. Perimeter: you add the length of the three edges to get the total distance around the shape.

c. Parallelogram: The area of a parallelogram can be divided into two congruent triangles with the same base and height as the parallelogram. Since there are two triangles in one parallelogram, do not divide the product of the base and height by two. Perimeter is the total length of the outside edges of a shape. You can add the lengths of the sides or since opposite sides are congruent, you can add two adjacent sides to get the distance halfway around and then double this for the total distance.

d. Circle: The area is a little more than 3, or π, times the area of a radius square. A radius square is a square with side length as long as the radius of the circle. Circumference is the distance around the outer edge of the circle. It is a little more than 3, or π, times the length of the diameter.

e. Irregular figure: The techniques described are the only ones available. There is no formula for the area of an irregular shape, nor for its perimeter. We must estimate the area by counting the squares that cover it. Better estimates are obtained using smaller grids.

Guide to the Unit Project

Assigning the Unit Project

Plan a Park is the final assessment in *Covering and Surrounding*. Students were told about a piece of land designated for a new city park and about the contest to design the layout of the park.

The Plan a Park Project gives students an opportunity to think about the size of things and the amount of area they occupy. They will need to use measurement skills, concepts of area and perimeter, ideas of scaling, and reasoning about size and space to create their design.

The project could be assigned as an individual or partner project. An ample supply of grid paper, as well as commonly available mathematical materials (calculators, rulers, measuring tapes, string, and compasses) should be available for students to use as they conduct research for their park designs. (Grid paper on large rolls is available through teacher-supply catalogs or stores.) We recommend that students use grid paper with small squares because of the size of the park. Most students will scale their drawings by using one square of grid paper for every square yard of the park.

Read through the description of the unit project, which starts on page 89 of the Student Edition. Make sure everyone understands the project, including the idea that The City Council of Roseville is not asking that the park be divided into two parts, but that *half of the total area* be reserved for what The Council specified. The elements required (the playground, the picnic area, and the trees) can be located anywhere in the park.

Talk with your students about what it means to make a scale drawing. You could discuss how to set up a one-to-one scale with grid paper. For example, if students use centimeter grid paper, one centimeter on the grid paper could represent one yard of the park. Your students have been informally making scale drawings throughout the unit, beginning with the tile models of bumper car floors. Because the audience for the design is more than the teacher, each design should include a key that gives the scaling ratio.

Although this project will take several hours to complete, most of the work can be done outside of class. You may want to take 10 or 15 minutes to launch the project in class and then a few minutes every couple of days to discuss questions and concerns your students have as they work on their projects. A week, including a weekend, is a reasonable amount of time to give students for this project.

Here are some common questions that students ask, along with suggested answers,

---

Classroom Dialogue Model

Student *How do I represent trees in the design? Do I show the trunk or the spread of the branches?*

Teacher *Most landscape drawings are aerial views, so you should show the spread of the branches.*

Student *Do I have to show calculations for the numbers of trees and picnic tables?*

Teacher *No, you can just find these by counting. You need to include the counts for these items, but not an addition equation to show the sum of the tables and the trees.*

Student *Do I have to give the perimeter and the area for each item in my park?*

Teacher *No, you should be selective about the measurements you include. For example, when you describe the amount of fencing needed for your park, you need only give the perimeter. When you specify the amount of space needed for the picnic area, you need only give the area.*

Remind students that their reports should be organized so the reader can easily find information about items in the park. Giving students your grading rubric for the project should help them understand what they need to do.

Suggested Scoring Rubric

A total of 50 points are possible for the project: 23 for the scale drawing, 22 for the report, and 5 for the letter to The City Council of Roseville.

Scale drawing

DIMENSIONS AND MEASUREMENTS—16 points

- Dimensions are labeled (3 pts)
- Dimensions are close to dimensions of actual items (9 pts)
- Scale is included (2 pts)
- Design meets problem constraints (2 pts)

COMPLETE DESIGN—7 points

- Design is reasonable and logical (4 pts)
- Design is neat, well-organized, and includes required items (3 pts)

Report

MATHEMATICS—16 points

- Dimensions are given and correctly match drawing (4 pts)
- Calculations are correct (6 pts)
- Necessary and correct measurements are given with explanations of what the measurements mean and why they are needed (6 pts)

ORGANIZATION—6 points

- Work is neat, easy to follow, and meets the requirements of the problem (3 pts)
- Information is easy to find (3 pts)

Letter

COMPOSITION—3 points

- Letter is easy to read and understand (1 pt)
- Justifications are given for decisions (1 pt)
- Reasons are given for why design should be chosen (1 pt)

STRUCTURE—2 points

- Letter is neat (1 pt)
- Grammar and spelling are correct (1 pt)

Sample

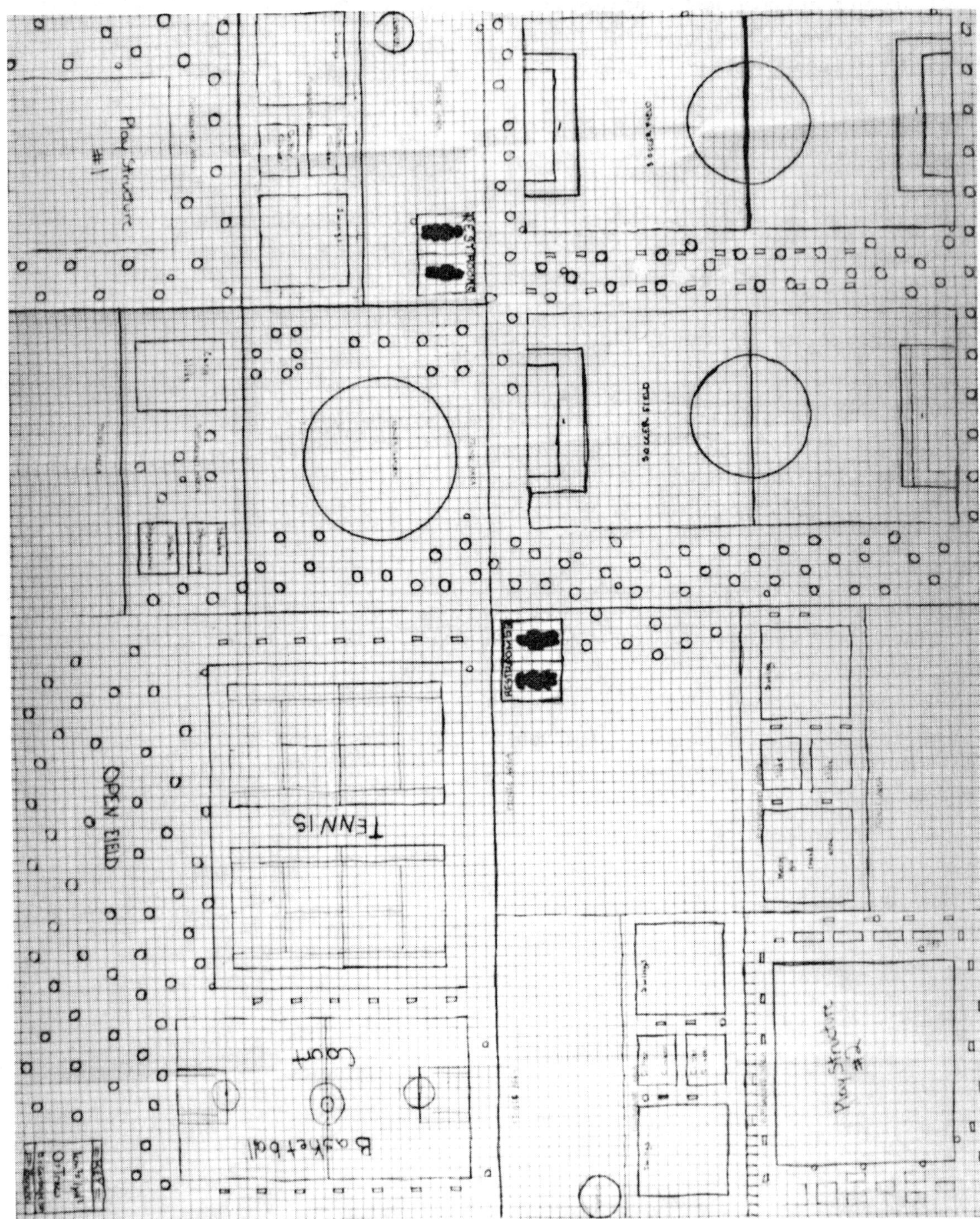
Play Structure #1
RESTROOMS
SOCCER FIELD
RESTROOMS
TENNIS
OPEN FIELD
Basketball Court
Play Structure #2

Dear Dr. Dolittle,

Our park was designed to ~~make~~ have families come and be able to spend a day outdoors together. We have a basketball court and tennis court in the top left corner and two soccer fields in the lower right corner. We included the sports fields so people can play for fun or the community can use the fields and courts for matches and tournaments.

To the left of our soccer fields we have picnic and playground areas. There are many fun and exciting play structures, climbers, swings and much more. We have covered the ground of our playground with sand for safety.

We have conveniently located benches around the sports fields so parents can sit down and relax while they watch their son or daughter play. This way they won't have to bring their own chairs.

We have added restrooms in the center so they can be used by anyone in the park. We also added both garbage and recycling ~~clean~~ cans for a clean park.

Our park meets all your constraints, has something for everyone, is ecologically minded with recycling and trees and will be a fun place for the family. We hope you will select our design.

Sincerely,

Katie

Rebecca

Land Used

2 soccer fields
21 yd by 45 yd
945 yd² area
132 yd perimeter

2 tennis courts
12 yd × 22 yd
264 yd² area
68 yd perimeter

basketball
16 yd × 30 yd
480 yd² area
92 yd perimeter

Total land used for soccer, tennis and basketball 945 + 945 yd² + 264 yd² + 264 yd² + 480 yd² =
2,898 yd²

Playground

5 sets of swings 9 yd × 9 yd
81 yd² area
36 yd perimeter

4 Critter Climbers 4 yd × 5 yd
20 yd² area
18 yd perimeter

1 curly slide 9 yd × 7 yd
63 yd² area
32 yd perimeter

2 slide area 4 yd × 5 yd
20 yd² area
18 yd perimeter

Play Structure #1 — 17yd × 17yd

289 yd² area

68 yd perimeter

Play structure #2 — 20yd × 18yd

360 yd² area

76 yd perimeter

Playground Area

4 — 30yd × 12.5yd = 1,500 yd²

2 — 30yd × 25yd = 1,500 yd²

3,000 yd² total playground

Small flower gardens

diameter	4 yd
radius (½ D)	2 yd
area r × r × π	12.57 yd²
circumference D × π	12.57 yd

Restrooms

6yd × 8yd

Area — 48yd²

perimeter — 28 yd

Picnic Area

4 — 30yd × 12.5yd = 1,500yd²

2 — 30yd × 25yd = 1,500yd²

3,000 yd² total picnic

Flower Garden

Big

diameter	16 yd
radius (½ d)	8 yd
area = r × r × π	201.06 yd²
circumference = D × π	50.27 yd

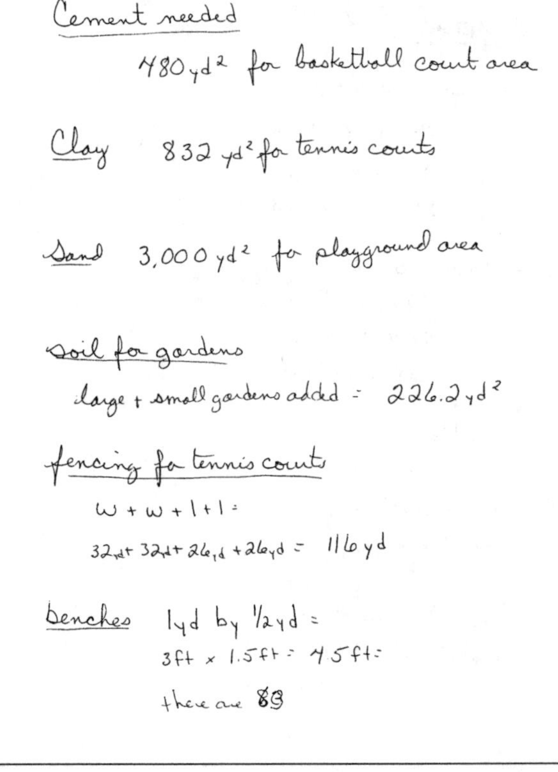

Cement needed

480 yd² for basketball court area

Clay — 832 yd² for tennis courts

Sand — 3,000 yd² for playground area

soil for gardens

large + small gardens added = 226.2 yd²

fencing for tennis courts

w + w + l + l =

32yd + 32yd + 26yd + 26yd = 116 yd

benches — 1yd by ½ yd =

3ft × 1.5ft = 4.5ft =

there are 8

trash cans

23 trash cans

trees =

d 1 yd

r .5 yd

a: .78 yd²

Total park area = 100yd x 120yd = 12,000yd

total park 12,000yd²

picnic & playground - 6,000yd²

6,000yd²

The total park area was 12,000yd². We subtracted the total area for the picnic and playground which was 3,000yd² + 3,000yd² = 6,000yd² leaving 6,000 yd² for other activities. We can tell this is ½ of 12,000. There is also open field areas around the tennis and basketball courts. We did not subtract the flower garden area but if we did it would equal

3,000yd² area for picnic

- 201.06yd² area for garden

2798.94 yd²

+3000 yd playground area

5798.94yd² picnic + playground

12000yd²) 5798.94yd² = .483 or 48%

A Teacher's Comments

In my class, students worked on the project in pairs. They put a lot of time and energy into the projects but had a hard time figuring out how to show the mathematics and organize the information. A pair of students that struggled with these issues made the sample project.

Scale drawing

Dimensions and measurements—9 out of 16 points Most of the items in the design are close to the correct scaled size. One exception is the soccer field.

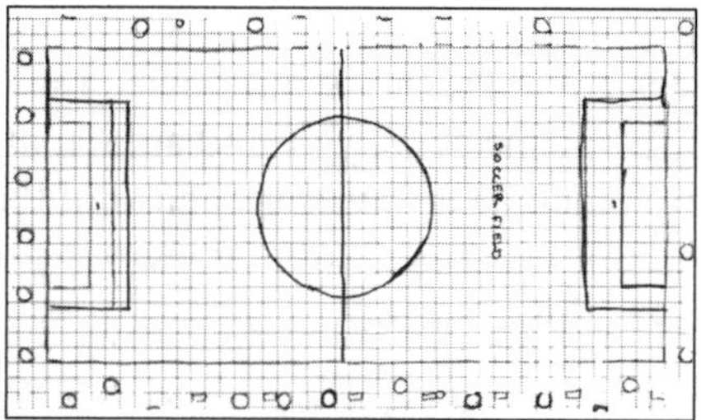

A regulation soccer field is 120 yards by 60 yards (more than half of the park). Although junior soccer fields are sometime smaller, there is no indication that the fields in the design were meant to be junior soccer fields. The letter to The City Council of Roseville states that the community could hold tournaments on these fields, which implies that they are regulation size.

Other problems are the sizes of the swings and play structures 1 and 2, which are shown as square areas.

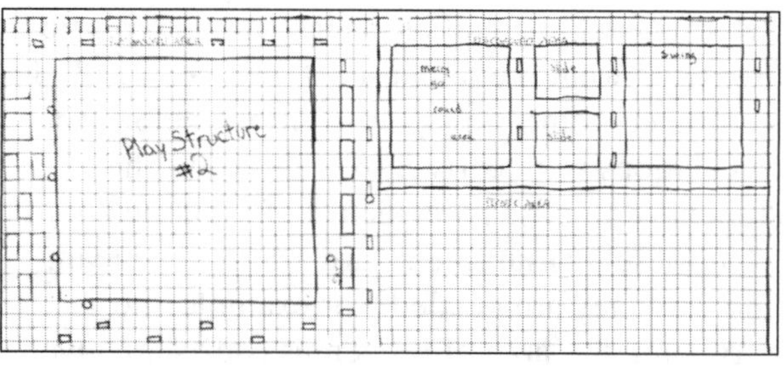

The report does not explain why these areas are squares or why they are the size that they are. Also, there is no explanation given about what "play structure area" means. Because of these concerns, I gave only 5 points for close and reasonable dimensions. I gave no points for labeling the dimensions of items in the park. The students must have missed this part of the assignment. They received 2 points for the key.

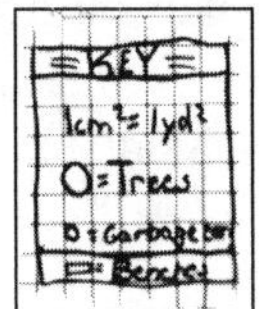

The design meets the requirements that half of the park be picnic or playground area, that the picnic area include a flower garden, and that the items in the park appeal to families, so I gave 2 points for this criteria.

COMPLETE DESIGN—6 out of 7 points

The design of the park seems reasonable, except for the size of the soccer field. One might question the fact that the picnic area has no tables or trash cans. Also, "open field" implies a piece of land with no trees or equipment, yet this drawing shows several trees in the open field.

Report

MATHEMATICS—11 out of 16 points

Most of the dimensions in the report (other than the soccer field) match the drawing. The biggest problem is that the reader has to work hard to determine what count as playground and picnic areas and what the dimensions are. As a result, I subtracted points for "Organization" below. The calculations were correct (6 points), but the students do not show evidence of thinking about what these measurements are, what they mean, and why they are needed. For example, the perimeter and area of the tennis courts are given with no explanation of why they are given or what they imply for the park design. The perimeters of the tennis courts are not needed, which is evident in the calculations of the amount of fencing required for this area. By examining the numbers for these calculations, it is clear that the fence is intended to surround both tennis courts and not each individual court. I gave 2 points for necessary and correct measurements with explanations.

ORGANIZATION—2 out of 6 points

The organization of the report is the weakest part of the project. Referring to the rubric, I awarded only 1 out of 3 points for "work is neat, easy to follow, and meets the requirements of the problem" and 1 out of 3 points for "information is easy to find."

Letter

COMPOSITION—3 out of 3 points

The letter is clear and attempts to justify the decisions that were made.

STRUCTURE—1 out of 2 points

The letter is not very neat and it contains crossed-out words.

I awarded 32 out of 50 points, a C, for this project. The students have addressed the basic elements of the project, but there are problems with completeness and reasonableness.

When I assign this project next time, I will need to help my students better understand what quality work is and what my expectations are. I need to help them think more about measurements and what they tell us. It is apparent that students can find areas and perimeters, but it is not clear that they are reasoning about these measures. I need to find ways to raise these issues when I teach this unit. Having students do more measuring of actual items may give them more frames of reference for size. Organizing information is a difficult task for my students. This was apparent in many of the reports turned in for this project. I need to talk more about organization with my students and model some of the ways I organize information.

Name ______________________________ Date ____________ Class ____________

Labsheet 1.2

Designs A–H

Design A

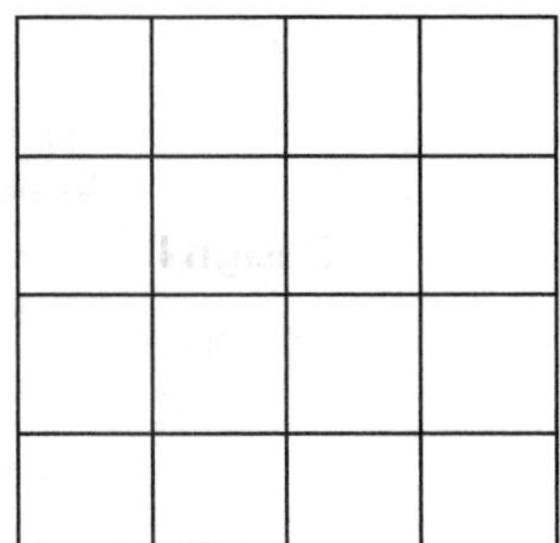

Design B

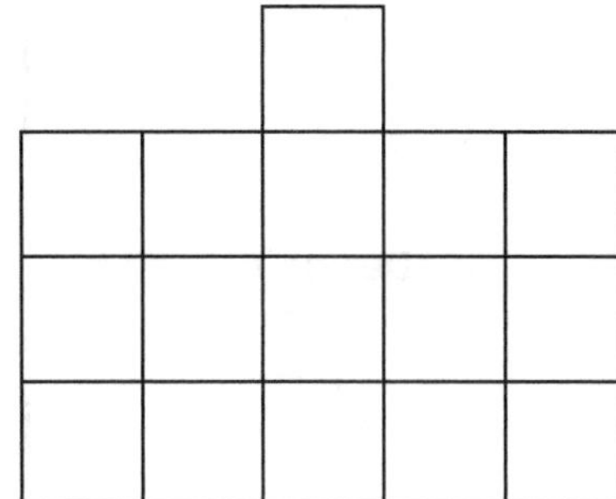

Design C

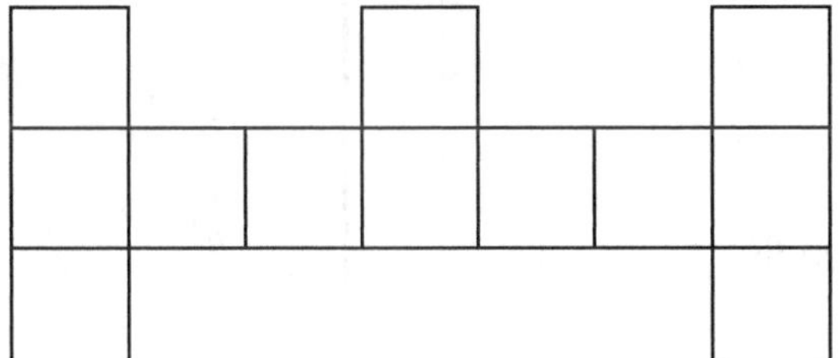

Design D

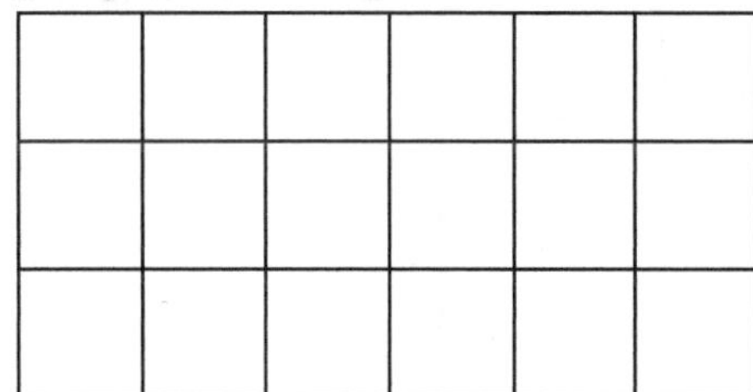

Design E

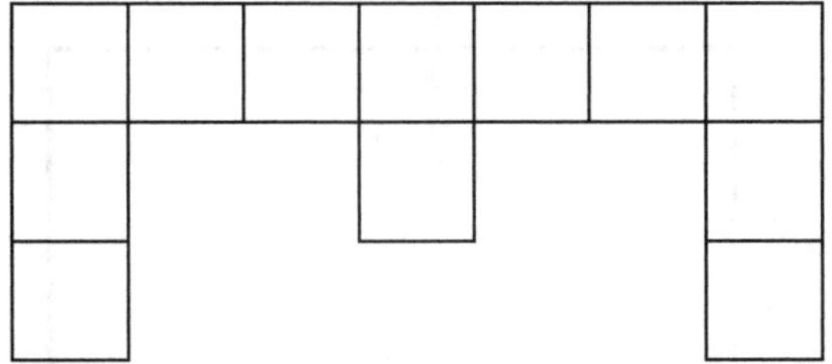

Design F

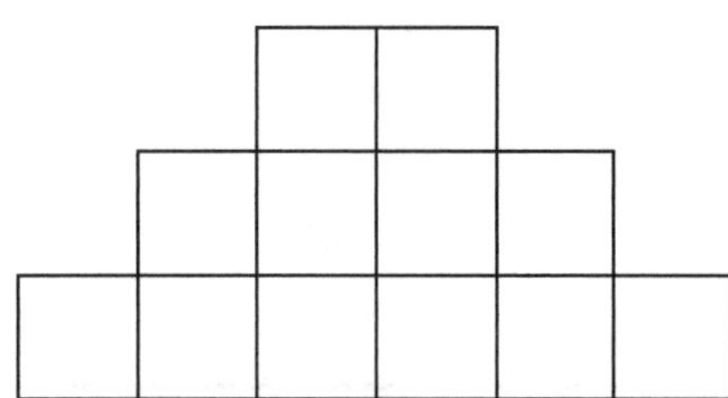

Design G

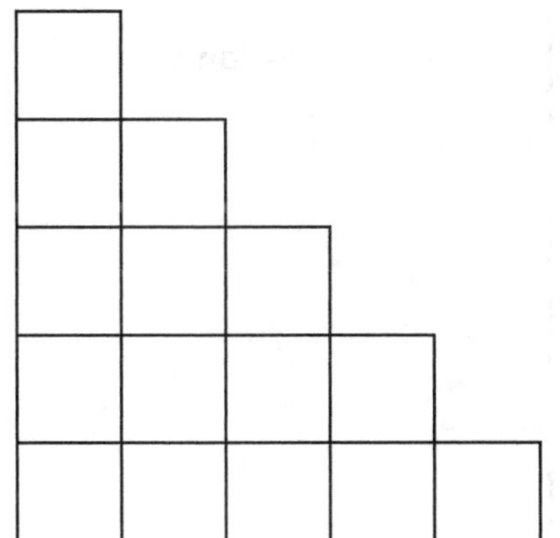

Design H

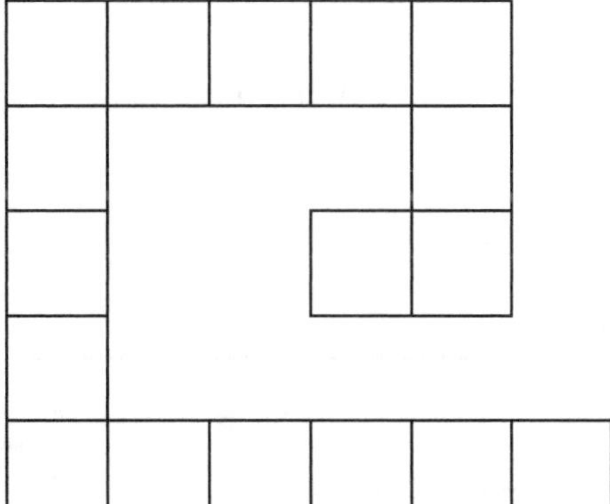

Name ______________________________ Date ____________ Class ____________

Labsheet 1.3

Designs I–V

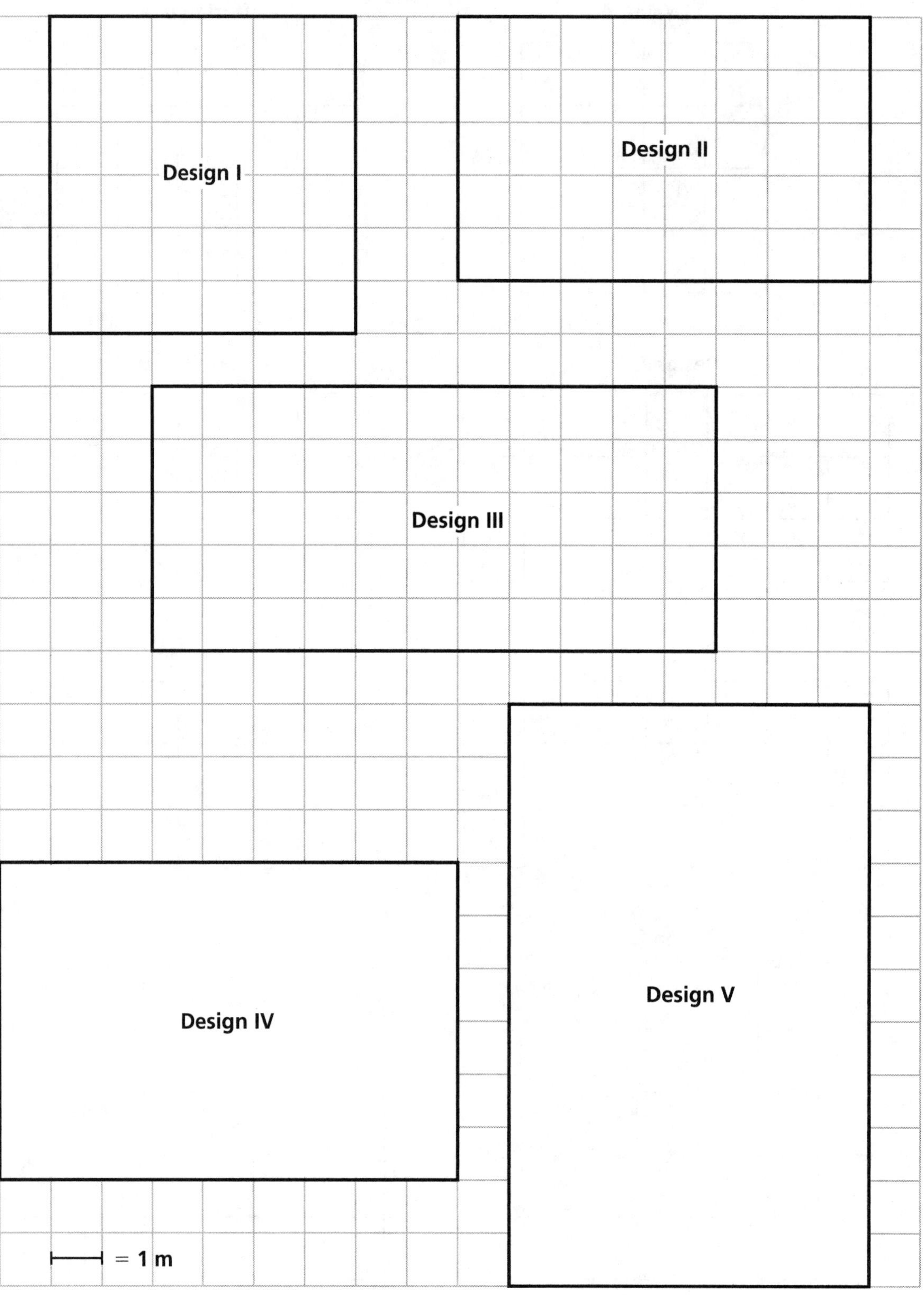

Name ______________________ Date ____________ Class ____________

Labsheet 2.1

Shelter Floor Plans

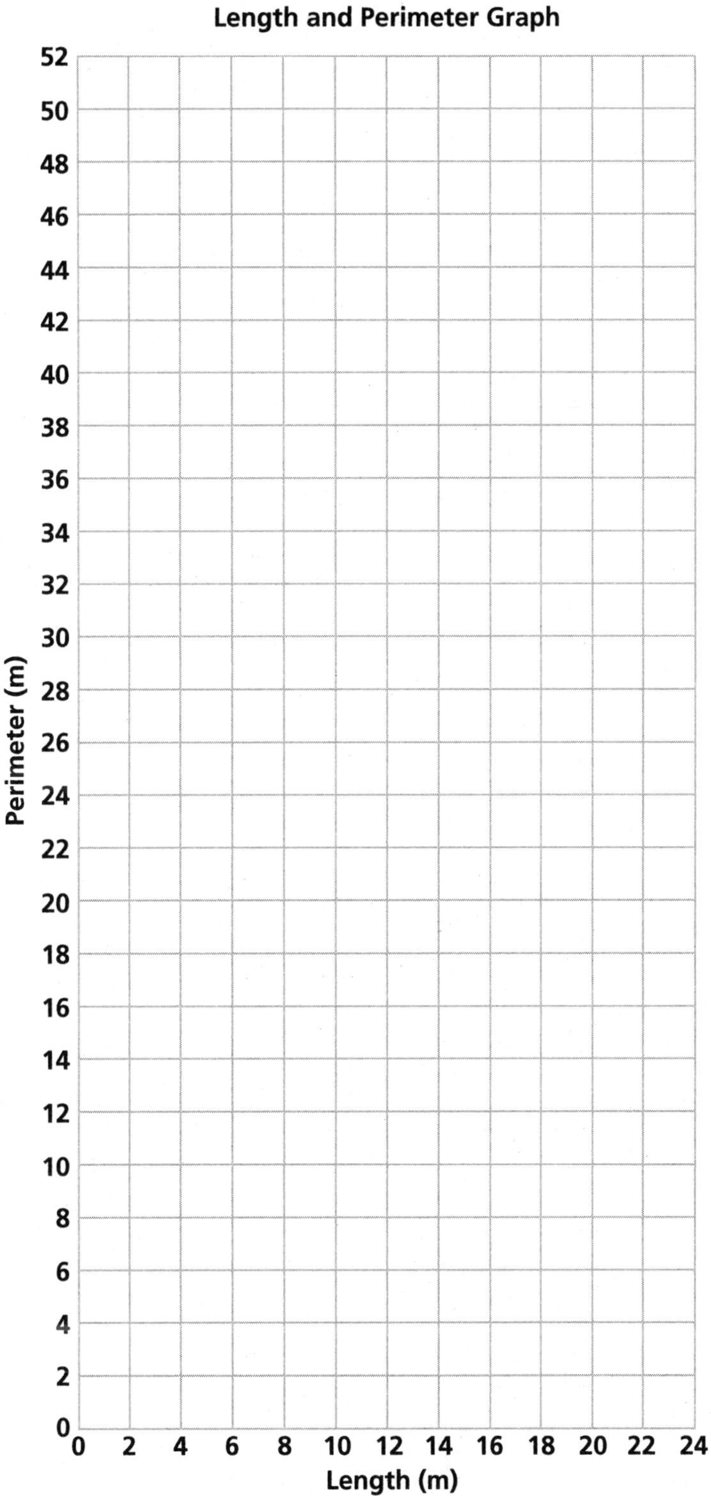

Length and Perimeter Graph

Perimeter (m): 0, 2, 4, 6, 8, 10, 12, 14, 16, 18, 20, 22, 24, 26, 28, 30, 32, 34, 36, 38, 40, 42, 44, 46, 48, 50, 52

Length (m): 0, 2, 4, 6, 8, 10, 12, 14, 16, 18, 20, 22, 24

Labsheet 2.3

Dog Pen Floor Plans

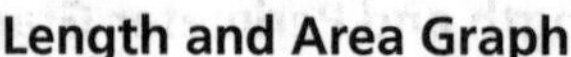

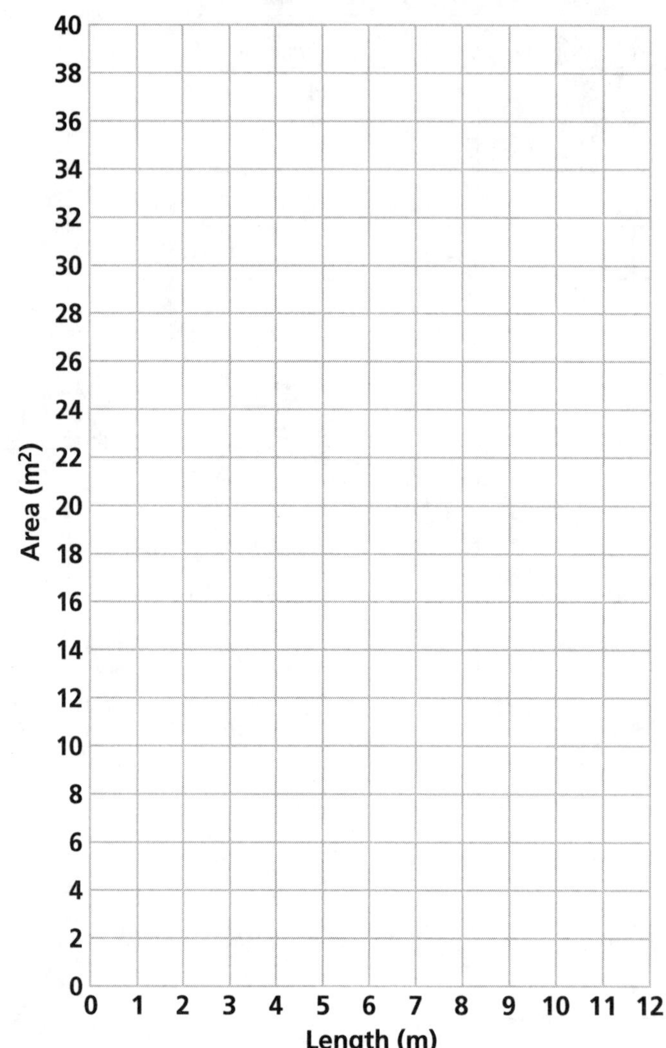

Name ______________________________ Date ____________ Class ____________

Labsheet 2ACE Exercises 3–5

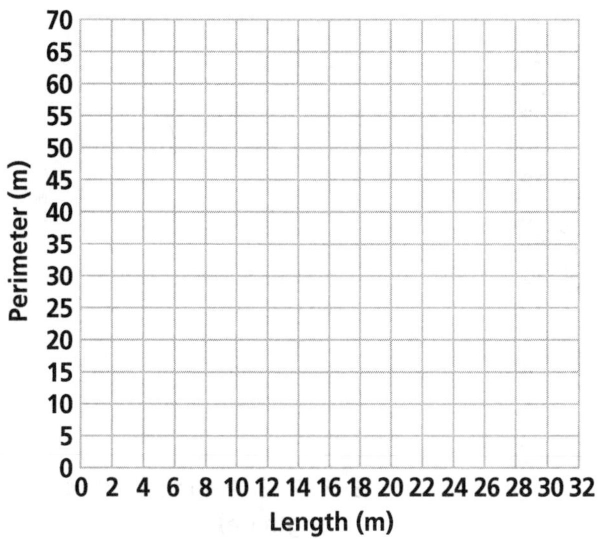

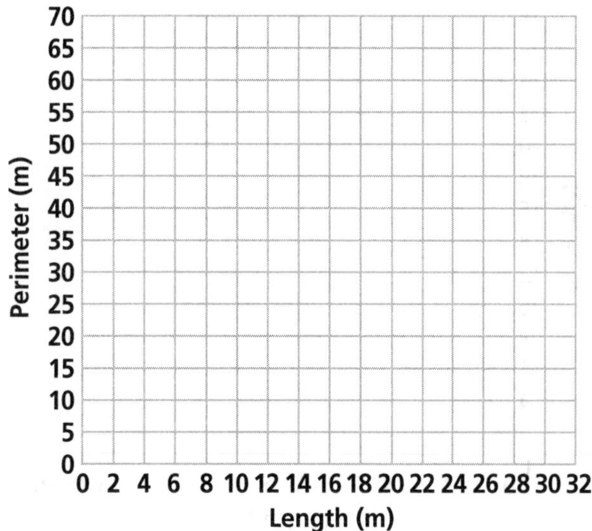

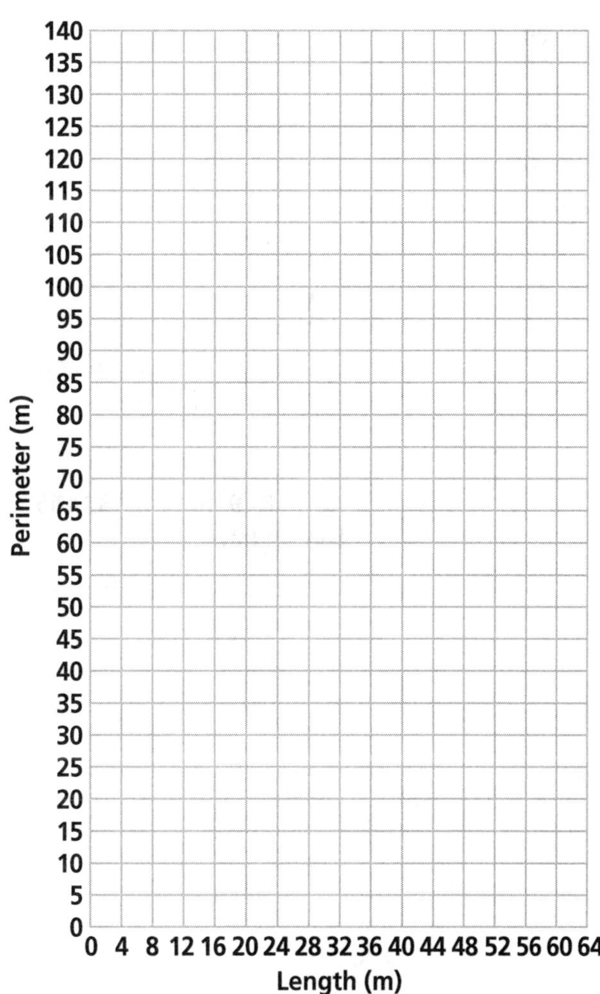

Name ______________________________ Date ____________ Class ____________

Labsheet 2ACE Exercises 10–12

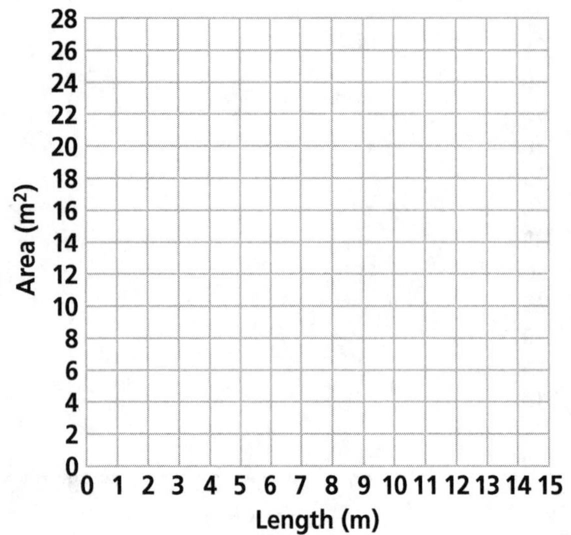

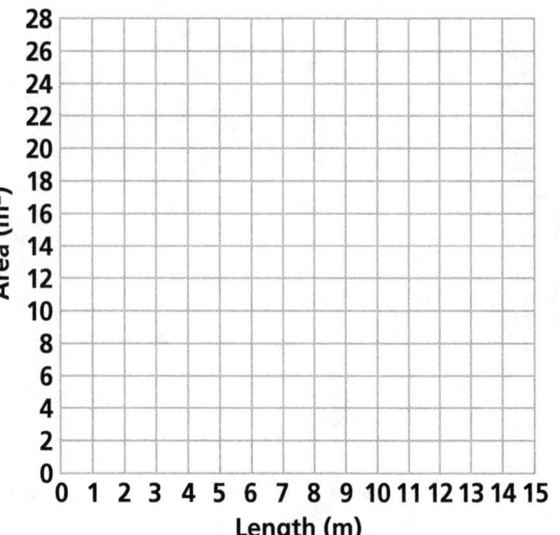

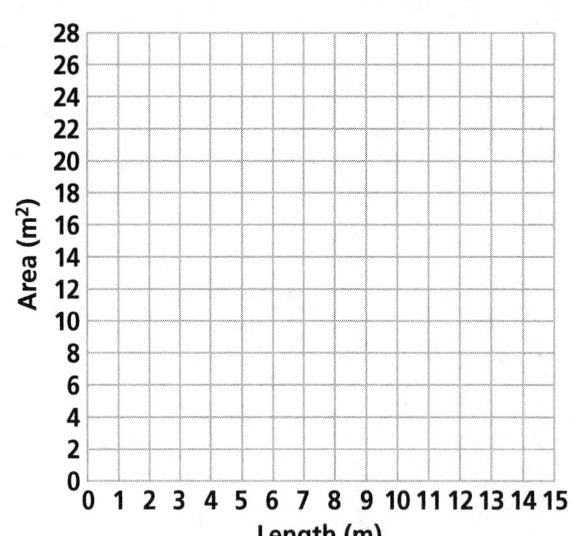

Name ______________________ Date ____________ Class ____________

Labsheet 2ACE Exercise 23

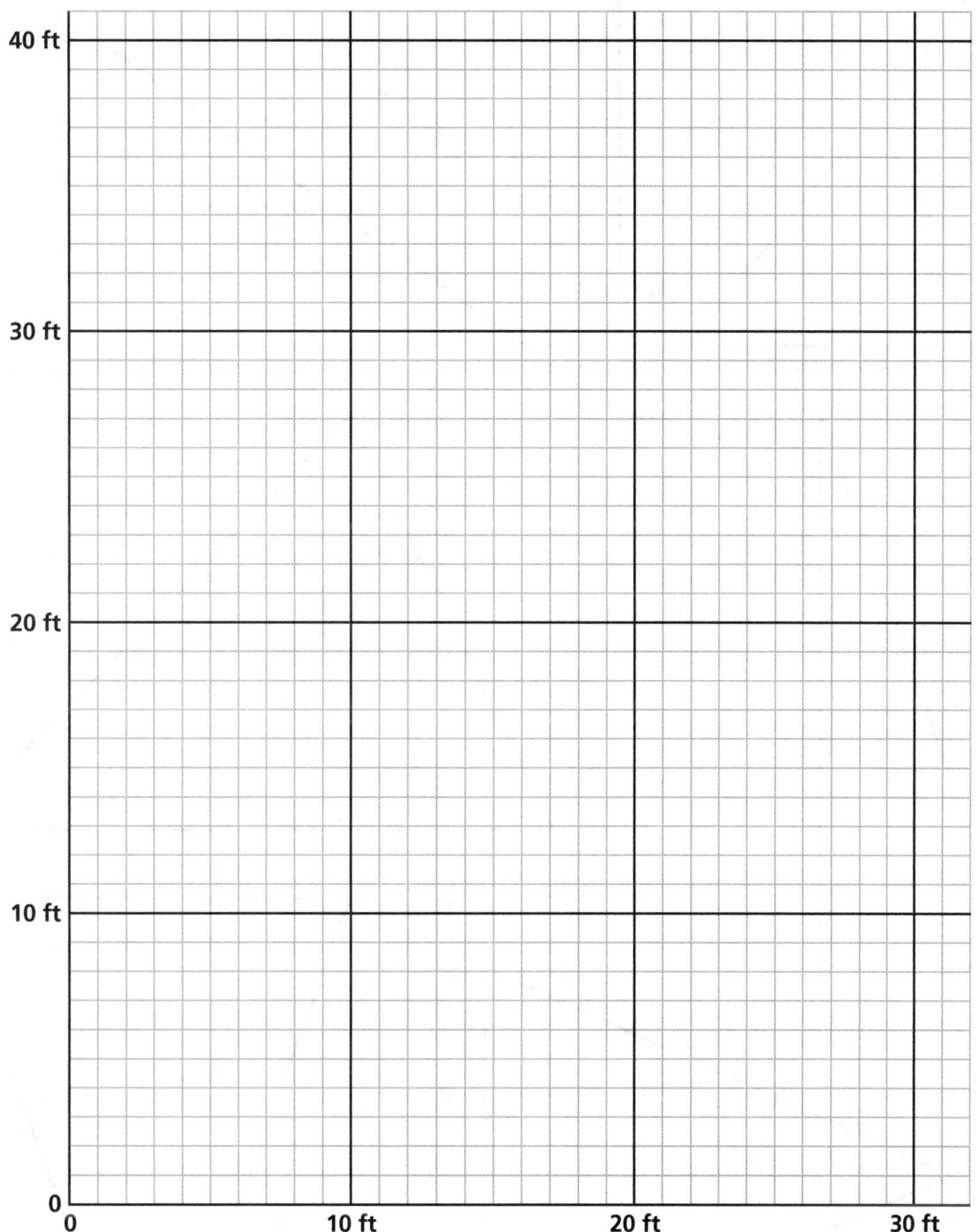

Name ______________________________ Date ____________ Class ____________

Labsheet 3.1 Triangles A–F

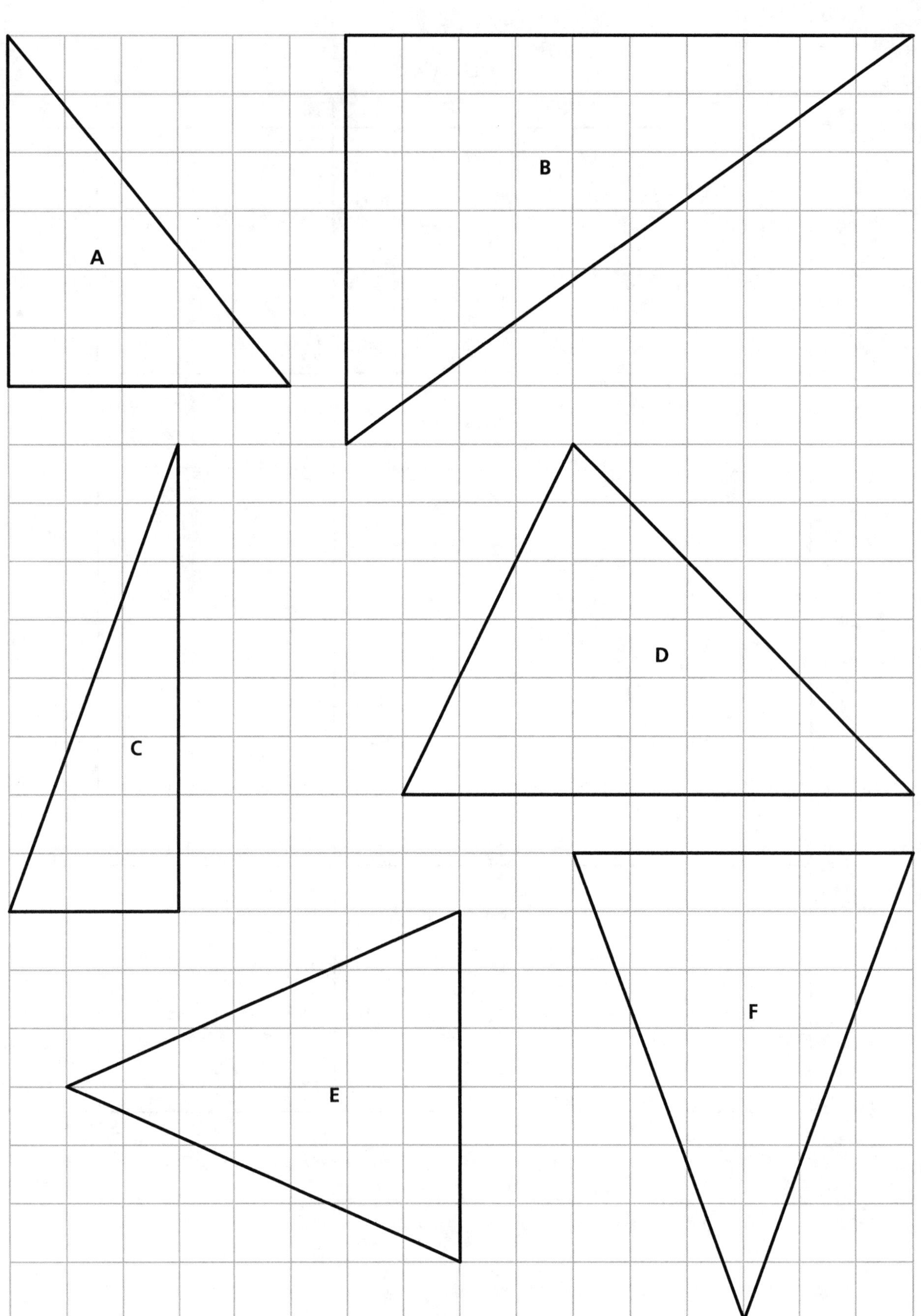

Name ______________________ Date ____________ Class ____________

Labsheet 3.2A

Two Triangles

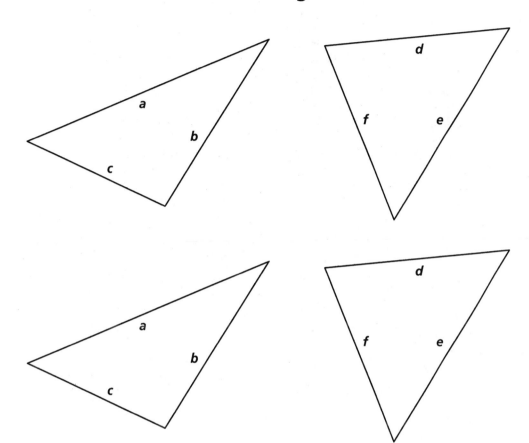

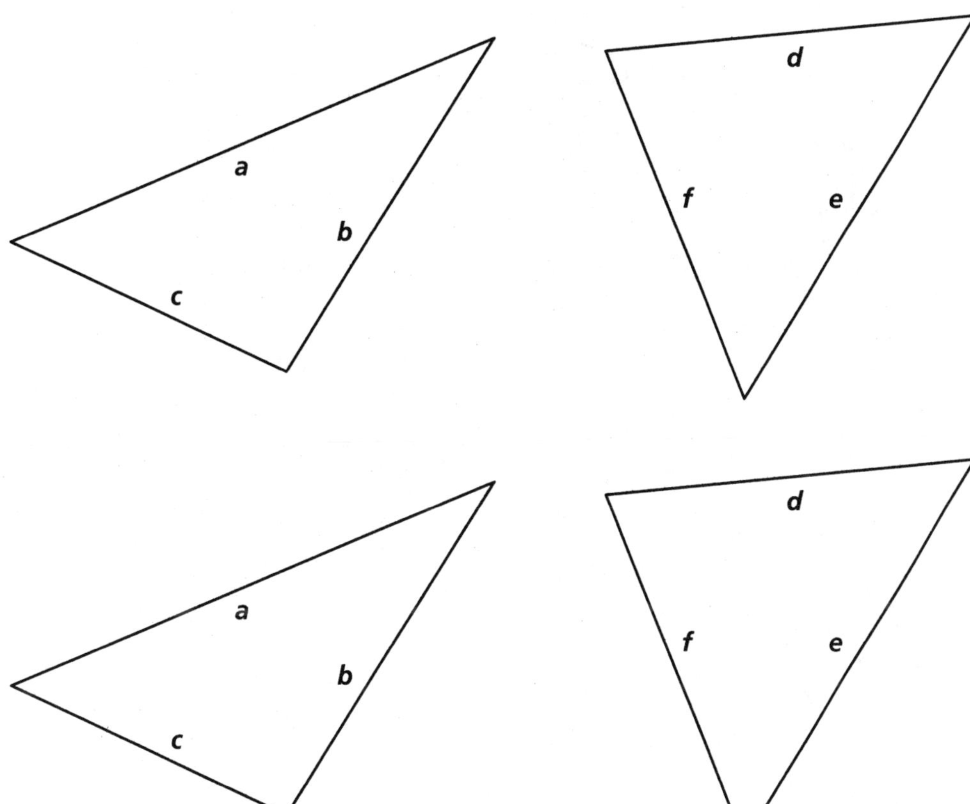

Name ______________________ Date ____________ Class ____________

Labsheet 3.2B

Two Shaded Triangles

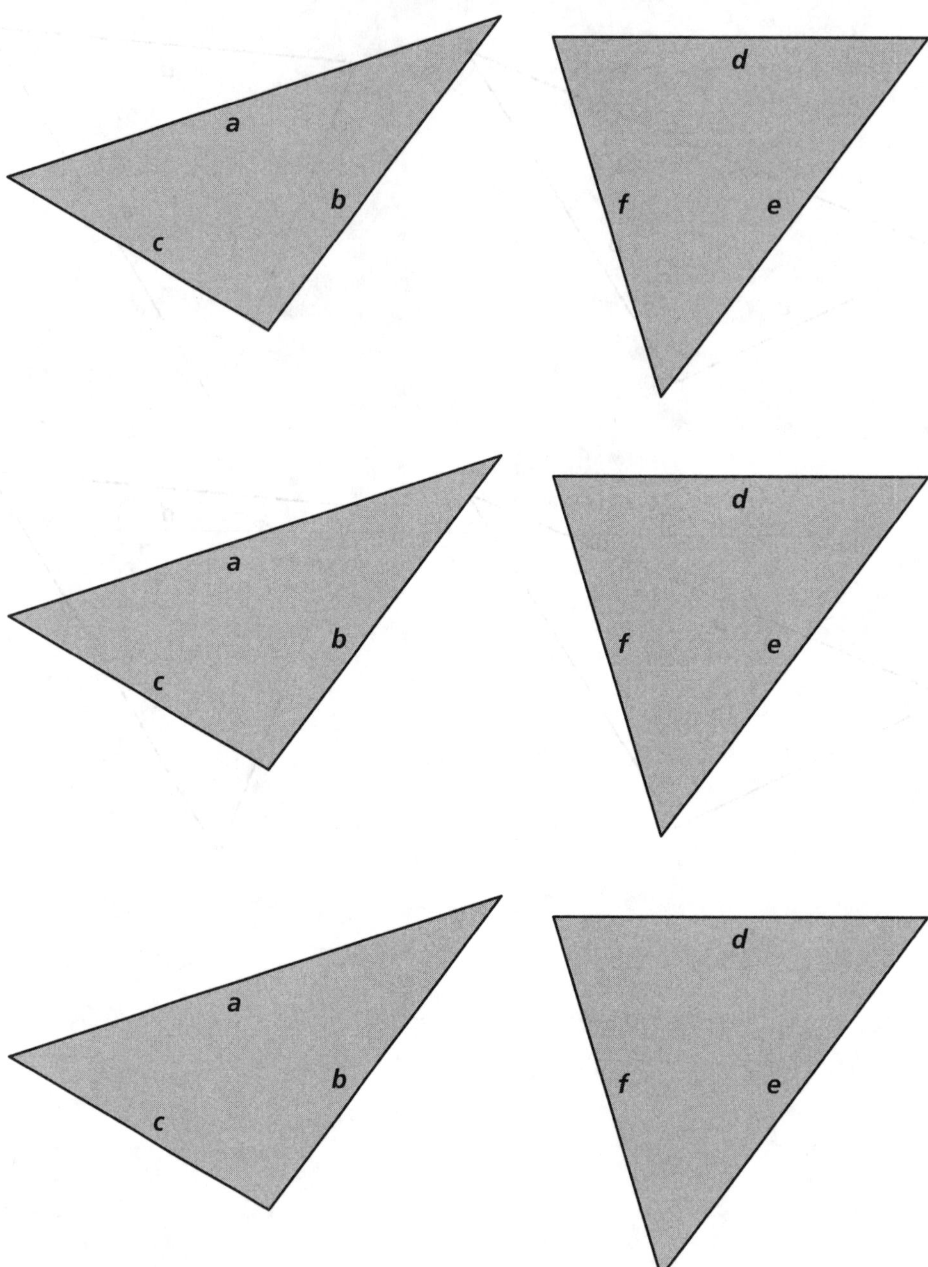

Name ______________________ Date ____________ Class ____________

Labsheet 3ACE Exercises 1–6

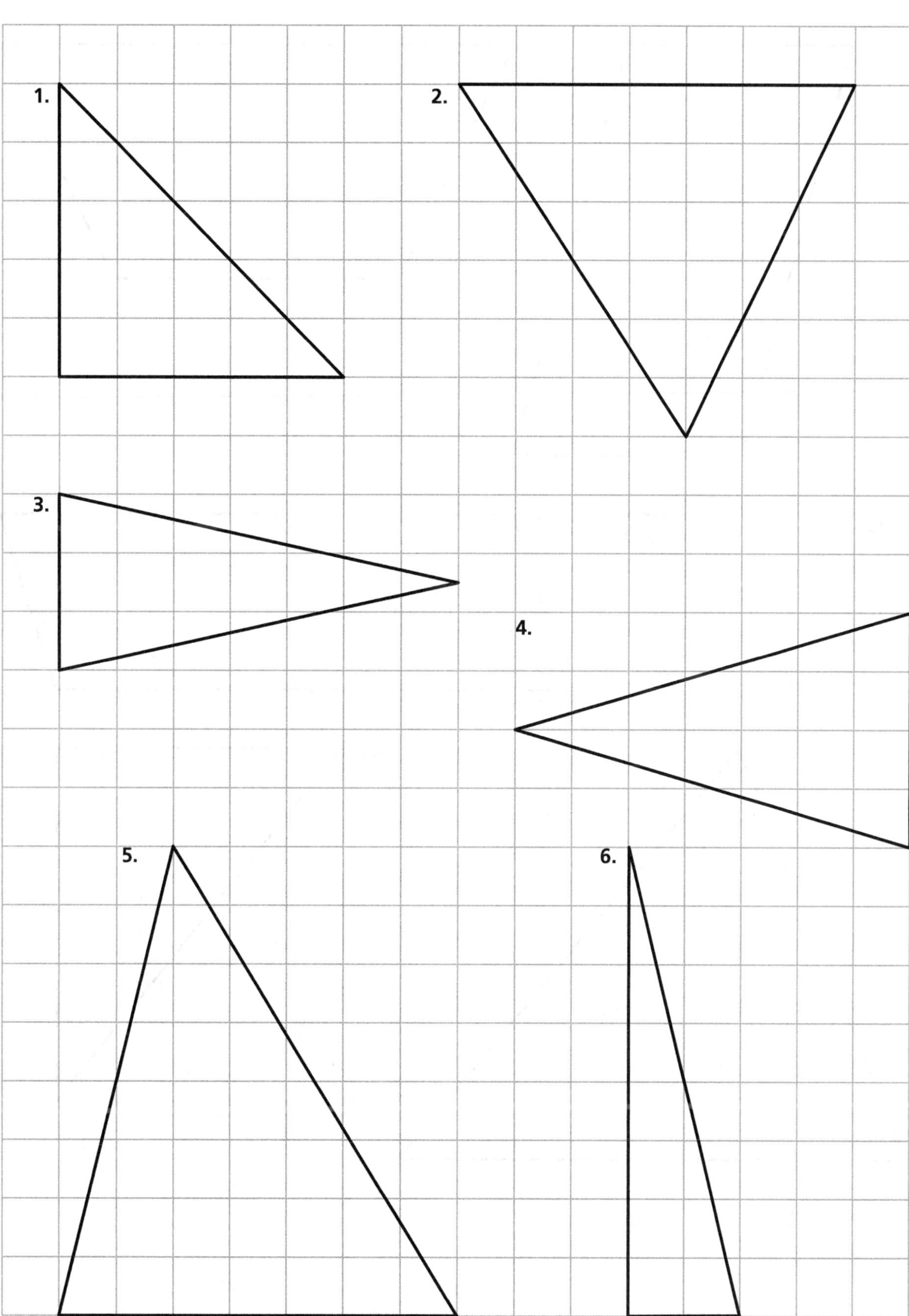

Name _______________ Date _______ Class _______

Labsheet 3ACE Exercises 26–31

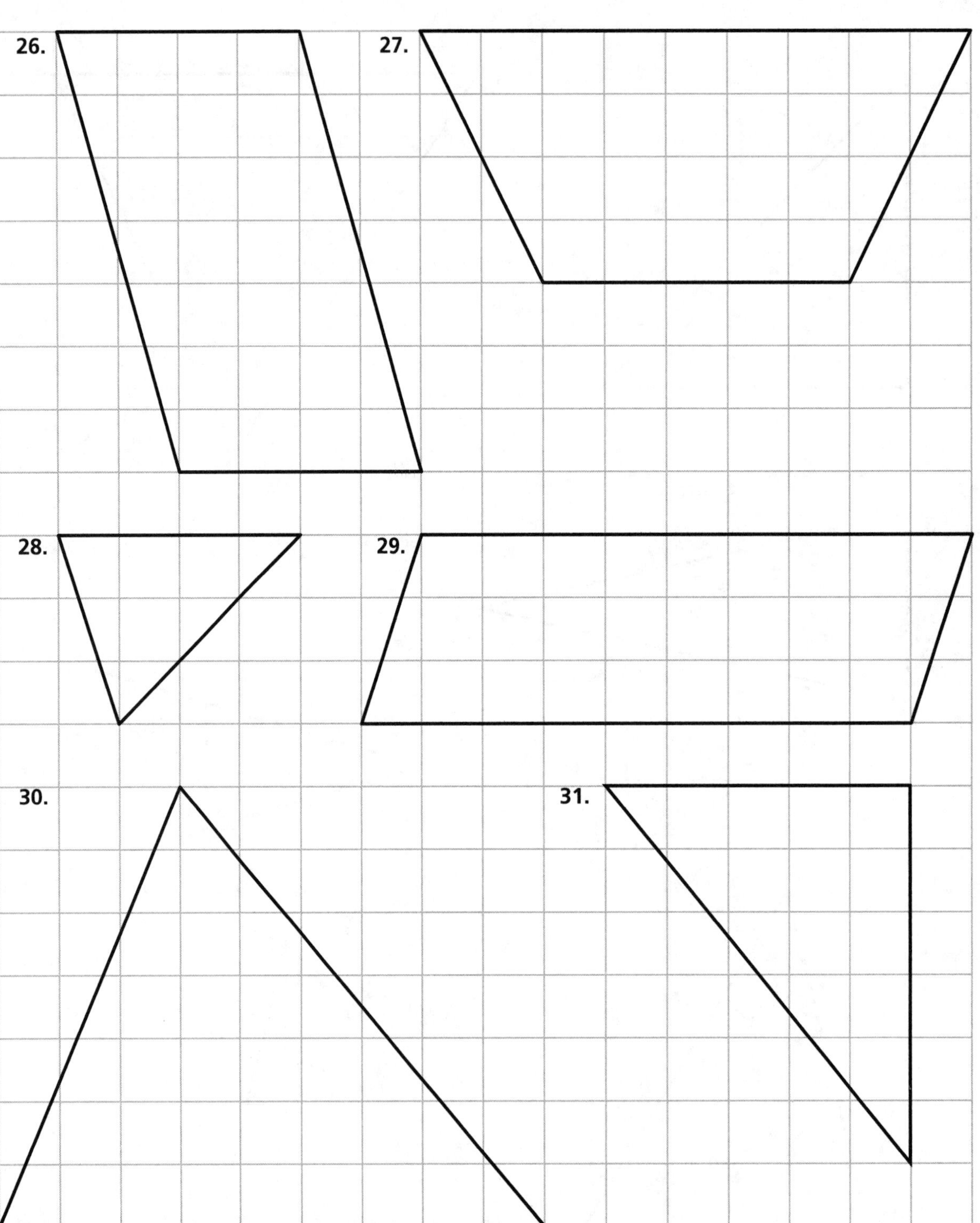

Name ______________________________ Date ____________ Class ____________

Labsheet 4.1

Parallelograms A–F

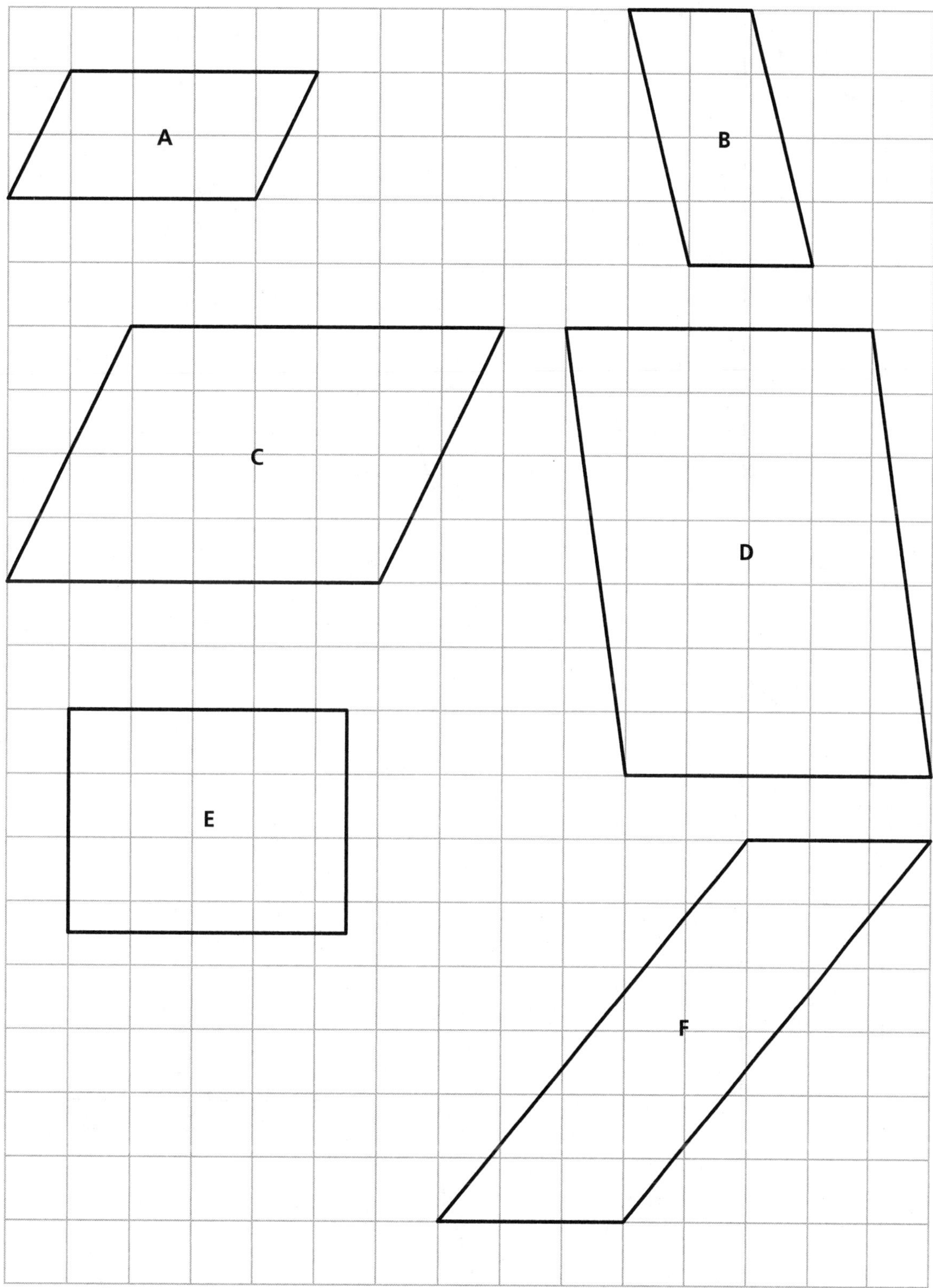

Name ______________________ Date ____________ Class ____________

Labsheet 4.2A

Two Parallelograms

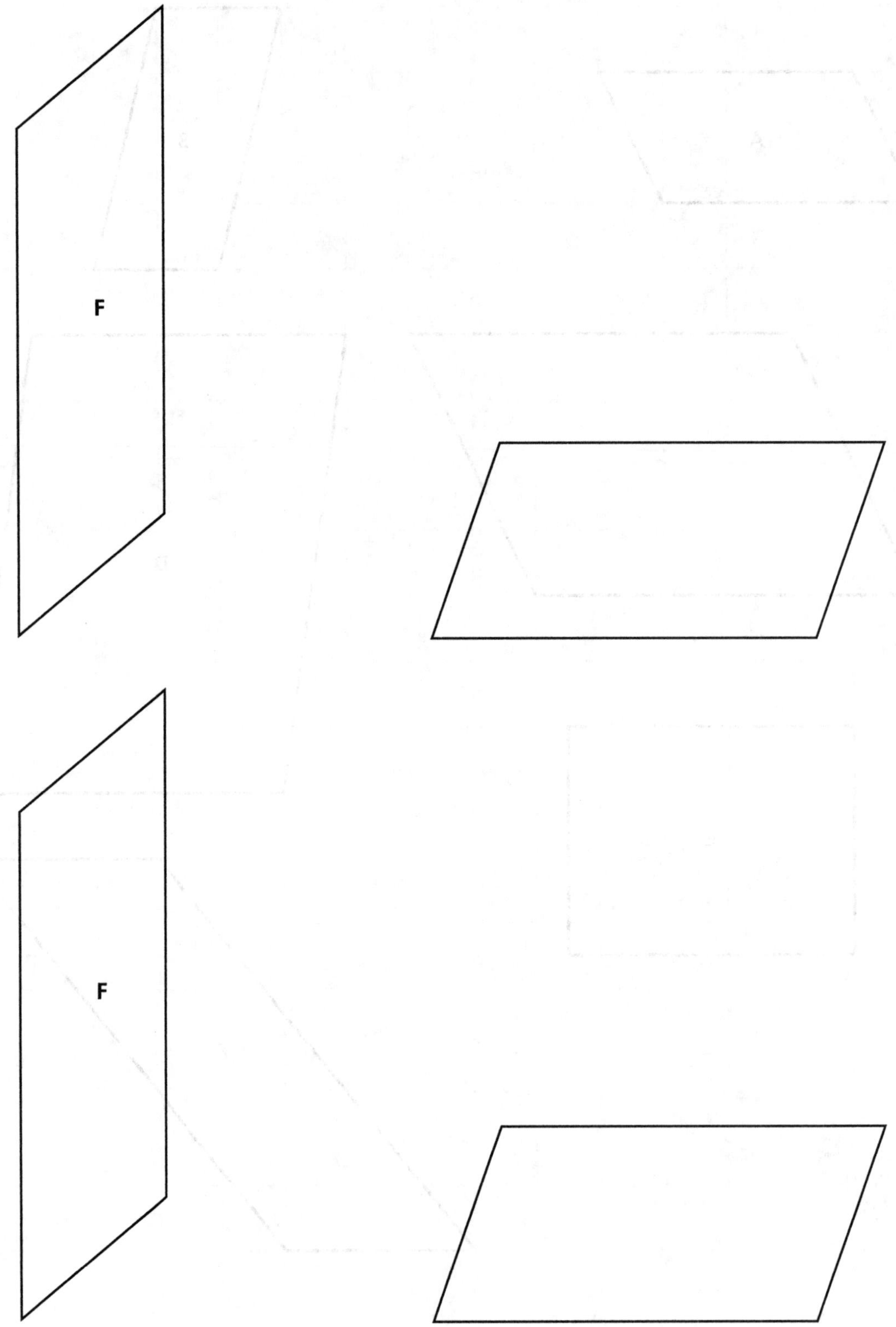

Name ______________________ Date ____________ Class ____________

Labsheet 4.2B

Two Shaded Parallelograms

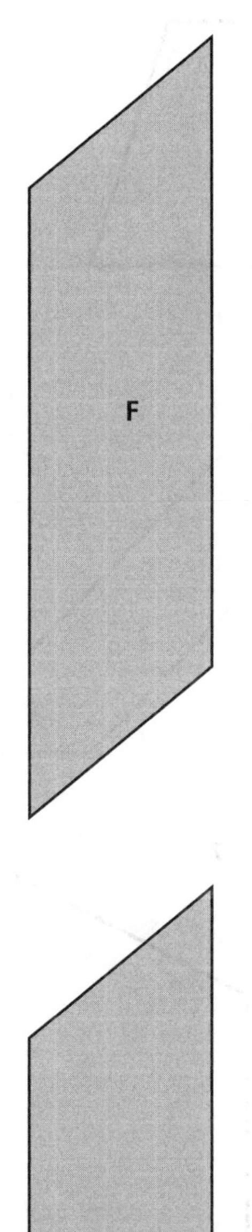

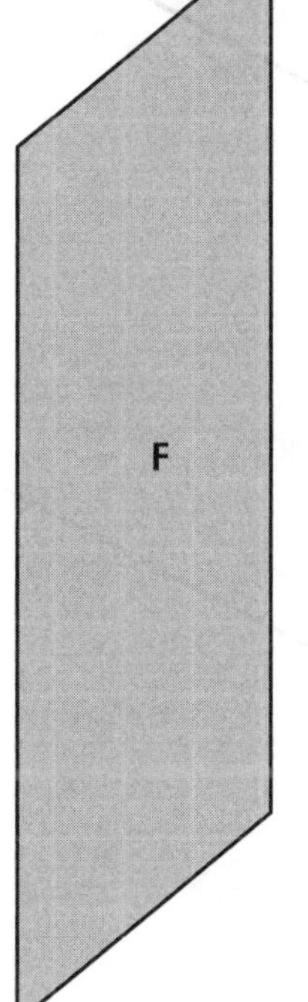

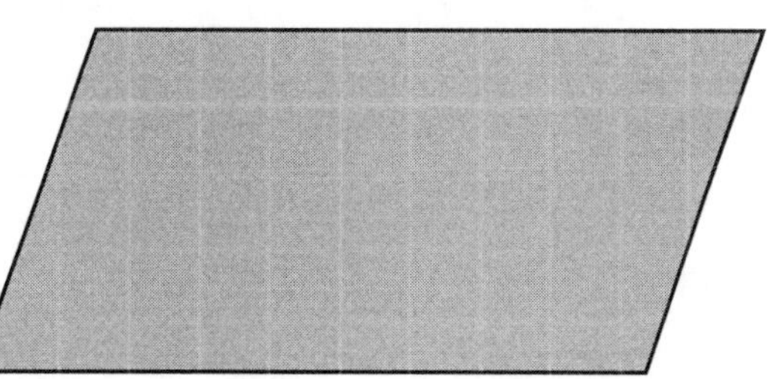

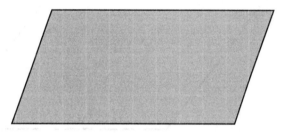

Name ______________________ Date __________ Class __________

Labsheet 4ACE Exercises 1–7

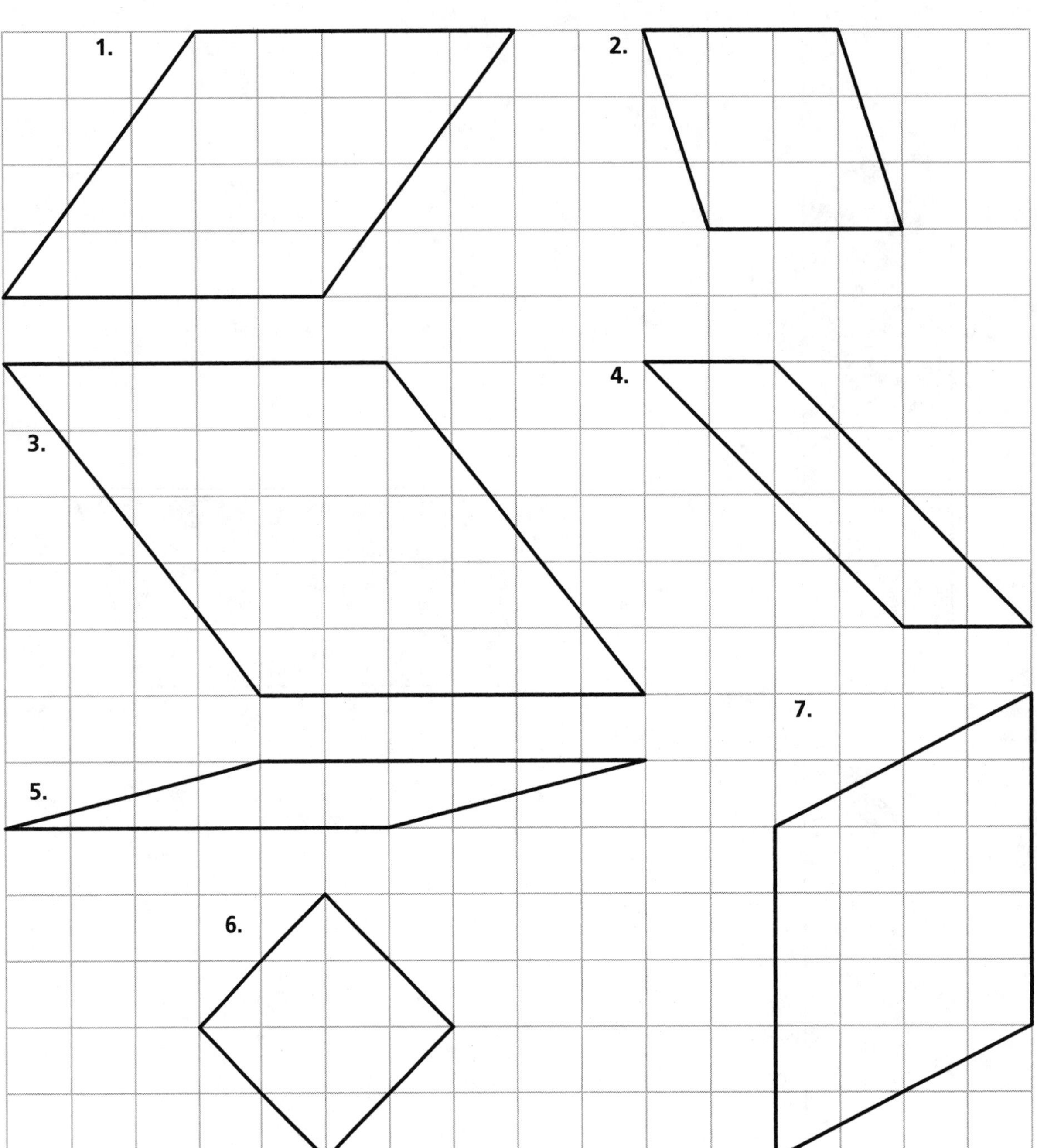

Name ______________________ Date ____________ Class ____________

Labsheet 4ACE Exercises 14–19

14.

15.

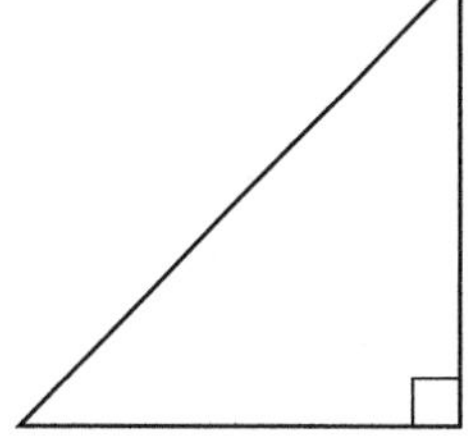

16.

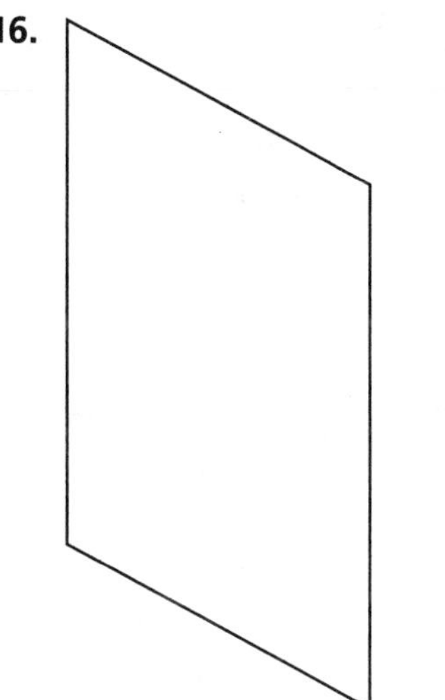

17.

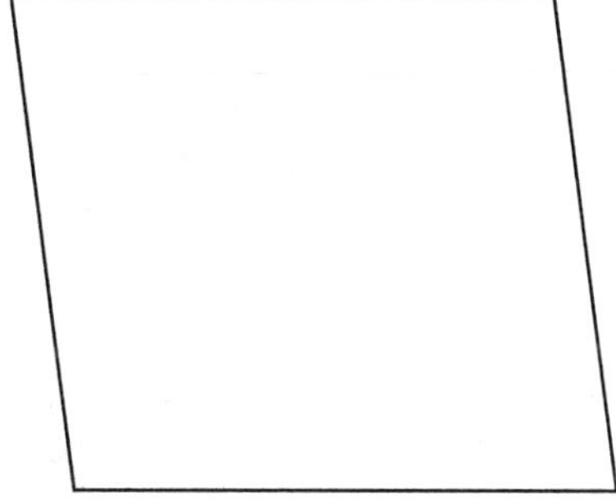

18.

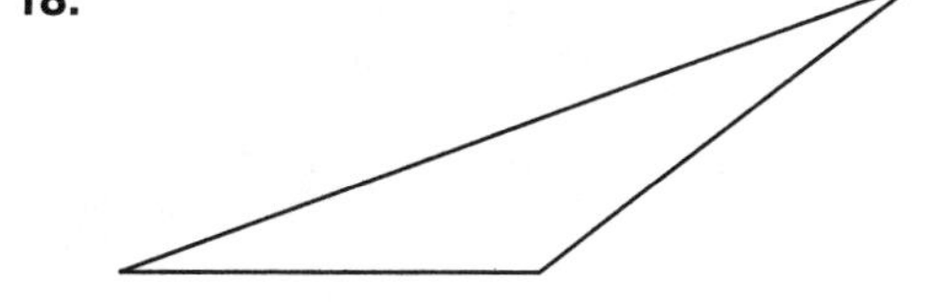

19.

Name ______________________ Date ____________ Class ____________

Labsheet 4ACE Exercises 39

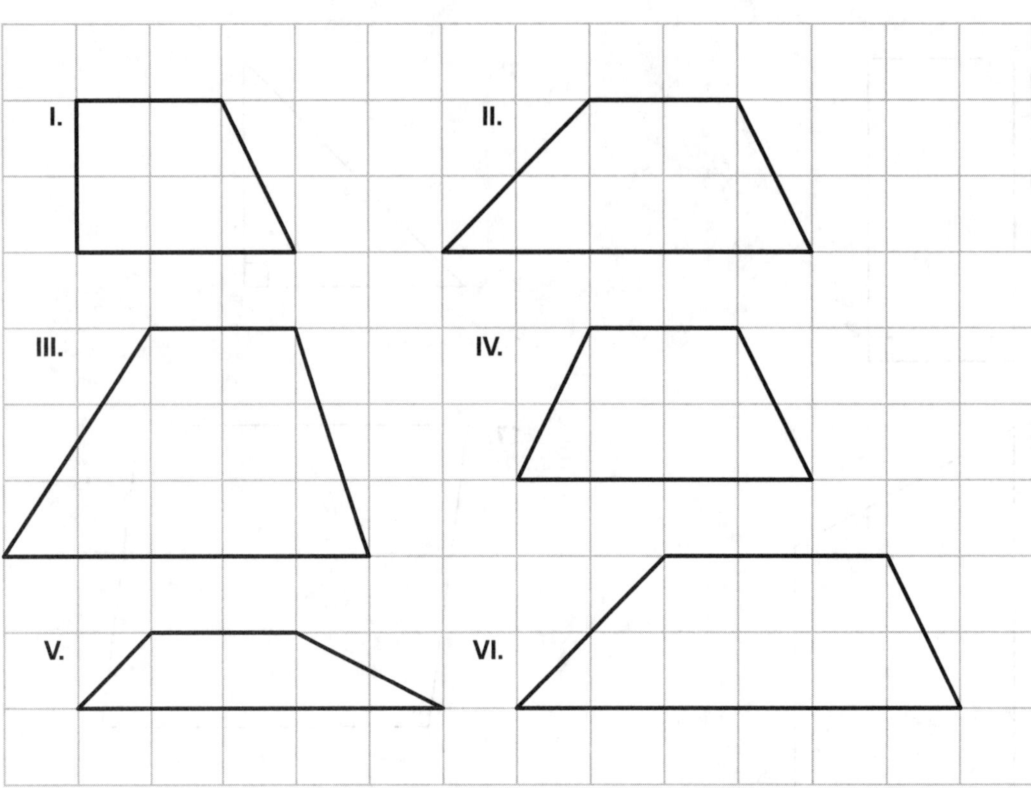

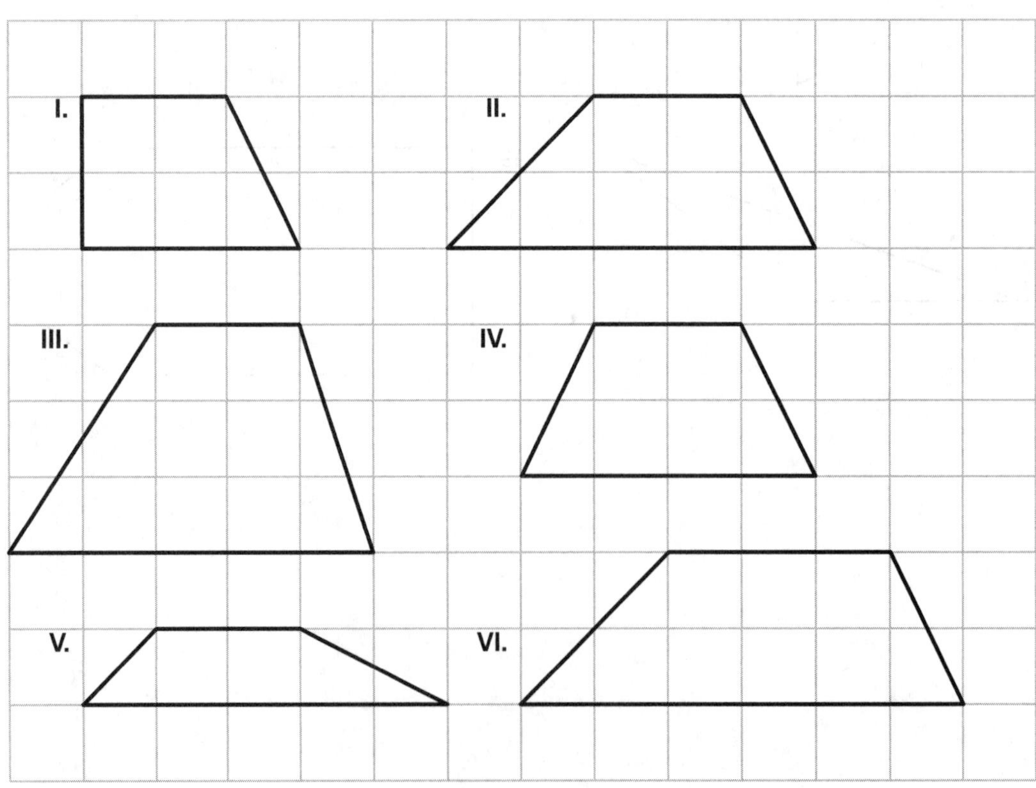

Name ______________________ Date ____________ Class ____________

Labsheet 5.1

Loon and Ghost Lakes

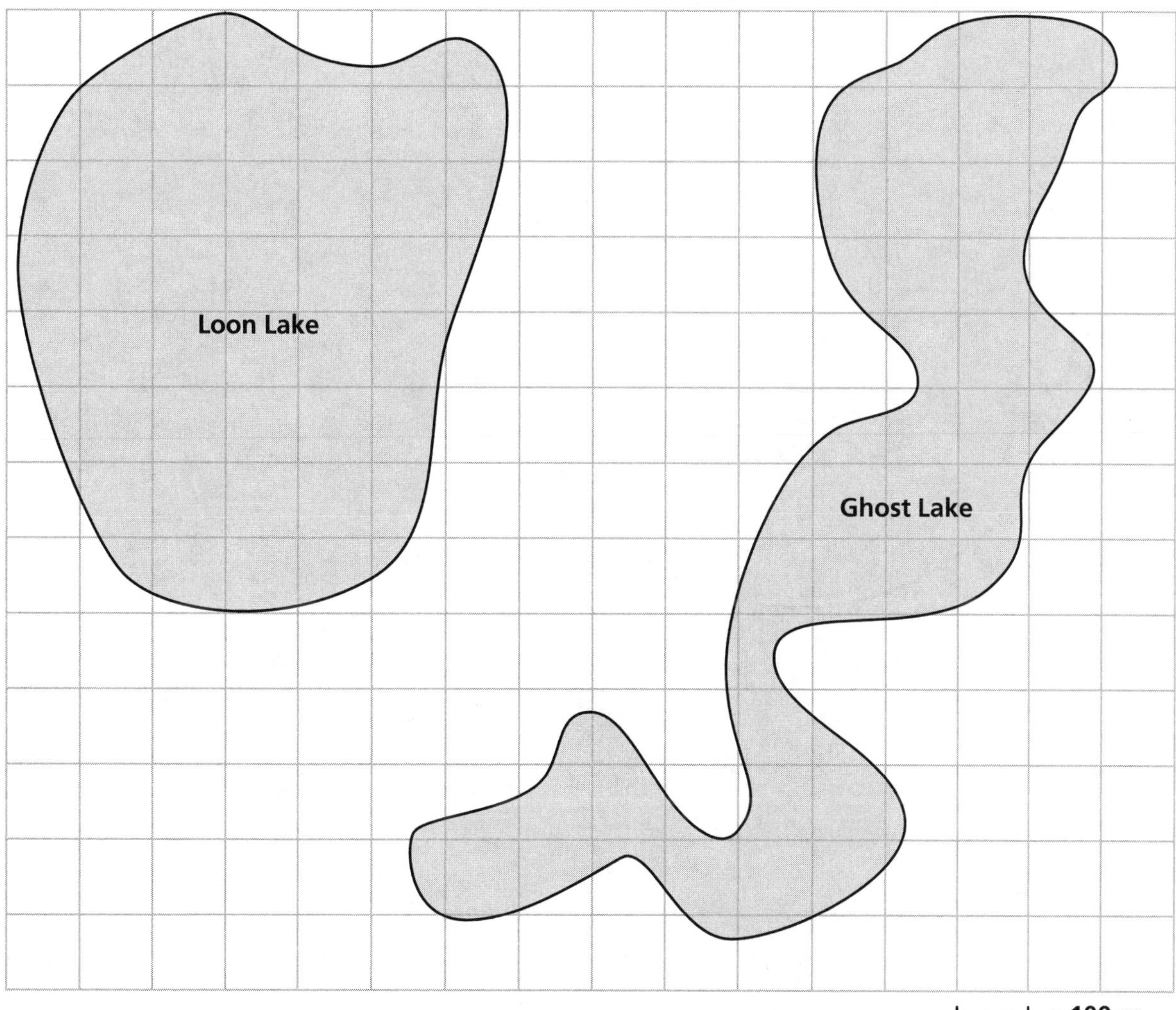

Name ______________________ Date ____________ Class ____________

Labsheet 5.3A

Small and Medium Pizzas

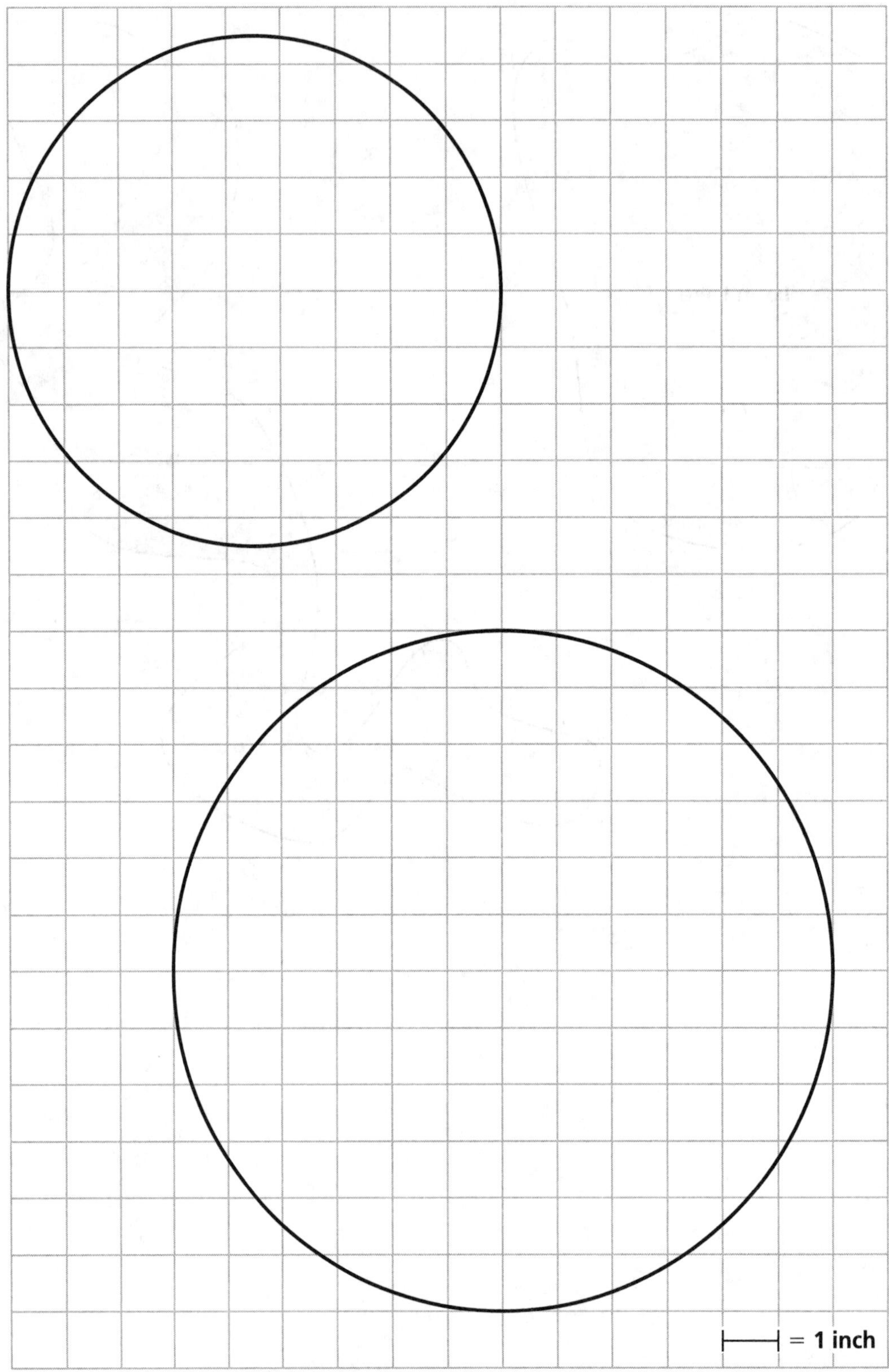

Name ________________________ Date ____________ Class ____________

Labsheet 5.3B

Large Pizza

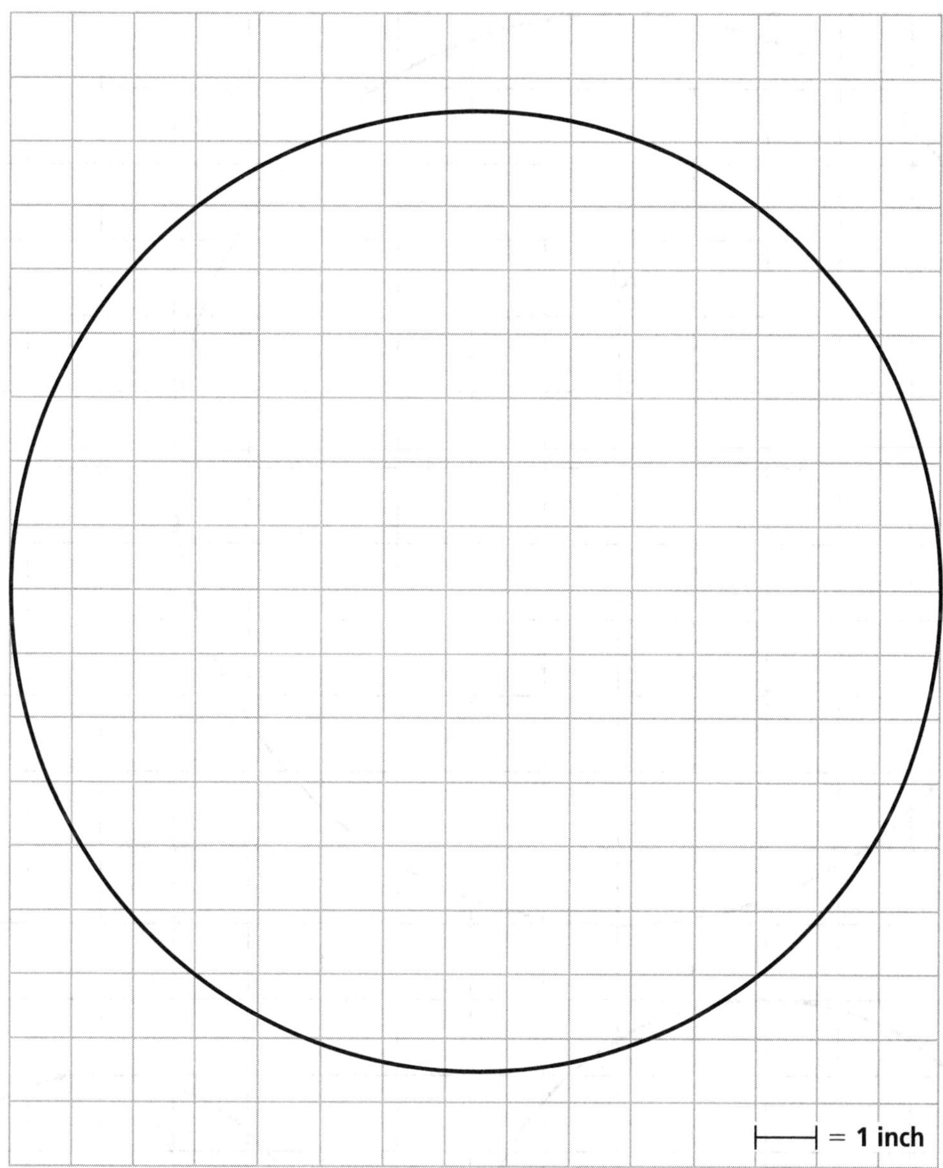

Name ____________________ Date __________ Class __________

Labsheet 5.4

Radius Squares

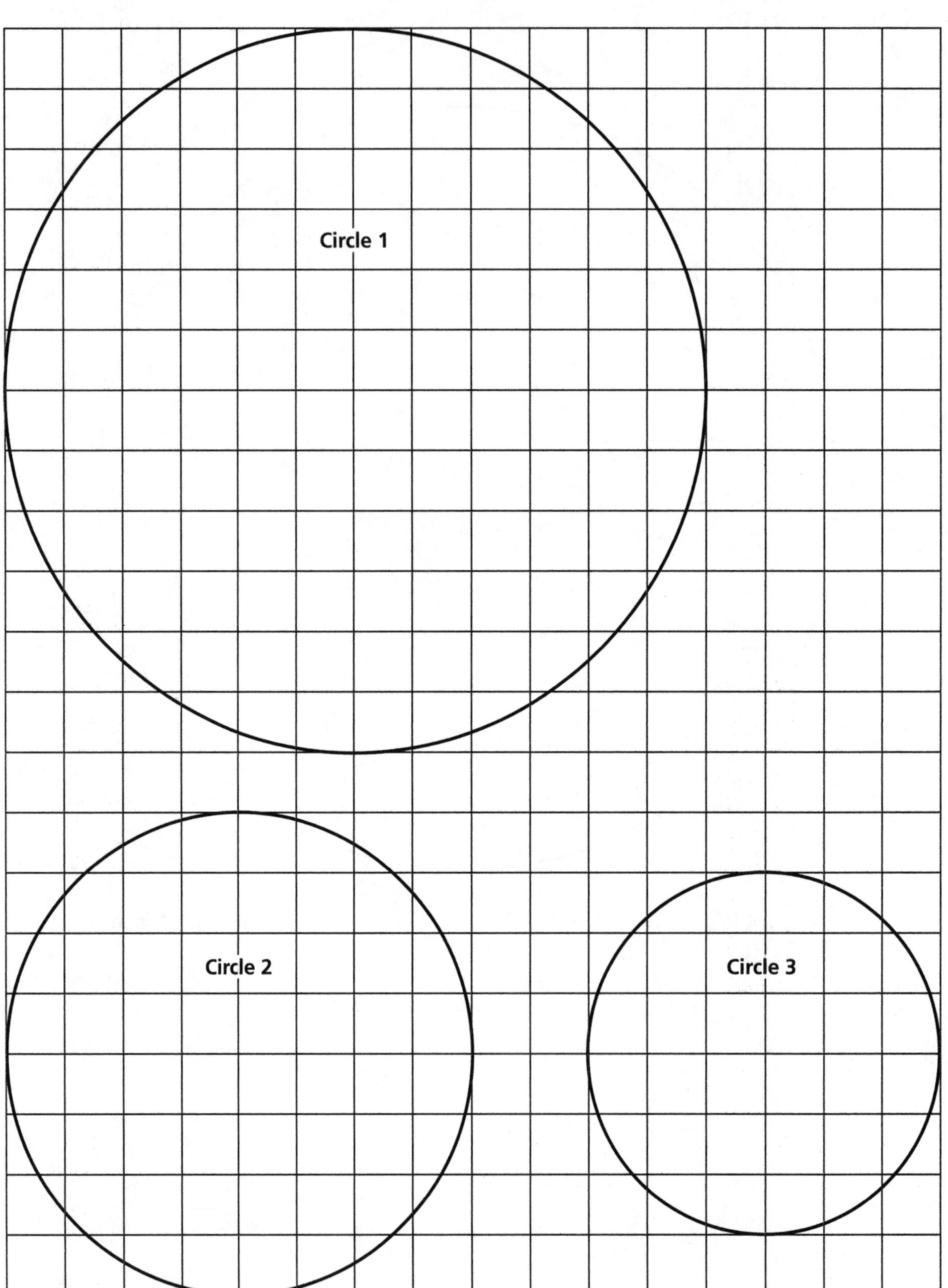

Name ______________________ Date __________ Class __________

Labsheet 5ACE Exercises 1 and 2

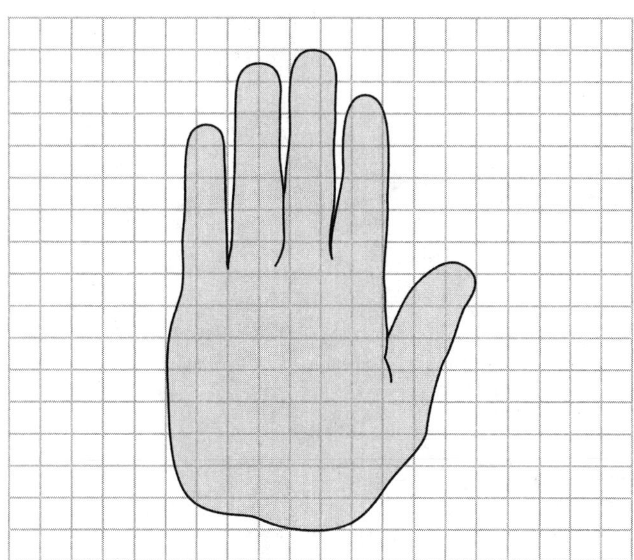

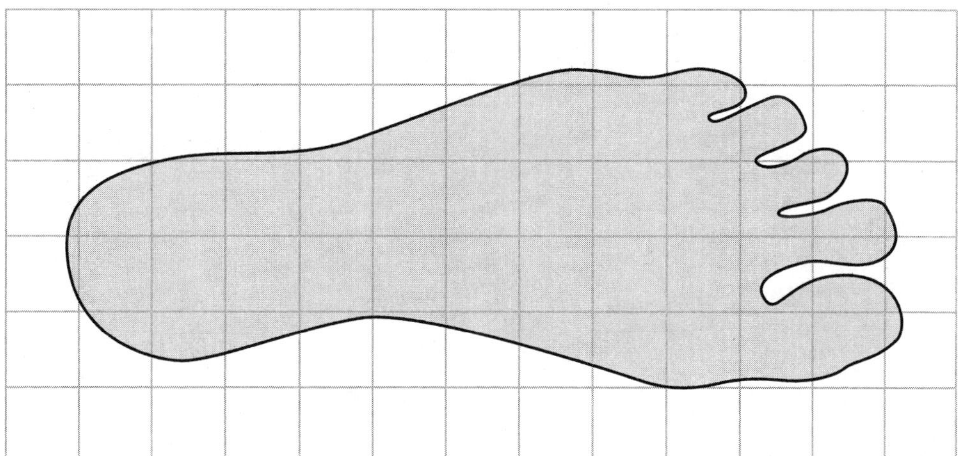

Name ______________________________ Date ____________ Class ____________

Labsheet 5ACE Exercises 3 and 4

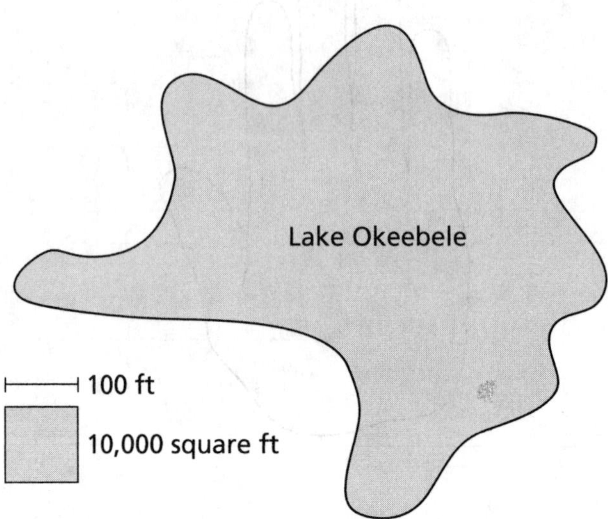

Name ______________________ Date ____________ Class ____________

Half-Centimeter Grid Paper

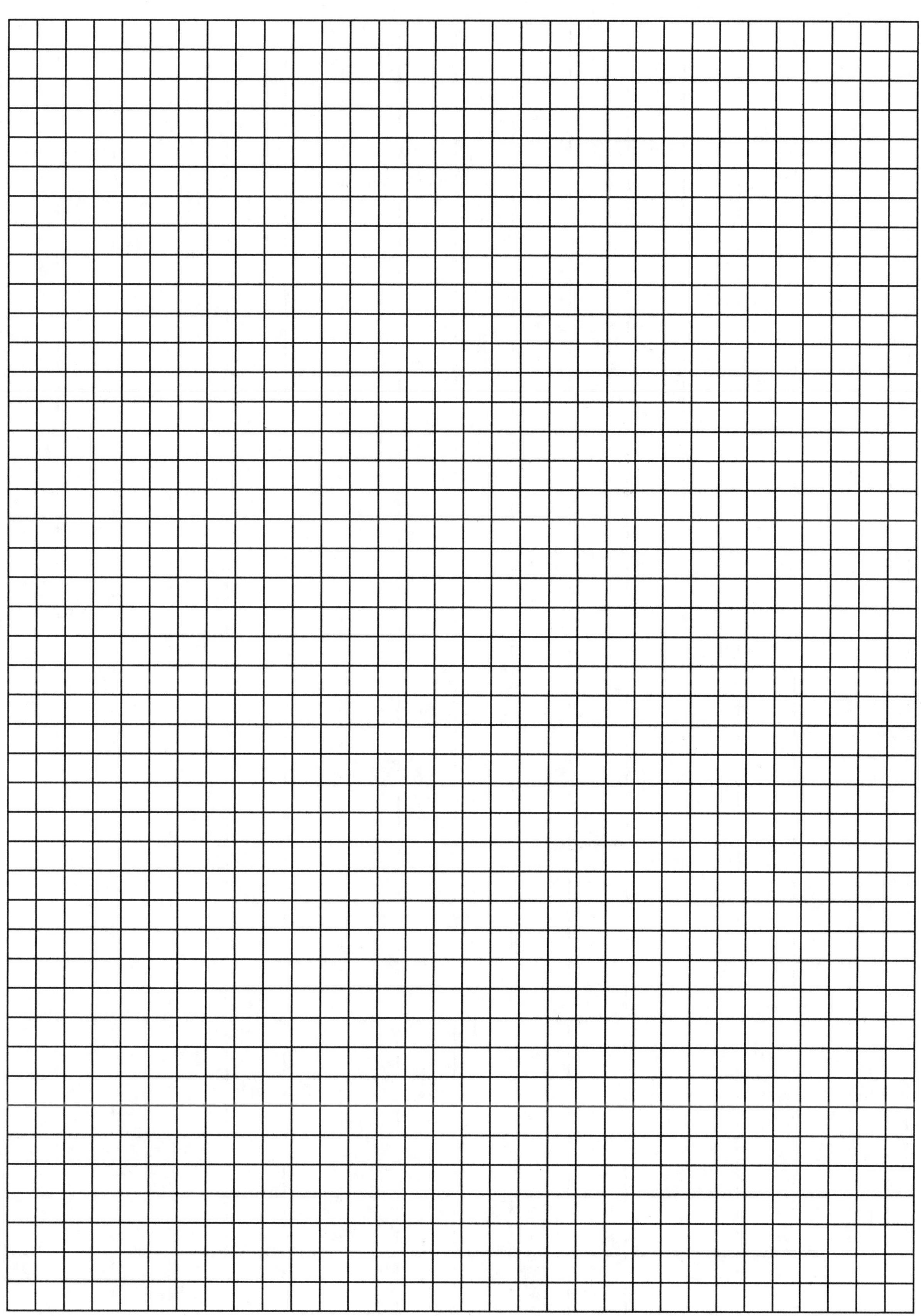

Name ______________________ Date ____________ Class ____________

Centimeter Grid Paper

Covering and Surrounding

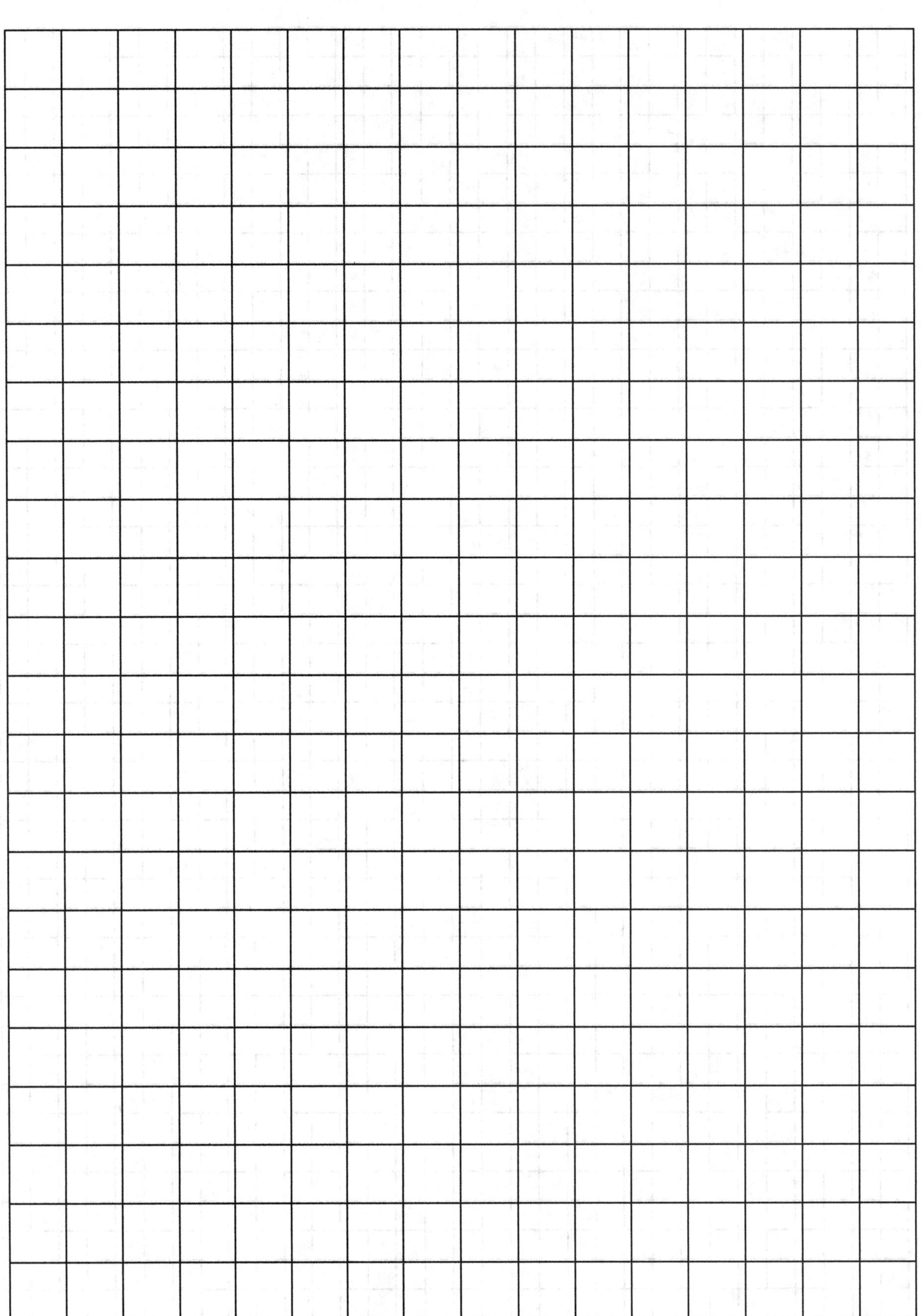

Name ____________________ Date ____________ Class ____________

Quarter-Inch Grid Paper

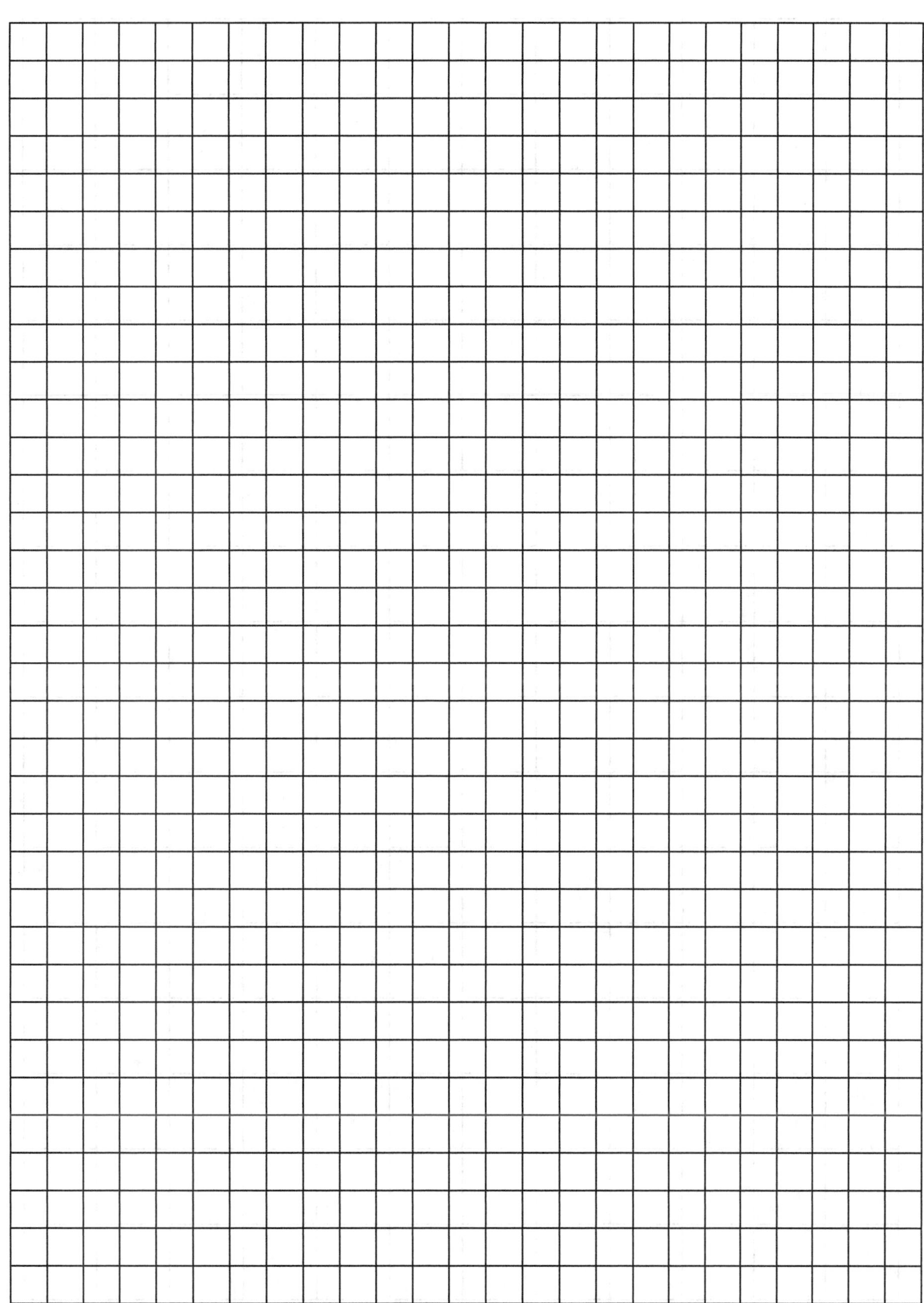

Name ______________________ Date ____________ Class ____________

Half-Inch Grid Paper

Name ______________________ Date ____________ Class ____________

Inch Grid Paper

At a Glance

PACING: ________

Mathematical Goals

Launch

Materials

Explore

Materials

Summarize

Materials

Glossary

A

area The measure of the amount of surface enclosed by the boundary of a figure. To find the area of a figure, you can count how many unit squares it takes to cover the figure. You can find the area of a rectangle by multiplying the length by the width. This is a shortcut method for finding the number of unit squares it takes to cover the rectangle. If a figure has curved or irregular sides, you can estimate the area. Cover the surface with a grid and count whole grid squares and parts of grid squares. When you find the area of a shape, write the units, such as square centimeters (cm^2) to indicate the unit square that was used to find the area.

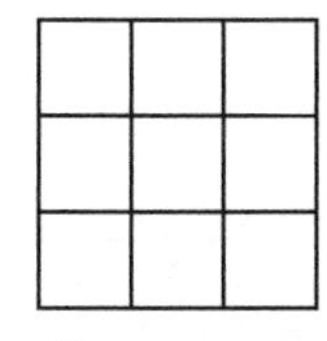

A = 9 square units

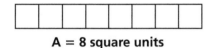

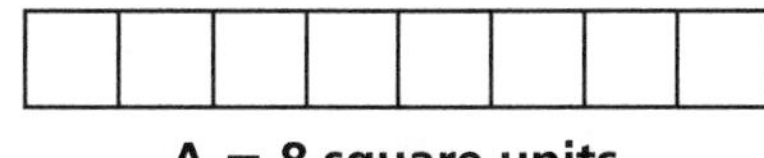

A = 8 square units

B

base See *linear dimensions*.

circle A two-dimensional object in which every point is the same distance from a point called the *center*. Point C is the center of this circle.

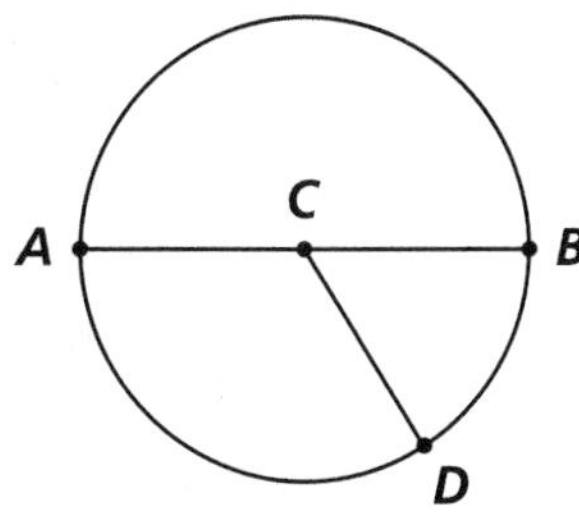

circumference The distance around (or perimeter of) a circle. It takes slightly more than three diameters to match the circumference of a circle. More formally, the circumference of a circle is pi (π) times the diameter of the circle.

D

diameter A segment that goes from one point on a circle through the center of the circle to another point on the circle. Also, diameter is used to indicate the length of this segment. In the definition of circle above, segment AB is a diameter.

height See *linear dimensions*.

length See *linear dimensions*.

linear dimensions Linear measurements, such as length, width, base, and height, which describe the size of figures. The longest dimension or the dimension along the bottom of a rectangle is usually called the *length*, and the other dimension is called the *width*, but it is not incorrect to reverse these labels. The word *base* is used when talking about triangles and parallelograms. The *base* is usually measured along a horizontal side, but it is sometimes convenient to think of one of the other sides as the base. For a triangle, the *height* is the perpendicular distance from a vertex opposite the base to the line containing the base. For a parallelogram, the height is the perpendicular distance from a point on the side opposite the base to the base. You need to be flexible when you encounter these terms, so you are able to determine their meanings from the context of the situation.

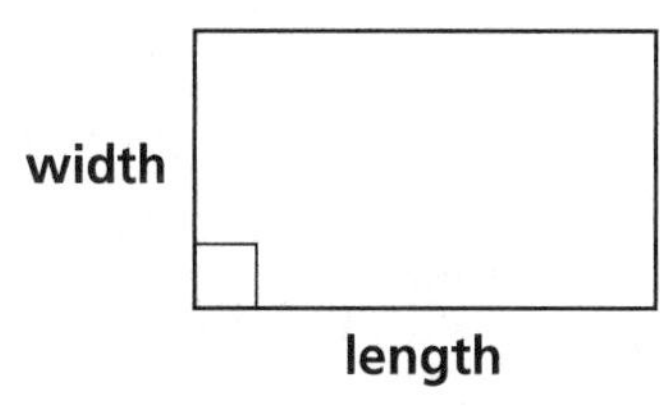

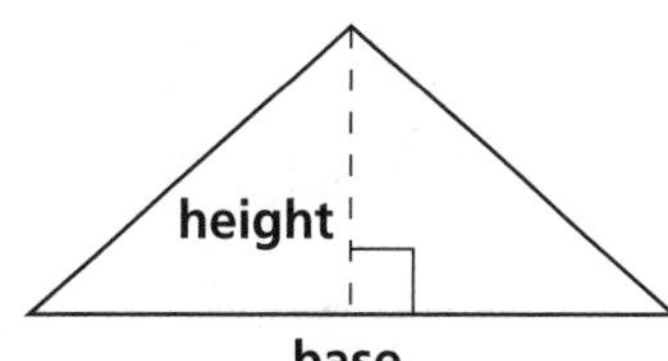

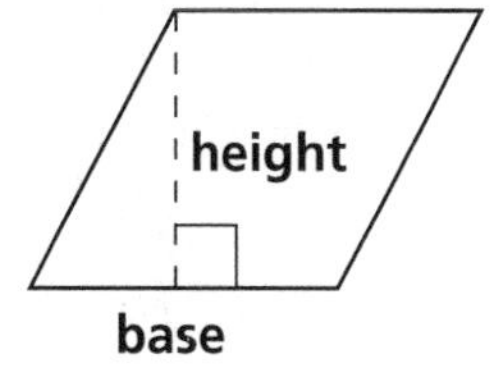

P

perimeter The measure of the distance around a figure. Perimeter is a measure of length. To find the perimeter of a figure, you count the number of unit lengths it takes to surround the figure. When you find the perimeter of a shape, write the units (such as centimeters, feet, or yards) to indicate the unit that was used to find the perimeter. The perimeter of the square below is 12 units, because 12 units of length surround the figure. The perimeter of the rectangle is 18 units. Notice that the rectangle has a larger perimeter, but a smaller area, than the square.

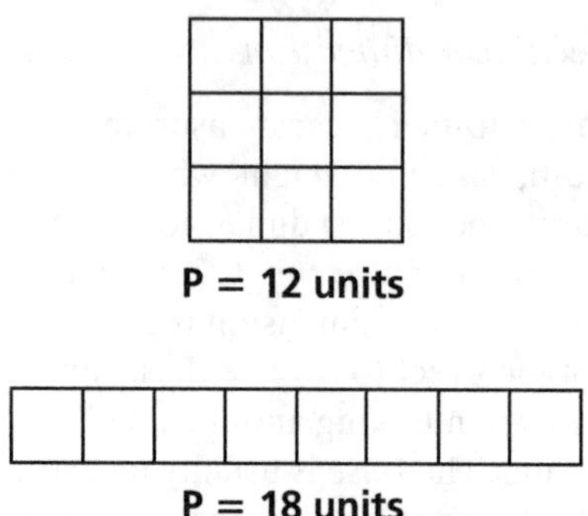

perpendicular lines Lines that meet at right angles. The length and width of a rectangle are perpendicular to each other and the base and height of a triangle are perpendicular to each other. In diagrams, perpendicular lines are often indicated by drawing a small square where the lines meet.

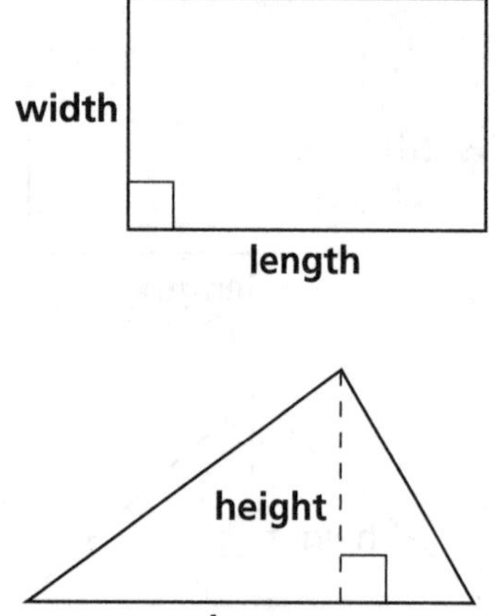

pi (π) The mathematical name for the ratio of a circle's circumference to its diameter. This ratio is the same for every circle, and is approximately equal to 3.1416.

R

radius A segment from the center of a circle to a point on the circle. The length of this segment is also called the radius. The radius is half of the diameter. *CD* is one radius of the circle below. The plural of radius is *radii*. All the radii of a circle have the same length.

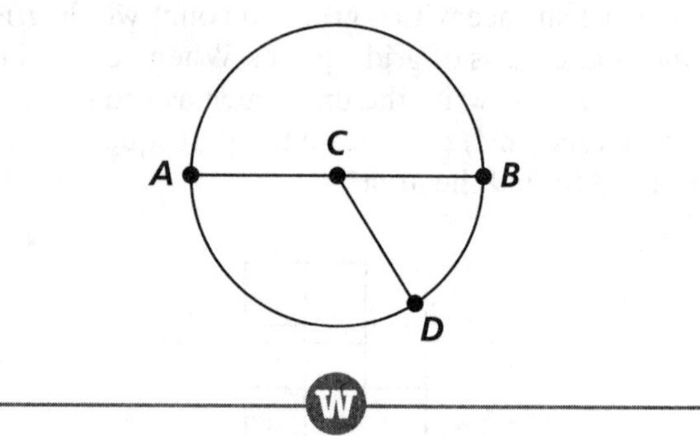

W

width See *linear dimensions*.

Index

Acknowledgments

Team Credits

The people who made up the **Connected Mathematics2** team—representing editorial, editorial services, design services, and production services—are listed below. Bold type denotes core team members.

Leora Adler, Judith Buice, Kerry Cashman, Patrick Culleton, Sheila DeFazio, Richard Heater, **Barbara Hollingdale, Jayne Holman,** Karen Holtzman, **Etta Jacobs,** Christine Lee, Carolyn Lock, Catherine Maglio, **Dotti Marshall,** Rich McMahon, Eve Melnechuk, Kristin Mingrone, Terri Mitchell, **Marsha Novak,** Irene Rubin, Donna Russo, Robin Samper, Siri Schwartzman, **Nancy Smith,** Emily Soltanoff, **Mark Tricca,** Paula Vergith, Roberta Warshaw, Helen Young

Additional Credits

Diana Bonfilio, Mairead Reddin, Michael Torocsik, nSight, Inc.

Technical Illustration

Schawk, Inc.

Cover Design

tom white.images